*Statistical Physics
for Students of Science
and Engineering*

Statistical Physics for Students of Science and Engineering

Robert D. Reed
Department of Physics
Colorado School of Mines

R. R. Roy
Department of Physics
Arizona State University

Intext Educational Publishers

College Division of Intext

Scranton   San Francisco   Toronto   London

ISBN 0·7002·2353·3

Library of Congress Catalog Number 72·151643

Copyright ©, 1971, International Textbook Company

Preface

This textbook has been written with the purpose in mind of filling what the authors feel is an existing hiatus in undergraduate level statistical physics textbooks designed for use in a one semester course. The authors do not assert that there is a dearth of books dealing with statistical physics, statistical mechanics, statistical thermodynamics, or other metonymy presently available for classroom use, but merely that the majority of such books: are too brief (very few fall within this category) or too lengthy and too detailed to be satisfactorily adopted for use in a one semester length course; suffer a complete absence of problems for students to test their understanding of the principles involved; contain a superabundant discussion of the fundamental and philosophical foundations of the topic with a consequent inanition of applications to problems of physical interest; direct the applications contained therein primarily to disciplines other than physics or engineering (principally chemistry); or place excessive emphasis on the formal and rigorous mathematical steps involved in obtaining a given result with the concomitant neglect of conceptual and physical principles involved. The authors hold no illusions that the present textbook is a panacea for all the above mentioned ills, but they offer it for the consideration of those who teach a course similar to that for which it was written.

A brief glance at the Table of Contents will indicate to the reader that this book is in no sense an imitation or carbon copy of other texts dealing with the subject of statistical physics. The first chapter collects together in one place the mathematical preliminaries and special tools required for a working knowledge of statistical physics. These mathematical preliminaries are discussed in such a manner that they can be readily followed by the student with a general mathematics background equivalent to that of most college sophomores with an engineering or science major. On the other hand, many seniors or first year graduate students will already be familiar with the topics discussed in the first chapter, and such students will need to refer only occasionally to this chapter. In addition, the mathematical "tools" or "tricks of the trade" developed in Chapter 1 are supplemented by three more detailed appendixes at the end of the text, dealing with the fundamental topics of Fourier series representation of an arbitrary function, complex variables and the Lagrangian and Hamiltonian functions encountered in junior level mechanics courses.

A casual inspection of the Table of Contents will also reveal that the reader is under no obligation to commence his reading of the text with the initial chapter but may begin with the description of the goals, aims, and perspectives of statistical physics found in Chapter 2, and refer back to Chapter 1 as his mathematical needs arise. This approach eliminates the possibility of frightening students who have not yet acquired any motivation to assimilate the mathematical techniques presented in the first chapter.

In Chapters 3, 4, and 5 the classical Maxwell-Boltzmann-Planck and the two quantum statistics are introduced jointly and severally. In Chapter 3 the number distribution is obtained in terms of the state energy and the usual Lagrange undetermined multipliers. The role of the system entropy is established in Chapter 4 and in Chapter 5 it is shown that a gas without cohesion and covolume which obeys any of the three statistics, will also obey the familiar ideal gas equation of state. The remainder of the book deals with physical applications of the techniques of statistical physics and the use of these applications as teaching devices to enable the student to grasp a *working knowledge* of statistical physics.

The authors feel that the text is concise enough to be comfortably covered in a one semester course. In the event that this text is to be used in a course taught for one quarter of the academic year, Chapter 11, dealing with quantum symmetry principles involved in systems containing identical particles possessing spin angular momentum, may be omitted without seriously affecting the transition to the remaining three chapters. Of course if some particular applications discussed herein are treated elsewhere in the students' curriculum, it would be natural to delete them here if the instructor feels pressed for time. Although applications to various problems and effects are generously sprinkled throughout the last half of the book, the authors would like to encourage the professor in charge of the course to reserve adequate time to cover Chapter 14 in some detail to illustrate the rather nontrivial results obtainable from a somewhat unsophisticated study of statistical physics.

The authors express their thanks and appreciation to Dr. B. P. Nigam and Dr. Douglas Henderson for enlightening and pleasurable discussions and conversations, Mr. Kenneth Rilling for his assistance with some of the problems, Dr. W. H. Parker for permission to reprint the general physical constants and conversion factors, and to Mrs. Beverly R. Reed for her patient assistance in typing the several drafts of the manuscript.

Although pains were taken to minimize the error content of this volume, the authors hold themselves solely responsible for any mistakes, factual or otherwise, which may remain in the final form of this endeavor.

Robert D. Reed
R. R. Roy

August, 1971

Contents

vii

General Physical Constants and Conversion Factors*

Symbol	Quantity	Value	
c	Velocity of light in vacuo	2.9979250×10^{10}	cm/sec
e	Electron charge	$1.6021917 \times 10^{-19}$ C	
		4.803250×10^{-10} esu	
h	Planck's constant	6.626196×10^{-34} J-sec	
$\hbar$	$= h/2\pi$	$1.0545919 \times 10^{-34}$ J-sec	
N_0	Avogadro's number	6.022169×10^{23}	molecules/gm-mole
R	Gas constant	8.31434	J/gm-mole-deg
$k = \dfrac{R}{N_0}$	Boltzmann's constant	1.380622×10^{-23} J/deg	
m_e	Electron rest mass	9.109558×10^{-31} kgm	
		0.5110041 MeV	
M_p	Proton rest mass	1.672614×10^{-27} kgm	
		938.2592 MeV	
M_n	Neutron rest mass	1.674920×10^{-27} kgm	
		939.5527 MeV	
ε_0	Permittivity of free space	8.854185×10^{-12} farad/m	
μ_0	Permeability of free space	$4\pi \times 10^{-7}$ henry/m	
1 u	Unified nuclidic mass on C^{12} scale	931.4812 MeV	
1eV	Electron volt	$1.6021917 \times 10^{-19}$ J	

*Taken in part from B. N. Taylor, W. H. Parker, and D. N. Langenberg, *Rev. Mod. Phys.* **41**, 375 (1969).

Statistical Physics
for Students of Science
and Engineering

1 | Mathematical Review

1-0 PREAMBLE

With the knowledge that many students and a few instructors decline to read the author's comments in the preface of a textbook, this short discursive paragraph is included to provide authority to dispense entirely with the present chapter (i) if the student is already quite familiar with the "mathematical tricks of the trade" treated herein, (ii) if the instructor feels pressed for time and would prefer to refer to this chapter as occasion develops, or (iii) for any other reason. It was the intention of the authors to develop most if not all of the special mathematical tools required for statistical mechanics in a single compact chapter, wherein the student might acquire some degree of familiarity with the implements he will encounter in the process of working with statistical physics. The primary advantage of such a program is that once the student has mastered Chapter 1 he need not be bothered with learning any "new" mathematics, but may learn to apply the "old" mathematics he has previously learned in this chapter. The obvious drawback to such a plan is that the students who, for the most part, have not acquired any motivation for the subject may become frightened of the vast array of mathematics presented to them at the outset. To avert such a result the professor in charge of the course may well want to begin with Chapter 2, which lays the foundation for the rest of the text, and to treat Chapter 1 as an appendix, to be referred to when the particular occasion warrants. Similarly, for a graduate-level course the students may be presumed to be familiar with the material in the present chapter, and Chapter 2 would be a logical starting point.

1-1 FACTORIALS AND THEIR APPROXIMATION FOR LARGE NUMBERS

The gamma function, first defined by Euler in 1729, and generally represented by $\Gamma(p)$, this notation being introduced by Legendre in 1814, may be taken to be defined by

$$\Gamma(p + 1) = \int_0^\infty x^p e^{-x}\, dx, \qquad p > -1 \tag{1-1}$$

We can obtain a recursion relation for the gamma function through an integration by parts of (1-1).

$$\Gamma(p + 1) = -\int_0^\infty x^p\, d(e^{-x})$$

$$= \left[-x^p e^{-x} \right]\Big|_0^\infty + p \int_0^\infty x^{p-1} e^{-x}\, dx$$

$$\Gamma(p + 1) = p\Gamma(p) \tag{1-2}$$

From (1-1), we see that

$$\Gamma(1) = \int_0^\infty e^{-x}\, dx = -e^{-x}\Big|_0^\infty = 1 \tag{1-3}$$

With the use of (1-3) we can write

$$\Gamma(p + 1) = p\,\Gamma([p - 1] + 1) = p(p - 1)\Gamma([p - 2] + 1)$$
$$= p(p - 1)(p - 2) \cdots 3 \cdot 2 \cdot 1 \cdot \Gamma(1)$$
$$\Gamma(p + 1) = p!, \qquad p = \text{integer} \tag{1-4}$$

In the defining equation for $\Gamma(p + 1)$, (1-1), p was not restricted to integral values, and consequently, some authors use the factorial notation of (1-4) for noninteger values of p. Another notation, common in the European literature is Gauss's function

$$\Pi(p) = \Gamma(p + 1) \tag{1-5}$$

which eliminates the superfluous factor of 1 in the argument of the gamma function in (1-4).

The integrand of (1-1)

$$y = x^p e^{-x} \tag{1-6}$$

has a maximum value when

$$\frac{dy}{dx} = x^{p-1} e^{-x}[p - x] = 0 \tag{1-7}$$

i.e., at $x = p$. That y takes its maximum value at $x = p$ can be seen from the fact that

$$\frac{d^2 y}{dx^2}\Big|_{x = p} = -p^{p-1} e^{-p} \tag{1-8}$$

which is negative for positive p. The function given by (1-6) is shown in Fig. 1-1, in which the maximum value

$$y_m = p^p e^{-p} = \left(\frac{p}{e}\right)^p \tag{1-9}$$

is clearly shown.

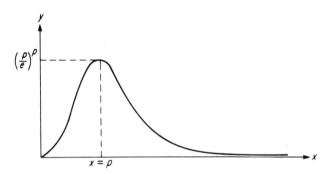

FIG. 1-1. Graph of $y = x^p e^{-x}$.

Let us change the function of (1-6) to

$$y = y_m e^{-t^2} \tag{1-10}$$

where y_m is given by (1-9) and, since $0 \le t^2 \le \infty$, we allow t to vary between $-\infty$ and $+\infty$. Also make another change of variable from x to θ by means of the transformation

$$x = p + \theta \tag{1-11}$$

where, since $0 \le x \le \infty$ and $p \ge 0$, we allow θ to vary between $-p$ and $+\infty$.

We now seek a relation between θ and t, by substituting (1-6), (1-9), and (1-11) into (1-10):

$$(p + \theta)^p e^{-(p + \theta)} = p^p e^{-p} e^{-t^2} \tag{1-12}$$

Dividing both sides of (1-12) by $y_m = p^p e^{-p}$, we find

$$\left(1 + \frac{\theta}{p}\right)^p e^{-\theta} = e^{-t^2}$$

or

$$e^{(\theta - t^2)} = \left(1 + \frac{\theta}{p}\right)^p \tag{1-13}$$

and taking the natural logarithm of both sides of (1-13) we see that

$$\theta - t^2 = p \ln\left(1 + \frac{\theta}{p}\right)$$

or

$$t^2 = \theta - p \ln\left(1 + \frac{\theta}{p}\right) \tag{1-14}$$

We now restrict θ to be in the vicinity where y takes its maximum value, i.e.,

$$\frac{\theta}{p} < 1 \tag{1-15}$$

For θ/p thus restricted, we can make use of the Maclaurin expansion[1] for the $\ln(1 + s)$

$$\ln(1 + s) = s - \frac{s^2}{2} + \frac{s^3}{3} + \cdots + \frac{(-1)^{n+1}s^n}{n} \tag{1-16}$$

$$-1 \leq s \leq 1$$

Thus we can write

$$t^2 = \theta - p\left[\frac{\theta}{p} - \frac{\theta^2}{2p^2} + \frac{\theta^3}{3p^3} + \cdots\right]$$

$$= \frac{\theta^2}{2p} - \frac{\theta^3}{3p^2} + \frac{\theta^4}{4p^3} - \cdots \tag{1-17}$$

For very large p, the right-hand side of (1-17) can be terminated, to a sufficient degree of accuracy, after the first term. This yields

$$\theta = \sqrt{2p}\, t \tag{1-18}$$

A higher-order approximation for θ can be obtained by expanding θ as a power series in t as

$$\theta = a_1 t + a_2 t^2 + a_3 t^3 + a_4 t^4 + \cdots \tag{1-19a}$$

$$\theta^2 = a_1^2 t^2 + 2a_1 a_2 t^3 + (a_2^2 + 2a_1 a_3)t^4 + \cdots \tag{1-19b}$$

$$\theta^3 = a_1^3 t^3 + 3a_1^2 a_2 t^4 + \cdots \tag{1-19c}$$

$$\theta^4 = a_1^4 t^4 + \cdots \tag{1-19d}$$

[1] L. P. Smail, *Analytic Geometry and Calculus* (New York: Appleton-Century-Crofts, Inc., 1953), p. 488.

and substituting (1-19) into (1-17) and solving for the expansion coefficients in (1-19a). This procedure leads to

$$t^2\left[\frac{a_1^2}{2p} - 1\right] + t^3\left[\frac{a_1a_2}{p} - \frac{a_1^3}{3p^2}\right]$$

$$+ t^4\left[\frac{(a_2^2 + 2a_1a_3)}{2p} - \frac{a_1^2a_2}{p^2} + \frac{a_1^4}{4p^3}\right] + \cdots = 0 \qquad (1\text{-}20)$$

Equation 1-20 will be satisfied if the coefficients of t^n are set equal to zero for all n. Thus

$$a_1 = \sqrt{2p} \qquad (1\text{-}21a)$$

$$a_2 = \frac{2}{3} \qquad (1\text{-}21b)$$

$$a_3 = \frac{1}{9\sqrt{2p}} \qquad (1\text{-}21c)$$

Substituting (1-21) back into (1-19a) leads to

$$\theta = \sqrt{2p}\,t + \frac{2t^2}{3} + \frac{t^3}{9\sqrt{2p}} + \cdots \qquad (1\text{-}22)$$

Using (1-11) and (1-22), we can write

$$dx = d\theta = dt\left[\sqrt{2p} + \frac{4}{3}t + \frac{1}{3\sqrt{2p}}t^2 + \cdots\right] \qquad (1\text{-}23)$$

and substituting (1-9), (1-10), and (1-23) into (1-1) we can express the gamma function, for large p, as

$$\Gamma(p+1) = \left(\frac{p}{e}\right)^p \int_{-\infty}^{\infty} e^{-t^2}\left[\sqrt{2p} + \frac{4}{3}t + \frac{1}{3\sqrt{3p}}t^2 + \cdots\right]dt$$

$$= \left(\frac{p}{e}\right)^p \sqrt{2p} \int_{-\infty}^{\infty} e^{-t^2}\,dt + \frac{4}{3}\left(\frac{p}{e}\right)^p \int_{-\infty}^{\infty} e^{-t^2}t\,dt$$

$$+ \frac{1}{3\sqrt{2p}}\left(\frac{p}{e}\right)^p \int_{-\infty}^{\infty} e^{-t^2}t^2\,dt + \cdots \qquad (1\text{-}24)$$

The range of t, remember from its defining equation 1-10, is from $-\infty$ to $+\infty$, thus all terms involving odd powers of t in the integrand on the right-hand side of (1-24) will vanish identically, and we can evaluate the remaining integrals as

$$I_1 = \int_{-\infty}^{\infty} e^{-t^2} \, dt = 2 \int_{0}^{\infty} e^{-t^2} \, dt = \sqrt{I_1^2} \tag{1-25}$$

$$I_1^2 = 4 \int_{0}^{\infty} e^{-x^2} \, dx \int_{0}^{\infty} e^{-y^2} \, dy$$

$$= 4 \int_{0}^{\infty} \int_{0}^{\infty} e^{-(x^2+y^2)} \, dx \, dy$$

$$= 4 \int_{\phi=0}^{\pi/2} \int_{r=0}^{\infty} e^{-r^2} \, (r \, d\phi \, dr)$$

$$= \pi \int_{0}^{\infty} e^{-r^2} \, (2r \, dr)$$

$$= \pi$$

Thus

$$I_1' = \sqrt{\pi} \tag{1-26}$$

$$I_2 = \int_{-\infty}^{\infty} e^{-t^2} t^2 \, dt = -\int_{0}^{\infty} t \, d(e^{-t^2}) = -(te^{-t^2})\Big|_{0}^{\infty} + \frac{I_1}{2}$$

$$I_2 = \frac{\sqrt{\pi}}{2} \tag{1-27}$$

It should be noted (cf. Prob. 1-1) that the integrals appearing on the right-hand side of (1-24) are themselves expressible in terms of the gamma function as

$$I_1 = 2I_2 = \Gamma\left(\frac{1}{2}\right) \tag{1-28}$$

Upon substitution of (1-28) into (1-24), we find

$$\Gamma(p+1) = \left(\frac{p}{e}\right)^p \sqrt{2\pi p} \left[1 + \frac{1}{12p} + \cdots\right] \tag{1-29}$$

The asymptotic expansion for large p of (1-29) is divergent as an infinite series. The resulting formula when only the first term in the square brackets is retained, is known as Stirling's formula:

$$p! \sim \left(\frac{p}{e}\right)^p \sqrt{2\pi p} \tag{1-30}$$

and is a good approximation for large p. Although the absolute error in using (1-30) to represent $p!$ may be large, the relative error, which can be estimated from the second term in the bracket of (1-29), tends to zero with increasing p, and in fact is less than 10 percent for $p = 1$. We shall always be primarily interested in the natural logarithm of $\Gamma(p + 1)$ in the work that follows.

1-2   THE RIEMANN ZETA FUNCTION AND ASSOCIATED FUNCTIONS

Riemann's zeta function is defined by the relation

$$\zeta(p) = \sum_{n=1}^{\infty} \frac{1}{n^p} \tag{1-31}$$

where p may take any value greater than unity. For our work we shall generally consider only positive integral values of p; however see Sec. 12-3 *infra*. There is no simple expression for $\zeta(p)$ when p is an odd integer. When p is an even integer the Riemann zeta function can be expressed in closed form in terms of the Bernoulli numbers.[2] We shall evaluate $\zeta(2)$ and $\zeta(4)$ explicitly, as well as some associated functions. First we shall need the series expansion for the sine and cosine functions.

$$\sin x = \frac{e^{ix} - e^{-ix}}{2i} = x - \frac{x^3}{3!} + \frac{x^5}{5!} - \frac{x^7}{7!} + \cdots \tag{1-32}$$

$$\cos x = \frac{e^{ix} + e^{-ix}}{2} = 1 - \frac{x^2}{2!} + \frac{x^4}{4!} - \frac{x^6}{6!} + \cdots \tag{1-33}$$

where we have made use of the Maclaurin expansion[3] of e^{ix}:

$$e^{\theta} = 1 + \theta + \frac{\theta^2}{2!} + \frac{\theta^3}{3!} + \frac{\theta^4}{4!} + \cdots \tag{1-34}$$

We also need the infinite product representation of $\sin \pi x$ and $\cos \pi x$, which we can obtain from a Fourier analysis.* We begin by writing

$$\cos \alpha x = \sum_{n=0}^{\infty} a_n \cos nx + \sum_{n=0}^{\infty} b_n \sin nx \tag{1-35}$$

Since $\cos \alpha x$ is an even, continuous, periodic function, the coefficients of the

---

[2]L. Brand, *Advanced Calculus* (New York: John Wiley & Sons, Inc., 1955), p. 486.

[3]See Ref. 1, p. 482.

*The student may wish to consult Appendix I at this point.

sine terms will all vanish in (1-35), and we have assumed that α is not an integer and the region of convergence of (1-35) is

$$-\pi \leq x \leq \pi \tag{1-36}$$

The Fourier coefficients, a_n, are obtained by the standard procedure of multiplying both sides of (1-35) by $\cos mx$ and integrating from $-\pi$ to π:

$$\int_{-\pi}^{\pi} \cos \alpha x \cos mx \, dx = \int_{-\pi}^{\pi} \cos mx \left[\sum_{n=0}^{\infty} a_n \cos nx \right] dx$$

We can interchange the order of integration and summation and write this result as

$$\sum_{n=0}^{\infty} a_n \int_{-\pi}^{\pi} \cos mx \cos nx \, dx = \int_{-\pi}^{\pi} \cos \alpha x \cos mx \, dx \tag{1-37}$$

We note that the integrals appearing on either side of the equation in (1-37) are of the same form (with the exception that n is an integer whereas α is not) and we thus need only evaluate it once. Let us represent the integral as

$$I = \int_{-\pi}^{\pi} \cos \alpha x \cos mx \, dx \tag{1-38}$$

which, since the integrand is an even function of x, we can write as

$$\begin{aligned}
I &= \frac{2}{m} \int_{0}^{\pi} \cos \alpha x \, d(\sin mx) \\
&= \frac{2}{m} \left[\cos \alpha x \sin mx \Big|_{0}^{\pi} + \alpha \int_{0}^{\pi} \sin mx \sin \alpha x \, dx \right] \\
&= -\frac{2\alpha}{m^2} \int_{0}^{\pi} \sin \alpha x \, d(\cos mx) \\
&= -\frac{2\alpha}{m^2} \left[\sin \alpha x \cos mx \Big|_{0}^{\pi} - \frac{\alpha}{2} I \right]
\end{aligned} \tag{1-39}$$

$$I \left(1 - \frac{\alpha^2}{m^2} \right) = -\frac{2\alpha(-1)^m \sin \alpha \pi}{m^2} \tag{1-40}$$

In (1-40) we have assumed that α and m are distinct, m being an integer and α not. If in (1-39) we replace α by n, we see that the first term in the square brackets vanishes at both limits, with the result that

$$I = \frac{n^2}{m^2} I \tag{1-41}$$

which implies that either $I = 0$ or $n = m$ (since both n and m are restricted to positive integers). This means that the only nonzero term in the infinite series on the left-hand side of (1-37) occurs when $n = m$. Thus

$$a_m 2 \int_0^\pi \cos^2 mx \, dx = \frac{2\alpha(-1)^m \sin \alpha\pi}{\alpha^2 - m^2} \tag{1-42}$$

The integral in (1-42) is easily evaluated as

$$\int_0^\pi \frac{1 + \cos 2mx}{2} \, dx = \frac{\pi}{2}$$

Thus

$$a_m = \frac{2}{\pi} \frac{\alpha(-1)^m \sin \alpha\pi}{\alpha^2 - m^2} \tag{1-43}$$

However, if $m = 0$, we cannot divide by m, as was done in the derivation of (1-39); thus we have to treat a_0 as a special case in (1-37).

$$\sum_{n=0}^\infty a_n 2 \int_0^\pi 1 \cos nx \, dx = 2 \int_0^\pi 1 \cos \alpha x \, dx \tag{1-44}$$

Again, we see that the integral on the left-hand side of (1-44) vanishes unless $n = 0$; in which case it becomes π. The integral on the right is easily seen to be $\sin \alpha\pi/\alpha$, and so

$$a_0 = \frac{\sin \alpha\pi}{\alpha\pi} \tag{1-45}$$

Substitution of (1-43) and (1-45) into (1-35) yields

$$\cos \alpha x = \frac{2\alpha \sin \alpha\pi}{\pi} \left[\frac{1}{2\alpha^2} - \frac{\cos x}{\alpha^2 - 1^2} + \frac{\cos 2x}{\alpha^2 - 2^2} + \cdots \right] \tag{1-46}$$

This series converges at $x = \pm \pi$, due to the continuity of $\cos \alpha x$; so if we let $x = \pi$, we can write

$$\pi \left[\cot \alpha\pi - \frac{1}{\alpha\pi} \right] = - \left[\frac{2\alpha}{1^2 - \alpha^2} + \frac{2\alpha}{2^2 - \alpha^2} + \cdots \right] \tag{1-47}$$

Both sides of (1-47) converge for $\alpha = 0$, and in fact converges for all α in the interval

$$0 \leq \alpha \leq a < 1 \tag{1-48}$$

Thus we can integrate both sides of (1-47) over α, term by term, from 0 to α:

$$\ln \sin \alpha\pi - \ln \alpha\pi = \lim_{n \to \infty} \sum_{j=1}^n \left[\ln(j^2 - \alpha^2) - \ln(j^2) \right]$$

Or, writing z in place of α,

$$\ln\left(\frac{\sin \pi z}{\pi z}\right) = \lim_{n \to \infty} \sum_{j=1}^{n} \ln\left(1 - \frac{z^2}{j^2}\right)$$

$$= \lim_{n \to \infty} \ln\left[\prod_{j=1}^{n}\left(1 - \frac{z^2}{j^2}\right)\right]$$

$$= \ln\left[\prod_{j=1}^{\infty}\left(1 - \frac{z^2}{j^2}\right)\right]$$

which can be expressed as

$$\frac{\sin \pi z}{\pi z} = \prod_{j=1}^{\infty}\left(1 - \frac{z^2}{j^2}\right) \tag{1-49}$$

We shall also be interested in obtaining an infinite product representation for the $\cos \pi z$; and it will be instructional to proceed on the basis of the Cauchy integral theorem.* Let $h(z)$ be analytic throughout the entire complex plane, except at a number (which may be infinite) of points

$$z = z_k, \quad k = 1, 2, \ldots m \tag{1-50}$$

Cauchy's integral formula and the residue theorem, then, lead to[4]

$$\oint_c h(z)\, dz = 2\pi i \sum_{k=1}^{m} (\text{residues of } h(z) \text{ within } c) \tag{1-51}$$

If we let $h(z) = f(z)/(z - z_0)$, then (1-51) becomes

$$\frac{1}{2\pi i}\oint_c \frac{f(z)}{z - z_0}\, dz = f(z_0) + \sum_{k=1}^{m}\left(\text{residues of } \frac{f(z)}{z - z_0} \text{ within } c\right) \tag{1-52}$$

when z_0 lies within the path of integration. Let $f(z)$ be analytic at $z = z_0$ so that the residues of $f(z)/(z - z_0)$ will be the same as the residues of $f(z)$ at $z = z_k$, $k = 1, 2, \ldots, m$. The residue of $f(z)/(z - z_0)$ at $z = z_k$, $k = 1, 2, \ldots, m$, can be written as

$$\frac{b_1(z = z_k)}{z_k - z_0}$$

where b_1 is the coefficient of the term $(z - z_k)^{-1}$ in the Laurent series[5] for $f(z)$ about the point $z = z_0$. Hence (1-52) can be expressed as

$$f(z_0) = \frac{1}{2\pi i}\oint_c \frac{f(z)\, dz}{z - z_0} - \sum_{k=1}^{m} \frac{b_1(z = z_k)}{z_k - z_0} \tag{1-53}$$

[4]M. L. Boas, *Mathematical Methods in the Physical Sciences* (New York: John Wiley & Sons, Inc., 1966), p. 491.

[5]See Ref. 4, p. 493.

*The student will find this discussed in Appendix II.

Through the use of partial fractions (see problem (1-5)) we can write

$$\frac{1}{z(z - z_0)} = \frac{1}{z_0(z - z_0)} - \frac{1}{z_0 z} \tag{1-54a}$$

or

$$\frac{1}{z - z_0} = \frac{1}{z} + \frac{z_0}{z(z - z_0)} \tag{1-54b}$$

and, from (1-54b), we can write

$$\frac{1}{2\pi i} \oint_c \frac{f(z)\, dz}{(z - z_0)} = \frac{1}{2\pi i} \oint_c \frac{f(z)\, dz}{z} + \frac{1}{2\pi i} \oint_c \frac{z_0 f(z)\, dz}{z(z - z_0)} \tag{1-55}$$

If we now limit for consideration those $f(z)$ such that $f(z)/(z^2 - z_0 z)$ decays faster than $1/|z|$ as $|z| \to \infty$, the second integral in (1-55) will vanish as c is extended to infinity, and we can write (1-55) as

$$\frac{1}{2\pi i} \oint_c \frac{f(z)\, dz}{z - z_0} = \frac{1}{2\pi i} \oint_c \frac{f(z)\, dz}{z}$$

$$= f(0) + \sum_{k=1}^{\infty} \frac{b_1(z = z_k)}{z_k} \tag{1-56}$$

Substituting (1-56) into (1-53), we find

$$f(z_0) = f(0) + \sum_{k=1}^{\infty} b_1(z = z_k)\left[\frac{1}{z_k} + \frac{1}{z_0 - z_k}\right] \tag{1-57}$$

We now restrict the form of $f(z)$ even further, requiring it to be expressible as

$$f(z) = \frac{g'(z)}{g(z)} \tag{1-58}$$

where $g(z)$ is a function that is analytic everywhere in the finite complex plane, and which has zeros at the isolated points $z = z_k$, and where we have defined

$$g'(z) \equiv \frac{dg}{dz} \tag{1-59}$$

Then (1-57) becomes

$$\frac{g'(z)}{g(z)} = \frac{g'(0)}{g(0)} + \sum_{k=1}^{\infty} b_1(z = z_k)\left[\frac{1}{z_k} + \frac{1}{z - z_k}\right] \tag{1-60}$$

which can be integrated from $z = 0$ to z, to yield

$$\ln\left[\frac{g(z)}{g(0)}\right] = \frac{g'(0)}{g(0)} z + \sum_{k=1}^{\infty} b_{1k}\left[\frac{z}{z_k} + \ln\left(\frac{z - z_k}{-z_k}\right)\right] \tag{1-61}$$

where we have defined

$$b_{1k} \equiv b_1(z = z_k) \tag{1-62}$$

We can take the antilogarithm of both sides of (1-61) to obtain

$$g(z) = g(0) \exp\left\{\frac{g'(0)}{g(0)} z\right\} \exp\left\{\sum_{k=1}^{\infty} \ln\left[(1 - z/z_k) e^{z/z_k}\right]^{b_{1k}}\right\}$$

$$g(z) = g(0) \exp\left\{\frac{g'(0)}{g(0)} z\right\} \exp\left\{\ln \prod_{k=1}^{\infty} \left[(1 - z/z_k) e^{z/z_k}\right]^{b_{1k}}\right\}$$

$$g(z) = g(0) \prod_{k=1}^{\infty} \left[(1 - z/z_k) e^{z/z_k}\right]^{b_{1k}} \exp\left[\frac{g'(0)}{g(0)} z\right] \tag{1-63}$$

We are now in a position to obtain the infinite product representation of the function $g(z) = \cos z$, which is analytic throughout the finite complex plane, and has simple zeros at $z_k = \pm (2k - 1)\,\pi/2$ with $k = 1, 2, 3, \ldots$. Further properties of $\cos z$, needed to evaluate (1-63), are

$$g(0) = 1 \qquad \text{and } g'(0) = 0$$

and

$$\frac{g'(z)}{g(z)} = \frac{-\sin z}{\cos z} = + \frac{\cos (z - z_k)}{\sin (z - z_k)}$$

$$= \frac{1 - (z - z_k)^2/2! + \cdots}{(z - z_k) - (z - z_k)^3/3! + \cdots}$$

from which we see that $b_{1k} = 1$ for all k. Thus

$$\cos z = \prod_{k=1}^{\infty} (1 - y_k) e^{y_k}(1 + y_k)e^{-y_k} = \prod_{k=1}^{\infty} (1 - y_k^2) \tag{1-64}$$

where

$$y_k = \frac{z}{+(2k - 1)\pi/2} \tag{1-65}$$

Making the change of variable from z to πz, we see that (1-64) can be written

$$\cos \pi z = \prod_{k=0}^{\infty} \left[1 - \frac{4z^2}{(2k + 1)^2}\right] \tag{1-66}$$

where we have relabeled the index k to start from 0 rather than 1. Of course we could have obtained (1-49) from (1-63) also, but we leave this as an exercise for the student (see Prob. 1-6).

We are now able to evaluate Riemann's zeta function and the associated so-called lambda function for even arguments. We begin by expanding the right-hand side of (1-49) as

$$\frac{\sin \pi z}{\pi z} = \left(1 - \frac{z^2}{1^2}\right)\left(1 - \frac{z^2}{2^2}\right)\left(1 - \frac{z^2}{3^2}\right)\cdots$$

$$= 1 - z^2 \sum_{k=1}^{\infty} \frac{1}{k^2} + z^4 \sum_{k=1}^{\infty} \sum_{j>k} \frac{1}{j^2 k^2} - \cdots \qquad (1\text{-}67)$$

From (1-32) we find

$$\frac{\sin \pi z}{\pi z} = 1 - z^2 \frac{\pi^2}{3!} + z^4 \frac{\pi^4}{5!} - \cdots \qquad (1\text{-}68)$$

and, by equating (1-67) to (1-68), we see that

$$\sum_{k=1}^{\infty} \frac{1}{k^2} = \frac{\pi^2}{3!}$$

or, from (1-31),

$$\zeta(2) = \frac{\pi^2}{6} \qquad (1\text{-}69)$$

From the equality of the coefficients of z^4 in (1-67) and (1-68) we can also evaluate

$$\sum_{k=1}^{\infty} \sum_{j>k} \frac{1}{j^2 k^2} = \frac{\pi^4}{5!} \qquad (1\text{-}70)$$

We can use (1-70) to evaluate $\zeta(4)$, which can be expressed in terms of the square of $\zeta(2)$, as

$$[\zeta(2)]^2 = \left[\sum_{k=1}^{\infty} \frac{1}{k^2}\right]^2 = \sum_{k=1}^{\infty} \frac{1}{k^2} \sum_{j=1}^{\infty} \frac{1}{j^2}$$

$$= \sum_{k=1}^{\infty} \frac{1}{k^2}\left[\sum_{j<k} \frac{1}{j^2} + \frac{1}{k^2} + \sum_{j=k+1}^{\infty} \frac{1}{j^2}\right]$$

$$= \sum_{k=1}^{\infty} \frac{1}{k^4} + \sum_{k=1}^{\infty} \sum_{j>k} \frac{1}{j^2 k^2} + \sum_{j=1}^{\infty} \sum_{k<j} \frac{1}{k^2 j^2} \qquad (1\text{-}71)$$

The last two sums in (1-71) are equal to each other and to the sum evaluated by (1-70), whereas the first sum in (1-71) is just $\zeta(4)$, thus

$$\zeta(4) = \left(\frac{\pi^2}{6}\right)^2 - 2\left(\frac{\pi^4}{5!}\right)$$

$$= \frac{\pi^4}{90} \qquad (1\text{-}72)$$

The so-called lambda function[6] can be defined as

$$\lambda(p) = \sum_{n=0}^{\infty} \frac{1}{(2n+1)^p} \tag{1-73}$$

We proceed, as we did in evaluating the zeta function, by expanding the infinite-product representation of (this time) $\cos \pi z$, (1-66), and equating this result to the series representation (1-33):

$$\cos \pi z = 1 - 4z^2 \sum_{k=0}^{\infty} \frac{1}{(2k+1)^2} + 16z^4 \sum_{k=0}^{\infty} \sum_{j>k} \frac{1}{(2k+1)^2(2j+1)^2} - \cdots$$

$$\cos \pi z = 1 - 4z^2 \lambda(2) + 16z^4 \sum_{k=0}^{\infty} \sum_{j>k} \frac{1}{(2k+1)^2(2j+1)^2} - \cdots \tag{1-74}$$

but, also

$$\cos \pi z = 1 - \frac{\pi^2 z^2}{2!} + \frac{\pi^4 z^4}{4!} - \cdots \tag{1-75}$$

and equating the coefficients of like powers of z from (1-74) and (1-75), we find

$$\lambda(2) = \frac{\pi^2}{8} \tag{1-76}$$

and

$$\sum_{k=0}^{\infty} \sum_{j>k} \frac{1}{(2k+1)^2(2j+1)^2} = \frac{\pi^4}{384} \tag{1-77}$$

We now square $\lambda(2)$ to obtain

$$[\lambda(2)]^2 = \sum_{k=0}^{\infty} \frac{1}{(2k+1)^2}$$

$$\left[\sum_{j<k} \frac{1}{(2j+1)^2} + \frac{1}{(2k+1)^2} + \sum_{j>k} \frac{1}{(2j+1)^2} \right]$$

$$= \sum_{k=0}^{\infty} \frac{1}{(2k+1)^4} + \sum_{k=0}^{\infty} \sum_{j>k} \frac{1}{(2k+1)^2(2j+1)^2}$$

$$+ \sum_{j=0}^{\infty} \frac{1}{(2j+1)^2} \sum_{k<j} \frac{1}{(2k+1)^2} \tag{1-78}$$

where the last sum was obtained by interchanging the dummy summation

---

[6]M. Abramowitz and I. Stegun (eds.), *Handbook of Mathematical Functions,* N.B.S. Applied Mathematics Series 55 (Washington, D.C.: Government Printing Office, 1964), Chap. 23 and references therein.

indices j and k, and, as a consequence, the last two terms in (1-78) are equal to each other and to (1-77), whereas the first term is just $\lambda(4)$. Thus

$$\lambda(4) = \left(\frac{\pi^2}{8}\right)^2 - 2\frac{\pi^4}{384}$$

$$= \frac{\pi^4}{96} \tag{1-79}$$

We can express the eta function, defined as

$$\eta(p) = \sum_{n=1}^{\infty} \frac{(-1)^{n+1}}{n^p} \tag{1-80}$$

as a linear combination of the zeta and lambda functions:

$$\eta(p) = \sum_{n=0}^{\infty} \frac{1}{(2n+1)^p} - \frac{1}{2^p} \sum_{n=1}^{\infty} \frac{1}{n^p}$$

$$\eta(p) = \lambda(p) - \frac{1}{2^p}\zeta(p) \tag{1-81}$$

Thus

$$\eta(2) = \frac{\pi^2}{8} - \frac{1}{4}\frac{\pi^2}{6}$$

$$\eta(2) = \frac{\pi^2}{12} \tag{1-82}$$

and

$$\eta(4) = \frac{7\pi^4}{720} \tag{1-83}$$

Other relations which the student should be able to show (see Prob. 1-26) are

$$\lambda(p) = [1 - 2^{-p}]\zeta(p) \tag{1-81a}$$

and

$$\eta(p) = [1 - 2^{1-p}]\zeta(p) \tag{1-81b}$$

1-3   PERMUTATIONS AND COMBINATIONS

The number of ways in which n distinct objects, each taken only one time, can be arranged is $n!$. We can choose any of the n objects first and any of the $(n-1)$ remaining objects second, and so on down to the last remaining object, which we then put last.

Assume that one has p numbered boxes into which N distinct objects are to be distributed such that there are n_1 objects in the first box, n_2 in the second box, ... and n_p in the pth box. The number of arrangements of these N objects into the p boxes with n_j objects in the jth box, such that no arrangement is repeated is

$$W = \frac{N!}{\prod\limits_{j=1}^{p} n_j!} \tag{1-84}$$

where, of course,

$$\sum_{j=1}^{p} n_j = N \tag{1-85}$$

As an example, consider the task of assigning the first nine letters of the alphabet to three boxes such that there are three letters in the first box, two letters in the second box, and four letters in the third and final box. In this case $N = 9$, $p = 3$, $n_1 = 3$, $n_2 = 2$, and $n_3 = 4$. By writing these letters in a series, there are $N! = 362880$ possible choices of arrangements, one of which might be

$$\underset{n_1 \quad n_2 \quad n_3}{|\,b\,a\,f\,|\,c\,d\,|\,e\,g\,h\,i\,|} \tag{1-86}$$

where the vertical bars have been used to separate the letters into groups of $n_1, n_2, \ldots,$ objects. However, the arrangement

$$|\,a\,f\,b\,|\,d\,c\,|\,g\,e\,i\,h\,| \tag{1-87}$$

which differs from (1-86) only by the order of the elements within the individual boxes, is not distinct from (1-86). In fact there are $n_1!$, $n_2!$, $n_3!$ ways of permuting the elements of the boxes which leaves the arrangements indistinguishable. Thus the 362,880 arrangements are not all distinguishable, but only

$$\frac{362880}{3!2!4!} = 1260$$

of the arrangements are independent, in consonance with (1-84).

Supposing that there are π numbered boxes and N distinct objects to be distributed within the boxes, we might ask: "What is the total number of ways of distributing the N particles in the π boxes?"

Let's take, as an example: $N = 3$; $\pi = 2$; we can denote the boxes as α and β, which we have supposed are distinguishable; and the distinct objects will be the first three letters of the alphabet. We can now construct the following table:

Box α	a b c	none	a	b c	b	a c	c	a b
Box β	none	a b c	b c	a	a c	b	a b	c
Label	$\alpha\,\alpha\,\alpha$	$\beta\,\beta\,\beta$	$\alpha\,\beta\,\beta$	$\beta\,\alpha\,\alpha$	$\beta\,\alpha\,\beta$	$\alpha\,\beta\,\alpha$	$\beta\,\beta\,\alpha$	$\alpha\,\alpha\,\beta$

The number we are looking for is the number of cases on the third line, in this example, 8. According to the third line, this is the number of ways of forming a group, containing three letters, with the use of only two letters, each letter being allowed to appear several times in the group. In this case, where α and β are distinguishable, two groups differing by the order of the letters in the group are counted as being different.

We have found, then, the number of *arrangements with repetition* of two distinguishable objects (α,β) taken three at a time. We can denote this number by

$$r_{A_r(2)_3} = 2^3 = 8 \qquad (1\text{-}88)$$

In principle, we could make a table for any N and π to evaluate $r_{A_r(\pi)_N}$, but this is not necessary, as we easily extend the analysis to see that there are π choices for the first element of the group, π for the second, ..., and π choices for the Nth and last element of the group (since we are allowing repetition of any and all of the π boxes). Thus, in general

$$r_{A_r(\pi)_N} = \pi^N \qquad (1\text{-}89)$$

The student should note that there is no restriction on π or N in (1-89); π may be greater than, less than, or equal to N.

Now assume that the N objects are not distinguishable (they may be identical, but not numbered). We retain the assumption that the π boxes are numbered (and thus distinguishable), and do not limit the number of objects which can be placed in any box. We then ask ourselves: What is the total number of ways of arranging the particles in the boxes?" Again let us take the case of $N = 3$ and $\pi = 2$ (α,β). We can label all the possible distributions again by a table as

Box α	3	0	2	1
Box β	0	3	1	2
Label	$\alpha\,\alpha\,\alpha$	$\beta\,\beta\,\beta$	$\alpha\,\alpha\,\beta$	$\alpha\,\beta\,\beta$
			or	or
			$\alpha\,\beta\,\alpha$	$\beta\,\alpha\,\beta$
			or	or
			$\beta\,\alpha\,\alpha$	$\beta\,\beta\,\alpha$

The three notations, separated by "or," in each of the two right-hand columns, correspond to the same distribution since the particles are assumed to be nondistinguishable. The total number of ways of distributing the three objects into the two boxes, then, is equal to the number of sets of three letters each that can be formed by using only two letters, each one of which (α or β) can appear several times, *but where the order of the letters in a set is irrelevant*. We can then denote the number of *combinations, with repetition*, of two objects taken three at a time as

$$r_{c(2)_3} = 4 \tag{1-90}$$

We can argue that the general formula for the number of combinations, with repetitions, of π objects taken N at a time, is given by

$$r_{c(\pi)_N} = \frac{(N + \pi - 1)!}{N! \, (\pi - 1)!} \tag{1-91}$$

as follows. Let the π boxes be labeled (α, β, ..., π). In one such distribution there will be m_α objects in box α, m_β objects in box β, ..., and m_π objects in box π. This distribution is subject to the restriction that

$$m_\alpha + m_\beta + \cdots + m_\pi = N \tag{1-92}$$

In the preceding example, the first distribution was of the form

$$m_\alpha = 3 \quad \text{and} \quad m_\beta = 0$$

Let us now suppose that we have numbered our N objects in order to render them discernible. We can now represent the numbered objects by 0 and the boxes by x. We now arrange, in all possible ways, the N objects and the first $\pi - 1$ boxes in a line, always putting the πth box on the extreme right-hand side of the line. There will then be $(N + \pi - 1)!$ permutations of the form

$$0x000x0x00xx0 \cdots x \tag{1-93}$$

which we interpret as meaning that we place in each numbered box the number of (distinguishable) objects appearing to the left of the box. Thus the distribution of (1-93) means one object is placed in the first box, three objects in the second box, one in the third box, two in the fourth box, none in the fifth, ..., etc. But all of the $(N + \pi - 1)!$ distributions are not distinct. Removing the individuality from the objects, it is necessary to divide by $N!$; furthermore, the order of the boxes is immaterial and so we need also to divide by $(\pi - 1)!$, which then leads to the general formula of (1-91). It is easily seen that (1-90) follows immediately from (1-91):

$$r_c(2)_3 = \frac{(3 + 2 - 1)!}{3! \, (2 - 1)!} = \frac{4!}{3!} = 4$$

Finally, let us suppose that each of the π-distinguishable boxes can hold at most one of the N indistinguishable objects (i.e., a given box either contains one particle or it is empty). Thus we must now require that the number of boxes be greater than the number of objects, $\pi > N$ (of course it is possible for $\pi = N$, but this means that every box is filled and there is only one possible distribution). To answer the question as to how many ways the objects can be distributed, we assume as an example that $\pi = 3$ and $N = 2$. Resorting to our table, we see that

Box α	1	1	0
Box β	1	0	1
Box γ	0	1	1
Label	$\alpha\,\beta$	$\alpha\,\gamma$	$\beta\,\gamma$
	or	or	or
	$\beta\,\alpha$	$\gamma\,\alpha$	$\gamma\,\beta$

Since the sets $\alpha\beta$ and $\beta\alpha$ are not distinct, the number we seek is the number of sets of two letters formed with three letters, the order of the letters being irrelevant. Thus the number of combinations *without repetition* of three objects taken two by two (with the order being immaterial) is given by

$$C(3)_2 = 3 \tag{1-94}$$

In order to find the general number $C(\pi)_N$ describing the number of different combinations which can be formed from π distinct objects taken N at a time, let us number the N indistinguishable objects. We then take the first object and deposit it into any one of the π boxes. We are then left with $(\pi - 1)$ choices of boxes in which to place the second particle, and $(\pi - 2)$ choices for the third object, ..., and $[\pi - (N - 1)]$ choices for the Nth and last object. The product of all these choices, is the number of different permutations which can be formed from π distinct objects taken N at a time, and is denoted by

$$\pi P_N = \pi(\pi - 1)(\pi - 2)\cdots \qquad (\pi - N + 1) \tag{1-95a}$$

$$= \frac{\pi!}{(\pi - N)!} \tag{1-95b}$$

In demonstrating the formulation of πP_N in (1-95) we assumed that the N objects were numbered, when in fact they were originally taken to be indistinguishable. Consequently we have overestimated the number of ways in which the N nondistinct objects could be distributed among the π boxes, with each box holding at most one particle, by the number of ways of permuting N particles, N at a time:

$$NP_N = N! \tag{1-96}$$

Thus our sought-for number can be represented as

$$C(\pi)_N = \frac{\pi P_N}{N!} \tag{1-97a}$$

$$= \frac{\pi!}{N!(\pi - N)!} \tag{1-97b}$$

Note that $C(\pi)_N = C(\pi)_{(\pi - N)}$ (see Prob. 1-7). In our example of $\pi = 3$ and $N = 2$, (1-97b) leads to

$$C(3)_2 = \frac{3!}{2!(3 - 2)!} = 3$$

in agreement with (1-94).

1-4 LIOUVILLE'S THEOREM

This is a theorem generally quoted in textbooks on classical mechanics.[7] The Lagrangian for a mechanical system having f degrees of freedom, and thus f generalized coordinates $(q_1, q_2, ..., q_f)$, may be expressed in terms of a potential energy function, ε_p, which is a function only of these generalized coordinates, and a kinetic energy function, ε_k, which is a function of these generalized coordinates and their time derivatives, as[*]

$$L(q_i, \dot{q}_i) = \varepsilon_k(q_i, \dot{q}_i) - \varepsilon_p(q_i) \quad i = 1, 2, ..., f \tag{1-98}$$

Frequently the kinetic energy may be expressed as a homogeneous function of the second degree in the generalized velocities $\dot{q}_j$, of the form

$$\varepsilon_k(q_j, \dot{q}_j) = \sum_{m=1}^{f} \sum_{n=1}^{f} A_{mn}(q_j)\, \dot{q}_m \dot{q}_n \quad j = 1, 2, ..., f \tag{1-99}$$

The canonical momentum conjugate to q_j can be defined as

$$p_j \equiv \frac{\partial L}{\partial \dot{q}_j}, \quad j = 1, 2, ..., f \tag{1-100}$$

and, in view of (1-98) and (1-99), p_j is a linear function of the $\dot{q}_j$. The f equations of (1-100) can be solved for the $\dot{q}_j$ in terms of the p_j, and upon substituting these $\dot{q}_j$ back into (1-99), we will have an expression for the kinetic energy as a function of the q_j and the p_j which is homogeneous and of the second degree in the p_j:

$$\varepsilon_k(q_j, p_j) = \sum_{m=1}^{f} \sum_{n=1}^{f} B_{mn}(q_j)p_m p_n \tag{1-101}$$

in analogy with (1-99).

The Hamiltonian function is defined to be

$$H(p_j, q_j) = \sum_{m=1}^{f} p_m \dot{q}_m - L(q_j, \dot{q}_j) \tag{1-102}$$

[7] See for example D. E. Christie, *Vector Mechanics*, 2nd ed. (New York: McGraw-Hill Book Company, 1964), p. 565.
[*] The student may wish to consult Appendix III at this time.

where the terms involving $\dot{q}_i$ on the right-hand side of (1-102) are expressed in terms of q_i and p_i from (1-100) so that the functional dependence of the Hamiltonian is in terms of the generalized coordinates q_i and the generalized momentum p_i (conjugate to q_i) given by (1-100). If the transformation equations defining the generalized coordinates, q_i, in terms of the rectilinear cartesian coordinates do not contain the time explicitly, and if the system is conservative, the Hamiltonian function will equal the total energy of the system; furthermore if the Lagrangian function does not depend explicitly on the time, the Hamiltonian will also be a constant of the motion.

In any event, the canonical equations of motion are given by

$$\dot{p}_i = -\frac{\partial H}{\partial q_i}(p_j, q_j) \tag{1-103a}$$

$$\dot{q}_i = \frac{\partial H}{\partial p_i}(p_j, q_j) \tag{1-103b}$$

As a simple example, consider the motion of a single-point particle of mass m in a force field derivable from a potential ε_p (x, y, z). In this case we take for our generalized coordinates

$$q_1 = x$$

$$q_2 = y \tag{1-104}$$

$$q_3 = z$$

and the kinetic energy may be written

$$\varepsilon_k = \frac{m}{2}(\dot{x}^2 + \dot{y}^2 + \dot{z}^2) \tag{1-105}$$

The generalized momenta are obtained from (1-100) with the aid of (1-98) and (1-105), as

$$p_x = m\dot{x} \Rightarrow \dot{x} = \frac{p_x}{m}$$

$$p_y = m\dot{y} \Rightarrow \dot{y} = \frac{p_y}{m} \tag{1-106}$$

$$p_z = m\dot{z} \Rightarrow \dot{z} = \frac{p_z}{m}$$

The Hamiltonian is then given by (1-102) as

$$H = \left[p_x \frac{p_x}{m} + p_y \frac{p_y}{m} + p_z \frac{p_z}{m} \right] - \left[\varepsilon_k - \varepsilon_p \right]$$

$$= \frac{1}{2m} \left[p_x^2 + p_y^2 + p_z^2 \right] + \varepsilon_p$$

$$= \varepsilon_k(\mathbf{p}) + \varepsilon_p(\mathbf{q})$$

Hamilton's canonical equations, (1-103), then give the equations of motion (for $q_1 = x$) as

$$\dot{p}_x = -\frac{\partial H}{\partial x} = -\frac{\partial \varepsilon_p}{\partial x}$$

$$\dot{x} = \frac{\partial H}{\partial p_x} = \frac{p_x}{m} \tag{1-107}$$

and similarly for the y and z components.

Also, we note from Hamilton's canonical equations that

$$\frac{\partial \dot{p}_i}{\partial p_i} = -\frac{\partial^2 H}{\partial p_i \partial q_i}$$

$$\frac{\partial \dot{q}_i}{\partial q_i} = +\frac{\partial^2 H}{\partial q_i \partial p_i} \tag{1-108}$$

For physically acceptable Hamiltonian functions the order of differentiation will be immaterial, and we obtain from (1-108) the important result that

$$\frac{\partial \dot{p}_i}{\partial p_i} + \frac{\partial \dot{q}_i}{\partial q_i} = 0 \tag{1-109}$$

Let us now consider a fluid having two dimensions formed by molecules moving parallel to the ξ-η plane, with the motion being the same in all planes parallel to the ξ-η plane. We also suppose that there exists a permanent velocity field such that

$$\dot{\xi} = \dot{\xi}(\xi, \eta)$$

$$\dot{\eta} = \dot{\eta}(\xi, \eta) \tag{1-110}$$

Let ρ be the mass per unit area of the fluid so that the mass of fluid in an infinitesimal rectangle is given by $\rho\, d\xi\, d\eta$. Assuming that there are no sources or sinks of fluid (no fluid is being created, and none is being annihilated), the condition that mass is conserved in the fluid is expressed by the equation of continuity

$$\nabla \cdot \mathbf{j} + \frac{\partial \rho}{\partial t} = 0 \tag{1-111}$$

where

$$\mathbf{j} = \rho \mathbf{v}$$

$$= \rho[\dot{\xi}\hat{\xi} + \dot{\eta}\hat{\eta}] \tag{1-112}$$

and $\hat{\xi}$ and $\hat{\eta}$ are unit vectors in the ξ-η plane. If the fluid is further assumed to be incompressible, then necessarily $\partial \rho / \partial t = 0$ and we have

$$\nabla \cdot \mathbf{j} = \frac{\partial}{\partial \xi} (\rho \dot{\xi}) + \frac{\partial}{\partial \eta} (\rho \dot{\eta}) = 0 \qquad (1\text{-}113)$$

If the incompressible fluid has constant density (1-113) becomes, upon dividing through both sides by the constant ρ,

$$\frac{\partial \dot{\xi}}{\partial \xi} + \frac{\partial \dot{\eta}}{\partial \eta} = 0 \qquad (1\text{-}114)$$

Comparison of (1-114) with (1-109) shows that *a phase point in the p-q plane, representing a mechanical system, moves in the same way as the particles of a two-dimensional incompressible fluid having a constant density.*

Boltzmann has given a concrete example of this theorem by considering the one-dimensional free-fall motion of a point particle of mass m. For this case,

$$\varepsilon_p = mgz$$

$$\varepsilon_k = \frac{p^2}{2m}$$

$$H = \frac{p^2}{2m} + mgz = E \qquad (1\text{-}115)$$

Substitution of (1-115) into (1-103) leads to

$$\dot{p} = -mg \Rightarrow p = p_0 - mgt \qquad (1\text{-}116)$$

$$\dot{z} = p/m = \frac{p_0}{m} - gt$$

$$z = z_0 + \frac{p_0 t}{m} - \frac{1}{2} g t^2 \qquad (1\text{-}117)$$

The trajectory of the particle in phase space for a given system energy is expressed by (1-115) and is seen to be a parabola. The same information is given in parametric form by (1-116) and (1-117) when the total, constant, system energy is identified with $p_0^2/2m + mgz_0$. If we now consider an infinite number of bodies, all having the same mass m, and filling the energy continuum between E and $E + \Delta E$. then all the phase points, at $t = 0$, within the rectangle determined by $p_1 \leq p_0 \leq p_1 + \Delta p_1$ and $z_1 \leq z_0 \leq z_1 + \Delta z_1$ will be completely occupied, as shown in Fig. 1-2.

After a time t the phase points will have moved to the region determined by

$$p_1 - mgt \leq p \leq p_1 + \Delta p_1 - mgt$$

$$z_1 + \frac{p_0 t}{m} - \frac{1}{2} g t^2 \leq z \leq z_1 + \Delta z_1 + \frac{p_0 t}{m} - \frac{1}{2} g t^2$$

The condition

$$\frac{p_0 t}{m} = \frac{pt}{m} + gt^2$$

from (1-116), can be substituted into the z inequality to yield

$$z_1 + \frac{pt}{m} + \frac{1}{2}gt^2 \le z \le z_1 + \Delta z_1 + \frac{pt}{m} + \frac{1}{2}gt^2$$

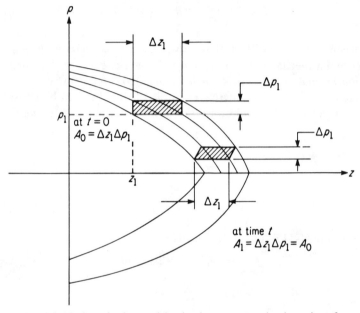

FIG. 1-2. Motion of point particles, in phase space, under the action of a
constant gravitational force.

We now have, by means of these two inequalities for p and z at the later time
t, the condition that all of the phase points must lie within the parallelogram
(no longer a rectangle) determined by the four lines

$$p = p_1 - mgt$$

$$p = p_1 - mgt + \Delta p_1$$

$$z = z_1 + \frac{pt}{m} + \frac{1}{2}gt^2$$

$$z = z_1 + \frac{pt}{m} + \frac{1}{2}gt^2 + \Delta z_1$$

This parallelogram is shown in Fig. 1-2 and has a base of length Δz_1 and
height Δp_1. The sides are inclined against the base at an angle (See Prob. 1-11)

$\delta = \tan^{-1} (m/t)$ ($\delta = \pi/2$ at $t = 0$ by our choice of determining $z = z_0$ and $p = p_0$ at $t = 0$), and the area of the parallelogram, being the product of the base and altitude, is independent of δ and in fact is equal to the area initially occupied by the phase points. Since the number of phase points is equal to the product of their density in phase space and the area occupied in phase space, and since the number of phase points (each point representing the kinematics of a single particle with a unique energy between E and $E + \Delta E$) is conserved, the fact that these points occupy a constant area at all times is consistent with the statement that the density of phase points is a constant.

We may add (1-109) for all f degrees of freedom in the system

$$\sum_{i=1}^{f} \left[\frac{\partial \dot{p}_i}{\partial p_i} + \frac{\partial \dot{q}_i}{\partial q_i} \right] = 0 \tag{1-118}$$

such that the resulting equation, which expresses the *Liouville Theorem*, can be formulated in the following manner:

Consider a hyperspace having $2f$ dimensions (p_i, q_i) $i = 1, 2, ..., f$. A point in this hyperspace is called a *phase point*, the domain available to these phase points is called the *phase space*, and an element of this domain is called an *element of extension in phase* or just a *differential element of phase space*. The Liouville theorem can then be expressed as *the phase points move in the phase space as an incompressible fluid* (having $2f$ dimensions).

Thus if the initial state of the system is given (q_{i0}, p_{i0}), then the later behavior of the system is completely determined. For example, let us write

$$q_i = g_i(q_{j0}, p_{j0}, t)$$
$$p_i = h_i(q_{j0}, p_{j0}, t)$$
$$\dot{q}_i = G_i(q_{j0}, p_{j0}, t)$$
$$\dot{p}_i = H_i(q_{j0}, p_{j0}, t), i, j = 1, 2, 3, ..., f \tag{1-119}$$

where we have allowed for the possibility that the time may explicitly appear in the functional form of the generalized coordinates and momenta.

We now assume that all the phase points are initially in the differential volume element

$$d\tau_0 = dp_{10}\, dp_{20} ... dp_{f0}\, dq_{10}\, dq_{20} ... dq_{f0} \tag{1-120}$$

and at some time dt later they are found to occupy the volume element

$$d\tau = dp_1\, dp_2 ... dp_f\, dq_1\, dq_2 ... dq_f \tag{1-121}$$

The generalized coordinate q_i, at time dt, is related to q_{i0}, at time 0, by means of

$$q_i = q_{i0} + \dot{q}_{i0}\, dt \tag{1-122a}$$

to first order in dt, and similarly

$$p_i = p_{io} + \dot{p}_{io}\, dt \qquad (1\text{-}122b)$$

The differential volume elements of (1-120) and (1-121) can be related by means of the Jacobian.[8]

$$d\tau = J\left(\frac{p_1, p_2, \ldots, p_f, q_1, \ldots, q_f}{p_{10}, p_{20}, \ldots, p_{f0}, q_{10}, \ldots, q_{f0}}\right) d\tau_0 \qquad (1\text{-}123)$$

where (suppressing the argument of J) we can write, using the transformation equations of (1-122).

$$J - \begin{vmatrix} \dfrac{\partial p_1}{\partial p_{10}} & \dfrac{\partial p_1}{\partial p_{20}} & \cdots & \dfrac{\partial p_1}{\partial p_{f0}} & \dfrac{\partial p_1}{\partial q_{10}} & \cdots & \dfrac{\partial p_1}{\partial q_{f0}} \\[2mm] \vdots & \vdots & & \vdots & \vdots & & \vdots \\[2mm] \dfrac{\partial q_f}{\partial p_{10}} & \dfrac{\partial q_f}{\partial p_{20}} & \cdots & \dfrac{\partial q_f}{\partial p_{f0}} & \dfrac{\partial q_f}{\partial q_{f0}} & \cdots & \dfrac{\partial q_f}{\partial q_{f0}} \end{vmatrix} \qquad (1\text{-}124a)$$

$$= \begin{vmatrix} \left(1 + \dfrac{\partial \dot{p}_{10}}{\partial p_{10}}\, dt\right) & \dfrac{\partial \dot{p}_{10}}{\partial p_{20}}\, dt & \cdots & \dfrac{\partial \dot{p}_{10}}{\partial q_{f0}}\, dt \\[3mm] \dfrac{\partial \dot{p}_{20}}{\partial p_{10}}\, dt & \left(1 + \dfrac{\partial \dot{p}_{20}}{\partial p_{20}} dt\right) & \cdots & \dfrac{\partial \dot{p}_{20}}{\partial q_{f0}}\, dt \\[3mm] \vdots & \vdots & & \vdots \\[3mm] \dfrac{\partial \dot{q}_{f0}}{\partial p_{10}}\, dt & \dfrac{\partial \dot{q}_{f0}}{\partial p_{20}}\, dt & \cdots & \left(1 + \dfrac{\partial \dot{q}_{f0}}{\partial q_{f0}}\, dt\right) \end{vmatrix} \qquad (1\text{-}124b)$$

The only terms of the first degree in dt resulting from the expansion of the determinant in (1-124b) arise from the product of the terms on the diagonal, yielding the result that

$$J = 1 + \left\{ \sum_{i=1}^{f} \left[\frac{\partial \dot{p}_{io}}{\partial p_{io}} + \frac{\partial \dot{q}_{io}}{\partial q_{io}}\right] \right\} dt + (\qquad)(dt)^2 \qquad (1\text{-}125)$$

We note that the term in braces in (1-125) vanishes identically from (1-118), and, to first order in the time, the Jacobian of the transformation of (1-122) is unity, with the result that (1-123) reduces to

$$d\tau = d\tau_0 \qquad (1\text{-}126)$$

[8] See Ref. 2, p. 177.

at all time, a fact we deduced earlier in the simple example of a freely falling body in one dimension.

Thus if we consider an aggregate of N molecules interacting within a volume V, the state of each molecule can be defined in terms of three position parameters, some parameters describing the orientation, the state of vibration, of rotation, etc. If the number of parameters is denoted by r, then there will be Nr parameters of the type q, and Nr of the type p. The entire collection will be represented by a phase point in a $2Nr$-dimensional space. In general there will be some potential energy of the system, dependent on the positions, orientations, states of vibration, rotation, etc., of each of the molecules. Suppose that the total energy of the system is given, and is constant. Then this conservative system, formed by the aggregate of the N molecules, will be represented by the phase point in the $2Nr$-dimensional space, and the phase point will move over the surface of constant energy. If instead of considering one such system, we were to assume a very large number of such systems, the corresponding phase points would move in the same manner as the molecules of an incompressible fluid.

As another example, consider a mole of N_0 identical interacting molecules (N_0 is, of course, Avogadro's number). Since each molecule moves in the force field due to the $N_0 - 1$ other molecules, the energy of each individual molecule will not be constant. Let r be the number of parameters needed to specify each molecule, and we shall designate the molecules by

$$a, b, c, \ldots, \quad N_0 \tag{1-127}$$

We shall be able to separate the Hamiltonian of the entire assembly into terms of the form: (1) which contain only the $2r$ parameters of molecule a, call this $H_a(p_a, q_a)$; (2) which contain only the $2r$ parameters of molecule b, call this $H_b(p_b q_b)$; and etc., for all N_0 molecules, and finally a term representing the interaction energy, which contains the parameters $(q_a, q_b, \ldots, q_{N_0})$, but not (we assume) the parameters $(p_a, p_b, \ldots, p_{N_0})$, and which is not separable. Thus the total Hamiltonian can be written as

$$H = H_a(p_a, q_a) + \cdots + H_{N_0}(p_{N_0}, q_{N_0}) + H_{int}(q_a, q_b, \ldots, q_{N_0}) \tag{1-128}$$

Let α be an index associated with molecule a ($\alpha = 1, 2, \ldots, r$), such that we can write Hamilton's canonical equations for molecule a in the form

$$-(\dot{p}_\alpha)_a = \frac{\partial H_a}{\partial q_{\alpha a}} + \frac{\partial H_{int}}{\partial q_{\alpha a}} \tag{1-129a}$$

$$(\dot{q}_\alpha)_a = \frac{\partial H_a}{\partial p_{\alpha a}} \tag{1-129b}$$

In addition, we can write (1-118) for molecule a as

$$\sum_{\alpha=1}^{r} \left[\frac{\partial \dot{p}_{\alpha a}}{\partial p_{\alpha a}} + \frac{\partial \dot{q}_{\alpha a}}{\partial q_{\alpha a}} \right] = 0 \qquad (1\text{-}130)$$

with analogous expressions for molecules b, c, ..., N_0.

We can now imagine a hyperspace having $2r$ parameters and suppose that to each molecule we make a corresponding phase point. The energy of the molecule will not be constant due to the interactions mentioned above, but in spite of this, the phase points of all the molecules a, b, c, ..., will move like an incompressible fluid because all of the molecules obey (1-130) separately. This is how we shall interpret the description of the collection of particles in the following sections of this text. An important case which we shall treat later in this text is that where the interaction energy is zero, $H_{int} = 0$. Then the energy of the collection of particles is just the sum of the energies of each of the molecules.

$$\varepsilon = \varepsilon_a + \varepsilon_b + \cdots + \varepsilon_N \qquad (1\text{-}131)$$

The energy ε_a is the sum of the kinetic energy of molecule a and the potential energy arising from the interaction forces arising between the particle and some body external to the system (e.g., the potential energy due to the force of gravity, or due to the orientation of the molecule in an external magnetic field) only, since the forces due to the other molecules of the system are all zero.

1-5 DELTA FUNCTIONS

We shall have occasion to make use of a generalized function[9] $\phi(x)$, which can be defined in terms of the operator x (which, for the present, we can take to be the position coordinate), as

$$x\,\phi(x) = \alpha\,\phi(x) \qquad (1\text{-}132)$$

where α may be called the eigenvalue of the operator. By transposing (1-132) we can write

$$(x - \alpha)\,\phi(x) = 0 \qquad (1\text{-}133)$$

To satisfy (1-133) we require

$$\text{if} \quad (x - \alpha) = 0; \quad \phi(x) \neq 0 \qquad (1\text{-}134a)$$

and

$$\text{if} \quad (x - \alpha) \neq 0; \quad \phi(x) = 0 \qquad (1\text{-}134b)$$

[9]M. J. Lighthill, *Introduction to Fourier Analysis and Generalized Functions* (London: Cambridge University Press, 1958), Chap. 2.

Thus, the generalized function $\phi(x)$ must vanish everywhere except at the point $x = \alpha$. Furthermore, we require that $\phi(x)$ satisfy the normalization condition

$$\int_{-\infty}^{\infty} \phi_{(x)}^{*} \, \phi_{(x)} \, dx = 1 \qquad (1\text{-}135)$$

Obviously, if $\phi(x)$ is a real function, $\phi_{(x)}^{*} \, \phi(x)$ will reduce to the simple square of $\phi(x)$. [$\phi_{(x)}^{*}$ is the complex conjugate of $\phi(x)$.] The conditions imposed on $\phi(x)$ by (1-134) and (1-135) can be reconciled if $\phi(x)$ has the form shown in Fig. 1-3.

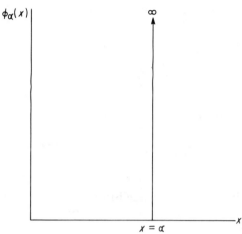

FIG. 1-3. The generalized function (x) which is defined to be zero everywhere, except at $x = \alpha$, where it is un-bounded so that (1-135) may be satisfied. The function is labeled with the subscript α to indicate the value of the argument at which the singularity occurs.

Since $\phi(x) = 0$ except when $x = \alpha$, it is necessary for $\phi(x)$ to become infinite at $x = \alpha$ in order for (1-135) to be satisfied. One can think of $\phi(x)$ being of the form of a rectangule of width ε, centered about $x = \alpha$, with height $\varepsilon^{-1/2}$ so that (1-135) is satisfied, and then letting ε become arbitrarily small (see Prob. 1-15). It is convenient to label $\phi_{\alpha}(x)$ by the subscript α to indicate the value of the argument at which the singularity occurs. Two generalized functions, characterized by different eigenvalues α and β, are orthogonal to each other in the sense that

$$\int_{-\infty}^{\infty} \phi_{\alpha}^{*}(x) \, \phi_{\beta}(x) \, dx = 0, \qquad \alpha \neq \beta \qquad (1\text{-}136)$$

since when $\phi_{\alpha} \neq 0$ (i.e. at $x = \alpha \neq \beta$) $\phi_{\beta} = 0$, and conversely. The relations (1-135) and (1-136) can be combined into one equation of the form

$$\int_{-\infty}^{\infty} \phi_{\alpha}^{*}(x) \, \phi_{\beta}(x) \, dx = \delta_{\alpha\beta} \qquad (1\text{-}137)$$

where the Kronecker delta, on the r.h.s. of (1-137), is defined by

$$\delta_{\alpha\beta} = \begin{matrix} 0 & \text{if } \alpha \neq \beta \\ \\ 1 & \text{if } \alpha = \beta \end{matrix} \qquad (1\text{-}138)$$

One can construct many representations of the generalized function $\phi(x)$, in addition to the one suggested by Prob. 1-15. As an example, we can write, from (1-25) and (1-26),

$$\int_{-\infty}^{\infty} e^{-t^2} dt = \sqrt{\pi} \qquad (1\text{-}139)$$

and by replacing t with $\sqrt{N}\,(y - \alpha)$, this becomes

$$\sqrt{\frac{N}{\pi}} \int_{-\infty}^{\infty} e^{-N(y-\alpha)^2} dy = 1,$$

from which we can identify

$$\phi_\alpha(y) = \lim_{N \to \infty} \left(\frac{N}{\pi}\right)^{1/4} e^{-N(y-\alpha)^2/2} \qquad (1\text{-}140)$$

The limiting process is required in order that $\phi_\alpha(y)$ have the properties shown in Fig. 1-3. The student can verify (see Prob. 1-16) that (1-40) satisfies (1-137).

Another representation which is sometimes used is the so-called Dirichlet function or diffraction grating function[10]

$$\phi_\alpha(y) = \lim_{N \to \infty} \sqrt{2N} \frac{\sin\left[2\pi N(y - \alpha)\right]}{\left[2\pi N(y - \alpha)\right]} \qquad (1\text{-}141)$$

This function becomes infinite at $y = \alpha$ as $\sqrt{2N}$, and although the function does not vanish for $y \neq \alpha$, nevertheless it does satisfy

$$\int_a^b \phi^2(x)\, dx = 0 \qquad (1\text{-}142)$$

when the interval $b - a$ does not include the origin. We can now demonstrate that the Dirichlet function is normalized in accord with (1-135); let

$$\int_{-\infty}^{\infty} \phi_\alpha^2(y) dy = \int_{-\infty}^{\infty} 2N \frac{\sin^2\left[2\pi N(y - \alpha)\right]}{\left[2\pi N(y - \alpha)\right]^2}\, dy$$

$$= \frac{1}{\pi} \int_{-\infty}^{\infty} \frac{\sin^2 x}{x^2}\, dx \qquad (1\text{-}143)$$

[10]A. Kyrala, *Theoretical Physics* (Philadelphia: W. B. Saunders Company, 1967), Chap. 7.

Now let

$$I = \int_{-\infty}^{\infty} \frac{\sin^2 x}{x^2} dx$$

$$= -\int_{-\infty}^{\infty} \sin^2 x \, d\left(\frac{1}{x}\right)$$

$$= -\left[\frac{\sin^2 x}{x}\right]\Big|_{-\infty}^{\infty} + \int_{-\infty}^{\infty} \frac{2\sin x \cos x \, dx}{x}$$

The integrated part vanishes at both limits, since $\sin x$ is a bounded function, and the integral can be written in the form

$$I = \int_{-\infty}^{\infty} \frac{\sin t}{t} dt$$

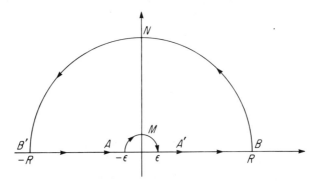

FIG. 1-4. Contour chosen for convenience in evaluating (1-144).

by replacing $2x$ with t. We can evaluate I most conveniently by means of the Cauchy integral formula. We begin by using (1-32) to write

$$I = 2\int_{0}^{\infty} \frac{e^{it} - e^{-it}}{2it} dt \qquad (1\text{-}144)$$

[remember $(\sin t)/t$ is an even function]. We now recognize that

$$f(z) = \frac{e^{iz}}{z} \qquad (1\text{-}145)$$

is analytic for all $z \neq 0$. Thus from (1-51) we have

$$\oint_C f(z) \, dz = 0 \qquad (1\text{-}146)$$

where the contour C excludes the origin of the complex plane. In particular we are interested in choosing C as shown in Fig. 1.4.

We can list the contributions to (1-146) separately as

$$0 = \int_{-R}^{-\varepsilon} f(x)\, dx + \int_{AMA'} f(z)\, dz + \int_{\varepsilon}^{R} f(x)\, dx + \int_{BNB'} f(z)\, dz \qquad (1\text{-}147)$$

The first integral in (1.147) can be written as

$$-\int_{R}^{\varepsilon} f(-x)\, dx = \int_{\varepsilon}^{R} f(-x)\, dx \qquad (1\text{-}148)$$

which can then be combined with the third integral in (1-147) to yield, in terms of I from (1-144),

$$iI = \lim_{\substack{\varepsilon \to 0 \\ R \to \infty}} \int_{-R}^{-\varepsilon} f(x)\, dx + \int_{\varepsilon}^{R} f(x)\, dx \qquad (1\text{-}149)$$

As ε approaches zero, the second integral in (1-147) takes the form

$$\lim_{\varepsilon \to 0} \int_{AMA'} f(z)\, dz = \lim_{\varepsilon \to 0} \int_{\theta = \pi}^{0} \frac{e^{i\varepsilon e^{i\theta}} i\varepsilon e^{i\theta}\, d\theta}{\varepsilon e^{i\theta}} = i \int_{\pi}^{0} d\theta = -i\pi \qquad (1\text{-}150)$$

where we have expressed $z = \varepsilon e^{i\theta}$ over the semicircular path of integration. The last integral in (1-147) can be evaluated by a similar procedure of replacing

$$z = Re^{i\theta} = R[\cos\theta + i\sin\theta]$$

along the semicircular path, labeled BNB' in Fig. 1-4.

$$\int_{BNB'} f(z)\, dz = i \int_{0}^{\pi} [e^{iR\cos\theta}] e^{-R\sin\theta}\, d\theta$$

$$< i \int_{0}^{\pi} e^{-R\sin\theta}\, d\theta \qquad (1\text{-}151a)$$

$$< 2i \int_{0}^{\pi/2} e^{-R\sin\theta}\, d\theta \qquad (1\text{-}151b)$$

where (1-151a) follows as a result of the fact that the magnitude of $e^{iR\cos\theta}$ is less than unity and (1-151b) can be obtained dividing the integral from 0 to π in (1-151a) into the sum of an integral from 0 to $\pi/2$ and one from $\pi/2$ to π, then replacing θ by $(\pi - \chi)$ in the latter (see Prob. 1-19). Since $(\sin\theta)/\theta$ decreases from unity at $\theta = 0$ to $2/\pi$ at $\theta = \pi/2$, we can set

$$R\sin\theta > \frac{2}{\pi} R\theta$$

and consequently

$$\int_{BNB'} f(z)\, dz < 2i \int_{0}^{\pi/2} e^{-2R\theta/\pi}\, d\theta < \frac{\pi i}{R}[1 - e^{-R}] \qquad (1\text{-}152)$$

Thus as R becomes very large the last integral in (1-147) contributes nothing and we can write (1-147), with the aid of (1-149) and (1-150), in the form

$$0 = iI - i\pi \tag{1-153}$$

which, when substituted into (1-143), shows that the Dirichlet function is indeed normalized.

The generalized function discussed in this section bears a strong resemblance to another generalized function known as the *Dirac delta* function, discussed in Ref. 9 and 10. The Dirac delta function, $\delta(x)$ [which should not be confused with the Kronecker δ of (1-138)] obeys (1-134), but instead of being normalized by (1-135), obeys

$$\int_{-\infty}^{\infty} \delta(x)\, dx = 1 \tag{1-154}$$

and can further be shown to satisfy

$$\int_{-\infty}^{\infty} f(x)\, \delta(x - a)\, dx = f(a) \tag{1-155}$$

1-6 THE EULER-MACLAURIN SUM FORMULA

One frequently encounters the problem of having to evaluate a sum of functions of the form

$$\sum_{n=0}^{p} f_{(n)} = f_{(0)} + f_{(1)} + \cdots + f_{(p)} \tag{1-156}$$

An alternative formulation of the problem is that of having to estimate the value of the sum of (1-156) for the situation when p is very large.

Let $f(x)$ denote any function which is defined over some interval for $x \geq 0$, and which has continuous derivatives existing up to an arbitrary order over this interval. For such a function we have

$$f(p) - f(n) = \int_{n}^{p} f'(x)\, dx \qquad (n = 0, 1, 2, ..., p) \tag{1-157}$$

where $f'(x)$ is the first derivative of the function. By simple addition (1-157) takes the form

$$(p + 1)f(p) - \sum_{n=0}^{p} f(n) = \sum_{n=0}^{p} \int_{n}^{p} f'(x)\, dx \tag{1-158}$$

If we now split up each integral in the sum of (1-158) into a sum of integrals of the form

$$\int_{0}^{p} = \int_{0}^{1} + \int_{1}^{2} + \int_{2}^{3} + \cdots + \int_{p-1}^{p} \tag{1-159}$$

where we have suppressed the argument $f'(x)\,dx$ of each integral, we find that the r.h.s. of (1-158) can be written as

$$\sum_{n=0}^{p}\int_{n}^{p}f'(x)\,dx = \int_{0}^{1} + \int_{1}^{2} + \int_{2}^{3} + \cdots + \int_{p-1}^{p}$$

$$+ \int_{1}^{2} + \int_{2}^{3} + \cdots + \int_{p-1}^{p}$$

$$+ \int_{2}^{3} + \cdots + \int_{p-1}^{p}$$

$$\cdots + \int_{p-1}^{p}$$

$$= 1\int_{0}^{1} + 2\int_{1}^{2} + 3\int_{2}^{3} + \cdots + p\int_{p-1}^{p}$$

$$\sum_{n=0}^{p}\int_{n}^{p}f'(x)\,dx = \sum_{k=0}^{p-1}(k+1)\int_{k}^{k+1}f'(x)\,dx \qquad (1\text{-}160)$$

which the student may easily (?) verify by actually expanding the sum over k (see Prob. 1-20). The sum of integrals on the r.h.s. of (1-160) can be recognized as the following integral in terms of the truncation function[11] $[x]$, which denotes the algebraically largest integer which does not exceed x,

$$\sum_{k=0}^{p-1}(k+1)\int_{k}^{k+1}f'(x)\,dx = \int_{0}^{p}([x]+1)f'(x)\,dx \qquad (1\text{-}161)$$

If we now introduce a new function $\phi(x)$ by means of

$$[x] + 1 = \phi(x) + x + 1/2 \qquad (1\text{-}162)$$

and combine (1-158) and (1-160) through (1-162), we find that we can express the sum of (1-156) in the form

$$\sum_{n=0}^{p} f(n) = (p+1)f(p) - \int_{0}^{p}\{\phi(x) + x + 1/2\}f'(x)\,dx$$

$$= (p+1)f(p) - \int_{0}^{p}\phi(x)f'(x)\,dx - \int_{0}^{p}x\,df - 1/2\{f(p) - f(0)\} \qquad (1\text{-}163)$$

When the second integral in (1-163) is integrated by parts and the various terms in $f(p)$ and $f(0)$ combined we obtain

$$\sum_{n=0}^{p} f(n) = \int_{0}^{p}f(x)\,dx + \frac{f(p) + f(0)}{2} - \int_{0}^{p}\phi(x)f'(x)\,dx \qquad (1\text{-}164)$$

---

[11]A. E. Taylor, *Advanced Calculus* (Waltham, Mass.: Blaisdell Publishing Company, 1955), Chap. 1.

Equation (1-164) is the simplest form of the *Euler-Maclaurin sum formula*; also known as the *Euler-Maclaurin series*, and the *Euler-Maclaurin integration formula*. As the last named appelation indicates, the formula finds frequent application in the numerical evaluation of definite integrals;[12] although in general the procedure yields only an asymptotic, rather than a convergent, series. Because of the asymptotic nature of the series obtained by integrating the last integral in (1-164) by parts, the form of the generalized Euler-Maclaurin formula is not unique,[13] but all forms involve the Bernouli numbers and Bernouli polynomials, B_n and $b_n(x)$, respectively, which themselves are not uniquely defined.[13] One form of the generalized Euler-Maclaurin sum formula can be written as[14]

$$\sum_{n=0}^{p} f(a + ns) = \frac{1}{s} \int_a^b f(x)\, dx + \frac{f(b) + f(a)}{2}$$

$$- \sum_{n=1}^{m-1} \frac{(-)^n B_n}{(2n)!} s^{2n-} [f(b)^{(2n-1)} - f(a)^{(2n-1)}] - R_m \quad (1\text{-}165)$$

when the first $2m$ derivatives of $f(x)$ are continuous on the interval (a,b) with $b = a + ps$, and when the interval is divided into p equal parts, where $s = (b - a)/p$. The remainder is given by

$$R_m = \frac{s^{2m}}{(2m)!} \int_0^1 b_{2m}(t) \sum_{n=0}^{p-1} f^{(2m)}(a + ns + st)\, dt \quad (1\text{-}166)$$

where the Bernoulli polynomial of order n, $b_n(x)$, is defined herein by

$$t\frac{e^{xt} - 1}{e^t - 1} = \sum_{n=1}^{\infty} b_n(x)\frac{t^n}{n!} \quad (1\text{-}167)$$

and the nth Bernoulli number, B_n, is defined herein by

$$\frac{t}{2} + \frac{t}{e^t - 1} = 1 + \sum_{n=1}^{\infty} \frac{(-)^{n+1} B_n}{(2n)!} t^{2n} \quad (1\text{-}168)$$

[12]R. G. Stanton, *Numerical Methods for Science and Engineering* (Englewood Cliffs, N.J.: Prentice-Hall, Inc., 1961), Chap. 5.

[13]In addition to Refs. 12 and 14, mention of the Euler-Maclaurin formula will be found in Ref. 6 *supra*; T. A. Bak and J. Lichtenberg, *Mathematics for Scientists* (New York: W. A. Benjamin, Inc., 1966), Chap. 8; J. Irving and N. Mullineux, *Mathematics in Physics and Engineering* (New York: Academic Press Inc., 1959), Chap. 11; H. Lass, *Elements of Pure and Applied Mathematics* (New York: McGraw-Hill Book Company, 1957), Chap. 10; P. Frank and R. von Mises, *Die Differential und Integralgleichungen der Mechanik und Physik* (New York: Dover Publications, Inc., 1961), Vol. I, Chap. 1.

[14]E. T. Whittaker and G. N. Watson, *A Course of Modern Analysis*, (London: Cambridge University Press, 1927) 4th ed., Chap. 7.

with $B_0 \equiv 1$. The first few Bernoulli numbers can be obtained from (1-168), and are found to be

$$B_1 = \frac{1}{6}, \quad B_2 = \frac{1}{30}, \quad B_3 = \frac{1}{42}, \quad B_4 = \frac{1}{30}, \quad B_5 = \frac{5}{66}, \ldots \qquad (1\text{-}169)$$

(see Prob. 1-22).

The special form of the Euler-Maclaurin sum formula, developed in (1-164) arises from (1-165) when $a = 0$ and $b = p$ (so that $s = 1$). In this case we see that the remainder term of (1-166) decays as the reciprocal of $(2m)!$, and if the higher derivatives of the function approach zero, this term may be (and in fact, for most physical applications, will be) negligible for sufficiently large m. In such a situation we may write (1-165) in the form analogous to (1-164) as

$$\sum_{n=0}^{p} f(n) = \int_0^p f(x)\,dx + \frac{f(p) + f(0)}{2}$$
$$+ \sum_{n=1}^{\infty} \frac{(-)^{n+1} B_n}{(2n)!} [f^{(2n-1)}(p) - f^{(2n-1)}(0)] \qquad (1\text{-}170)$$

Frequently the sum in (1-170) converges rapidly and in such case we can make use of (1-169) to write

$$\sum_{n=0}^{p} f(n) = \int_0^p f(x)\,dx + \frac{1}{2}[f(p) + f(0)] + \frac{1}{12}[f'(p) - f'(0)]$$
$$- \frac{1}{720}[f'''(p) - f'''(0)] + \frac{1}{30{,}240}[f^{(V)}(p) - f^{(V)}(0)]$$
$$- \frac{1}{1{,}209{,}600}[f^{(VII)}(p) - f^{(VII)}(0)] + \cdots \qquad (1\text{-}171)$$

which is a convenient form for numerical calculations.

Let us use (1-171) to evaluate, for example, the Riemann Zeta function of argument 4, given by (1-31) which we write as

$$\zeta(4) = \sum_{m=0}^{\infty} \frac{1}{(m+1)^4} \qquad (1\text{-}172)$$

with n replaced by $m + 1$ so that the sum begins with the term $m = 0$ in consonance with (1-171). If we take $f(x) = (x + 1)^{-4}$ and $p = \infty$, we note that $f(p) = 0$ and $f(0) = 1$. The student can easily verify that

$$f(x)^{(n)} = (-)^n \frac{(n+3)!}{3!}(x+1)^{-(n+4)} \qquad (1\text{-}173a)$$

from which we see that $f(p)^{(2n-1)} = 0$, but

$$f(0)^{(2n-1)} = -\frac{[2(n+1)]!}{3!} \qquad (1\text{-}173b)$$

so that $f(0)^{(2n-1)}$ increases rapidly with n, having the value of $-79,833,600$ for $n = 5$. Thus, the sum on the r.h.s. of (1-170) is strongly divergent, and we should not expect to obtain a reasonable approximation to $\zeta(4)$ if we persist in using $f(x) = (x + 1)^{-4}$ in (1-171). However, for the benefit of pertinacious students we proceed to evaluate (1-171). The integral is easily evaluated

$$\int_0^\infty f(x)\, dx = \int_0^\infty (x + 1)^{-4}\, dx = \frac{1}{3} \tag{1-174}$$

and we have

$$\sum_{m=0}^\infty \frac{1}{(m+1)^4} = \frac{1}{3} + \frac{1}{2}\cdot 1 + \frac{1}{12}\cdot 4 - \frac{1}{720}\cdot 120 + \frac{1}{30,240}\, 6,720$$

$$= \frac{1}{1,209,600}\cdot 604,800 + \cdots$$

$$= \frac{1}{3} + \frac{1}{2} + \frac{1}{3} - \frac{1}{6} + \frac{2}{9} - \frac{1}{2} + \cdots$$

$$= 0.8333 \tag{1-175}$$

And, as we anticipated, this result bears little resemblance to (1-72)

$$\zeta(4) = \frac{\pi^4}{90} = 1.0823232 \tag{1-176}$$

It would hardly do for the authors to have spent so much time developing the Euler-Maclaurin sum formula only to demonstrate that it is terribly restricted in scope of application. Let us rewrite (1-172) in the form

$$\zeta(4) = \frac{1}{1^4} + \frac{1}{2^4} + \frac{1}{3^4} + \frac{1}{4^4} + \sum_{m=0}^\infty \frac{1}{(m+5)^4} \tag{1-177}$$

which is certainly equivalent to (1-172) and (1-31). If we now take

$$f(x) = (x + 5)^{-4} \tag{1-178a}$$

we easily see that $f(p) = 0, f(0) = 1/5^4$, and

$$f(x)^{(2n-1)} = -\frac{[2(n+1)]!}{3!}(x + 5)^{-(2n+3)} \tag{1-178b}$$

and

$$f(0)^{(2n-1)} = -\frac{[2(n+1)]!}{3!(5)^{2n+3}} \tag{1-178c}$$

which diverges much more slowly than (1-173b), being -0.0654 for $n = 5$ and $-18,858$ for $n = 10$. The first four terms on the r.h.s. of (1-177) add to 1.0787518 and the integral of $f(x)$ given by (1-178a) has the value

$$\int_0^\infty (x + 5)^{-4}\, dx = \frac{1}{375} = 0.0026666 \tag{1-179}$$

and thus (1-171) and (1-177) lead to

$$\zeta(4) = 1.0787518 + 0.0026666 + \frac{1}{2(5^4)} + \frac{1}{3(5^5)}$$

$$- \frac{1}{6(5^7)} + \frac{2}{9(5^9)} - \frac{1}{2(5^{11})} + \cdots \tag{1-180}$$

$$= 1.0823230$$

which agrees with (1-176) to seven significant figures.

We conclude this section (and this somewhat prolix chapter) with a final application of the Euler-Maclaurin sum formula leading to the Stirling formula discussed in Sec. 1.1 *supra*. Toward this end we take

$$f(x) = \ln(x + 1) \tag{1-181}$$

so that

$$f(x)^{(2n-1)} = \frac{(2n)!}{(x+1)^{2n-1}} \tag{1-182}$$

The integral in (1-170) of the function of (1-181) can be integrated by parts to yield

$$\int_0^p \ln(x+1)\,dx = (p+1)\ln(p+1) - p \tag{1-183}$$

and, by the properties of logarithms, the sum on the l.h.s. of (1-170) takes the form

$$\sum_{n=0}^p \ln(n+1) = \ln\left[(p+1)!\right] \tag{1-184}$$

so that (1-170) can be written

$$\ln\left[(p+1)!\right] = (p+1)\ln(p+1) - p + \frac{1}{2}\ln(p+1)$$

$$+ \sum_{n=1}^{\infty} (-)^n B_n \left[\frac{1}{(p+1)^{2n-1}} - 1\right] \tag{1-185}$$

We can rewrite (1-185) as

$$\ln(p!) = \left(p + \frac{1}{2}\right)\ln(p+1) - p + \sum_{n=1}^{\infty} (-)^n B_n \left[\frac{1}{(p+1)^{2n-1}} - 1\right] \tag{1-186}$$

and by comparison with the asymptotic expansion of $\ln\left[(p+1)\right]$ (as given, e.g., in Chapter 13 of ref. 14) it can be found that the remaining sum in

(1-186) can be identified, in the limit of large p, as $\frac{1}{2} \ln (2\pi)$. When this result is incorporated into (1-186) we find that

$$\ln p! = \left(p + \frac{1}{2}\right) \ln (p + 1) - p + \frac{1}{2} \ln (2\pi) \qquad (1\text{-}187)$$

We note that

$$\ln (p + 1) = \ln \left[p \left(1 + \frac{1}{p} \right) \right] = \ln p + \ln \left(1 + \frac{1}{p} \right) \qquad (1\text{-}188)$$

and, for large p, we can utilize (1-16) to write

$$\ln \left(1 + \frac{1}{p} \right) = \frac{1}{p} \qquad (1\text{-}189)$$

so that

$$\lim_{p \to \infty} \ln (p + 1) = \ln p$$

and thus we can write (1-187) in the form

$$\ln p! \simeq \left(p + \frac{1}{2}\right) \ln p - p + \frac{1}{2} \ln (2\pi) \qquad (1\text{-}190)$$

which the student can easily show is equivalent to (1-30).

PROBLEMS

1-1. Show that the integral of (1-25) can be expressed in terms of the gamma function of (1-28) by transforming $t^2 = u$ and making use of the defining Eq. 1-1.

1-2. Evaluate the coefficients a_4 and a_5 in the expansion of θ in (1-19a) and retaining terms to order t^4 in (1-24), find the next nonzero term in the expansion $\Gamma(p + 1)$ of (1-29).

1-3. Make a table of the relative error in using (1-30) to represent $\Pi(p)$, as a function of p, for values of $p = 1, 10, 100, 1000,$ and 10^{23}. Make a suitable graph of this table.

1-4. Using (1-34), obtain the series expansions for $\sin x$ and $\cos x$ in (1-32) and (1-33) respectively.

1-5. Verify (1-54a) and (1-54b) by expressing

$$\frac{1}{z(z - z_0)} = \frac{A}{z} + \frac{B}{(z - z_0)}$$

and solving for A and B.

1-6. Obtain (1-49) from (1-63) by letting $g(z) = (\sin z)/z$ and verifying that $g(z)$ satisfies all the requirements assumed in obtaining (1-63) in the text.

1-7. (a) Obtain (1-95b) from (1-95a). (b) Using (1-3) and (1-4), obtain (1-96) from (1-95b). (c) From (1-97b) show that $C(\pi)_N = C(\pi)_{(\pi - N)}$.

1-8.   How many different 5-card hands can be obtained from a deck of 52 cards? State any conditions or assumptions you make.

1-9.   In how many ways can a committee of five be formed from seven women and five men if the committee's bylaws require the membership to consist of (a) three women and two men? or (b) of at least two women and at least one man?

1-10. Show that $C(\pi)_N = C(\pi - 1)_N + C(\pi - 1)_{(N-1)}$

1-11. Show that the angle between the base and the side of the parallelogram in Fig. 1-2 is given by $\delta = \tan^{-1}(m/t)$.

1-12. (a) Set up the Lagrangian for the one dimensional simple harmonic oscillator with potential energy $\varepsilon_p = \frac{1}{2}kx^2$. (b) Find the corresponding generalized momentum and obtain the functionally correct Hamiltonian function. (c) Write and solve Hamilton's canonical equations. Now consider a large number of identical particles, all of which obey the equations of (a), (b), and (c) above, and which have, initially, all their positions and momenta such that

$$- \xi \le x \le \xi$$
$$+ \eta \le p \le \eta + \Delta\eta$$

(d) Show on a phase diagram the initial region occupied by the corresponding phase points, and the region occupied at some later time, t. Show by direct calculation that the area occupied by the phase points doesn't change with time. (e) Explain briefly how you would go about solving this problem for a three-dimensional SHMO; discuss the effects of degeneracy.

1-13. Expand the determinant of the Jacobian of (1-124b) by minors (or evaluate the determinant by any method of your choice) and obtain (1-125).

1-14. Show that the last two terms on the r.h.s. of (1-71) are equal to each other. (*Hint*: carry out the indicated sum and compare terms.)

1-15. Define

$$\phi(x) = \begin{cases} 0 & x < \alpha - \varepsilon/2 \\ \varepsilon^{-1/2} & \alpha - \varepsilon/2 \le x \le \alpha + \varepsilon/2 \\ 0 & x < \alpha - \varepsilon/2 \end{cases}$$

show that $\phi(x)$ satisfies (1-135), and when $\varepsilon \to 0$ show that (1-134) is also satisfied. Plot this function and compare with Fig. 1-3.

1-16. Plot $\phi_\alpha(y)$ given by (1-140) for $N = 2, 20, 200$ and demonstrate that (1-140) satisfies (1-137).

1-17. Plot the Dirichlet function of (1-141) as a function of $\theta = 2\pi N(y - \alpha)$ and verify (1-142).

1-18. Use (1-144), (1-145), and (1-148) to verify (1-149).

1-19. Obtain (1-151b) by writing

$$\int_0^\pi e^{-R\sin\theta}d\theta = \int_0^{\pi/2} e^{-R\sin\theta}d\theta + \int_{\pi/2}^\pi e^{-R\sin\theta}d\theta$$

and changing variables in the last term from θ to $\pi - \chi$.

1-20. Satisfy yourself of the veracity of (1-160) by actual expansion of the sum over k [or by any other means of your choice].

1-21. Write the r.h.s. of (1-161) as

$$\int_0^1 (0 + 1)f'(x)\, dx + \int_1^2 (1 + 1)f'(x)\, dx + \cdots,$$

thus making use of the definition of the truncation function $[x]$, and verify that the result is compatible with (1-160).

1-22. Verify that the first three Bernoulli numbers as defined by (1-168), are given by (1-169).

1-23. Fill in all the steps which are not obvious to you between (1-172) and (1-180) and verify the numerical calculations.

1-24. Follow the procedure outlined to evaluate $\zeta(4)$ in Sec. 1.6 by means of the Euler-Maclaurin sum formula to compute $\zeta(3)$ correct to seven decimals. Take $f(x) = (x + 10)^{-3}$. (*Hint*: see Ref. 12.)

1-25. Supply any steps which are not intuitively obvious to you between (1-181) and (1-190) and verify that (1-190) is equivalent to (1-30).

1-26. Verify the relations (1-81a) and (1-81b). [*Hint*: add and subtract

$$\sum_{n=1}^{\infty} \frac{1}{(2n)^p}$$

to (1-73) and regroup terms in units of $\zeta(p)$].

1-27. How many ways may 3 balls be placed in 4 distinguishable boxes (a) if the balls are distinguishable and there is no limit on the number of balls in a box? (b) if the balls are distinguishable but with at most one ball in a box? (c) if the balls are indistinguishable and there is no limit to the number of balls in a box? (d) if the balls are indistinguishable but with at most one ball in a box?

1-28. Show that the harmonic series of order p

$$\sum_{n=1}^{\infty} \frac{1}{n^p} = 1 + \frac{1}{2^p} + \frac{1}{3^p} + \cdots$$

diverges for $p \le 1$ and converges to the zeta function for $p > 1$.

1-29. (a) By direct multiplication, evaluate $5!$ and $10!$ (b) Use Eq. 1-30, Stirling's approximation, to evaluate $5!$ and $10!$ and compare your result with that of part (a).

1-30. Consider 3 digits which can have values of zero to nine for each digit. (a) How many combinations can occur if each digit takes on values from 0 to 9 independently of the other digits? (b) How many combinations will occur if no two digits have the same value?

1-31. Show that the Hamiltonian is conserved if the potential is velocity independent and the Lagrangian has no explicit time dependence, where

$$\frac{\partial L}{\partial q_i} = \frac{d}{dt}\left(\frac{\partial L}{\partial \dot{q}_i}\right)$$

is Lagrange's equation. (*Hint*: See Appendix III.)

2 | *Exordium*

2-1 INTRODUCTION

The subject of statistical mechanics has often been alluded to by students as a somewhat difficult, and perhaps even esoteric discipline. Certainly there can be no doubt (as the student who has perused the preceding chapter can readily attest) that the subject is mathematical in nature. Yet many of the most vocal opprobriums have been issued by competent mathematicians. Some of this feeling may have been justified, in part at least, due to the manner in which the subject formerly was presented to the student. The subject of statistical mechanics has traditionally been considered as one element of a trilogy, the other members of which are thermodynamics and kinetic theory. The more modern practice is to lump all three subjects together under the title *statistical physics*. Some proponents of statistical mechanics have strongly felt that the subject should stand on its own merits, and should be presented to the student independently of thermodynamics or kinetic theory, with the result that the student generally sees no connection or continuity between the subjects. Consequently in this text there has been no attempt to separate or compartmentalize the various constituents of statistical physics into specious categories; to the contrary, an affirmative effort has been made to weave all the elements of statistical physics into an integrated fabric which the authors anticipate will cover the subject satisfactorily.

All three topics—thermodynamics, kinetic theory, and statistical mechanics—concern themselves with heat transfer associated with some kind of system as the state of the system changes in some manner determined by constraints that are imposed on the system.

As the student may recall from a previous thermodynamics course, the subject of what we now call thermodynamics is the oldest of the three, having come of age prior to the development and acceptance of a workable atomic model of matter. The replacement of the caloric theory of heat by the suggestion that heat is a form of energy was made by Benjamin Thompson (later Count Rumford) and Humphry Davy near the close of the eighteenth century. This suggestion gained widespread acceptance toward the middle of the nineteenth century, only after careful experimental attention was devoted to the possibility by James Prescott Joule, and subsequent to the theoretical considerations of Sadi Carnot. The present state of thermodynamic theory owes its sound footing, in part at least, to the efforts of Rudolf Clausius and William Thomson (later Lord Kelvin) and to the ensuing work by J. Willard Gibbs. Thermodynamics is restricted to a consideration of the macroscopic properties of aggregated matter as predicted by a relatively few empirically determined relationships, or laws, completely independent of any assumptions concerning the underlying atomic structure of the substance comprising the aggregated matter. In the words of J. Willard Gibbs,[1]

> The laws of thermodynamics, as empirically determined, express the approximate and probable behavior of systems of a great number of particles, or, more precisely, they express the laws of mechanics for such systems as they appear to beings who have not the fineness of perception to enable them to appreciate quantities of the order of magnitude of those which relate to single particles, and who cannot repeat their experiments often enough to obtain any but the most probable results.

The main goal of statistical mechanics then, is to produce a set of tools, capable of predicting the thermodynamic functions applicable to a given thermodynamic system, taking as the starting point the molecular structure and the intermolecular forces within the aggregated matter, and the development of techniques for skillful application of these tools.

Once the thermodynamic functions, appropriate to the system under consideration, have been determined by statistical mechanics, the thermodynamic laws and relationships can be used to deduce whatever information is desired concerning the system. Thus the areas covered by thermodynamics and statistical mechanics are interdependent, mutually complementary, and in many respects overlap each other.

The nascent stages of statistical mechanics appeared during the latter half of the nineteenth century, when the atomic nature of matter began to be understood, and now is known as the kinetic theory (of matter in general, and of dilute gases in particular). This was the first attempt to apply an atomic approach to macroscopic problems and the first successes were found in the consideration of dilute gases, where the interactions between molecules are minimal. Among the first workers in the study of the kinetic theory were Rudolf Clausius, James Clerk Maxwell, who formulated the distribution

[1]J. W. Gibbs, *Elementary Principles in Statistical Mechanics* (reprint of 1902 ed., (New York: Dover Publications, Inc., 1960), p. viii.

law of molecular velocities, given by (6-2) *infra*, and Ludwig Boltzmann, whose name appears throughout this volume. Further refinements leading to the modern form of the kinetic theory were provided by Sidney Chapman and David Enskog in the second decade of the present century.

The primary stimulus to the more ambitious descipline of what we now refer to as statistical mechanics was provided by Ludwig Boltzmann and J. Willard Gibbs. From the foregoing brief history of the trilogy of thermodynamics, kinetic theory, and statistical mechanics, the reader notices that the same names crop up repeatedly, thus indicating that the original workers in these fields recognized no artificial boundaries between these disciplines.

To realize our goal in statistical mechanics, i.e., to derive or predict the properties of matter in bulk, on a macroscopic scale, from the known, or assumed, or hypothesized atomic structure of matter and the laws of inter-action among its constituent atoms, we make use of the fact that we are dealing with an enormous quantity of atoms or molecules within the matter [of the order of 10^{23} atoms (Avogadro's number) per cm^3] and play the actuarial game practiced (and profited) by insurance companies. In other words, we ignore the detailed behavior of each of the individual atoms in the substance and concentrate our attention on the average or probable values of the aggregate effects of related atomic properties, such as pressure or temperature. Statistical mechanics does not concern itself with the behavior of an individual atom or molecule, reacting to the influence of all the other atoms or molecules within the substance, but merely seeks to discover the (average, or most probable) result of the combined behavior of the entire collection of particles comprising the substance.

The primary goal of thermodynamics is to determine the resulting macro-scopic equilibrium state of a thermodynamic system subject to constraints which characterize the system. The number of parameters required to des-cribe this equilibrium macroscopic state is generally quite small (e.g., in an ideal gas three suffice: the number of particles N, the volume occupied by the particles V, and the temperature T) compared to the number of particles (of the order of 10^{23}) making up the macroscopic system. Thus the number of macroscopic parameters is certainly quite inadequate to specify the detailed molecular or microscopic state of the system. Hence, there will be an extremely large number of different microscopic states which are com-patible with the given macroscopic thermodynamic state. Usually the microscopic states will refer to *energy states*, although we will have occasion to consider *momentum* or *velocity* states. These energy states are rigorously the energy eigenstates or stationary states determined from the application of quantum mechanics to the microstates of the system. The Bohr Corre-spondance Principle however, asserts that quantum-mechanical results merge with results obtained by classical mechanical analysis in the limit of large quantum numbers, or when Planck's constant may be neglected. These conditions are generally found to exist except at very low temperatures Consequently, we shall postpone until Chap. 11 a detailed discussion of quantum-mechanically determining the energy eigenstates of the system (but cf. Sec. 10-3), without introducing appreciable error into our results.

We make use of the fact that there is an enormous number of distinct stationary microstates, all of which are consistent with the particular macroscopic equilibrium thermodynamic state under investigation, by applying the fundamental assumption of statistical mechanics: the value of any physical quantity describing an equilibrium macroscopic thermodynamic system is found by taking the average of the physical quantity over all possible (or accessible) stationary microstates of the system which are consistent with the macroscopic system. This assumption is rephrased in Secs. 3-1 and 5-1 in the form that every distinct stationary microstate of the system has the same a priori probability.

The task before us then is to develop a procedure which will enable us to calculate the macroscopic properties characterizing a system under consideration from the molecular properties of the substance which makes up our system. Since the laws or rules of thermodynamics are valid independently of any theoretical models depicting the nature of molecular interactions within the substance, we shall make frequent appeal to such thermodynamic laws for a complete description of the macroscopic properties of our system. In order to avail ourselves of the thermodynamic relations, we pause in the following section to reflect on some generalities.

2-2   GENERALITIES OF THERMODYNAMICS

We have seen in the preceding chapter (Sec. 1-4) that the state of a mechanical system is completely specified by Newton's laws of motion at any given time if the initial position and velocity of each particle of the system is known. The student with some background in modern physics may already be aware that Newton's laws are inapplicable to describe motion of atomic-sized particles. Even if we are successful in formulating the proper equations to deal with atoms and molecules, we saw in the preceding section of the instant chapter that there is an enormous number of particles (Avogadro's number) to which the equations must be applied. Consequently in thermodynamics a different and much simpler concept of the state of a system is employed than that used to characterize a mechanical system. In thermodynamic considerations, the equilibrium state of a simple (macroscopic) system may be specified by a knowledge of the *internal energy U* of the system, the *volume V* occupied by the system, and the *number of atoms N* (assuming the system to be a chemically pure element; otherwise we would need to specify the number of atoms or molecules in each of the chemically pure components of which the system is composed) in the system. As the complexity of the system is increased more parameters will be required to completely determine an equilibrium state of the system, as for example electric or magnetic dipole moments, or certain elastic strain parameters, or moments and products of inertia.

The parameters which are used to describe the equilibrium thermo-dynamic state of the system such as N, U, and V are proportional to the amount of substance in the system, that is, their value in a composite system is just the sum of their values in any subsystems of which the composite system is composed. Parameters having this property are known as *extensive parameters*.

On the other hand, there exist parameters identifying the state of a system, such as the *temperature T*, the *pressure P*, the *chemical potential μ*, *etc.* which have a single value describing both a composite system and the subsystems comprising the composite system. Parameters possessing this property of being independent of the amount of substance present in the system are called *intensive parameters*.

A third class of parameters may be derived from the extensive para-meters by dividing the extensive parameters by the mass of the system, by the volume of the system, by the number of moles in the system, or by the number of particles in the system. Such quantities are known as *specific parameters* and examples are the density $\rho = M/V$, the specific volume $v = V/M = 1/\rho$, the molar specific heat of the system $c = C/n$, and the specific internal energy per particle $u = U/N$. Since specific para-meters represent the value of an extensive parameter *per unit* volume mass, mole, or particle, it is common to designate the specific parameter as the lowercase of the letter symbol representing the extensive parameter. The student should use care to ascertain whether it is the mass, or volume, or number of moles, or number of particles which is being divided into the extensive quantity.

When the intensive parameters are expressed in terms of the independent extensive parameters, the resulting relationships are known as *equations of state* of the system. In general there will be more than a single equation of state describing a given thermodynamic system, and different forms of a particular equation of state, each form being valid over a limited range of the independent variables upon which the equation of state is expressed. The term equation of state is also used to describe other relationships and the student should be aware that the term has a nonunique meaning. How-ever, the protean nature of the expression should cause the student no great anxiety, and we will not concern ourselves herein with the various nuances of the term. Some authors define the relation expressing the extensive parameters in terms of the independent intensive parameters as the equation of state of the system, which is a kind of inverse of our definition. Furthermore the relation

$$V = V(P, T) \tag{2-1}$$

has been termed a mechanical[2] and a thermal[3] equation of state by different authors; whereas these same authors [for example] denote the entropy, expressed as

$$S = S(P, T) \tag{2-2}$$

as the thermal[2] equation of state, and the internal energy

$$U = U(T, V) \tag{2-3}$$

as a caloric[3] equation of state, even though (2-2) and (2-3) are related to each other by a Legendre transformation[4] [see App. III]

$$S(P, T) = \frac{1}{T} PV + \frac{1}{T} U(T, V) \tag{2-4}$$

Whatever the nature of this thing called an equation of state, it will generally be much too complex to express as a simple mathematical expression when we attempt to deal with actual substances found in nature, and it will thus usually be presented in graphical or tabular form.

Knowledge of the form of a single equation of state will not suffice to enable us to obtain all possible thermodynamic information about the system. To obtain complete thermodynamic knowledge of the system we should have to know all of the equations of state of the system. There is however, a relation among the parameters of the system which is equivalent to the knowledge of all the equations of state of the system. This relation is called the *fundamental relation* of the system and can be expressed analytically as the relation which gives the entropy of the system as a function of the extensive parameters required to characterize the system.

Thus if (somehow) we can find the fundamental relation for a particular system, we are in the position of being able to calculate every conceivable property of the system. In other words, everything that is thermodynamically knowable about the system can be found from the fundamental relation of the system (through the use of thermodynamic laws and relations).

This is the point at which statistical mechanics comes into play. Statistical

---

[2] W. P. Allis and M. A. Herlin, *Thermodynamics and Statistical Mechanics* (New York: McGraw-Hill Book Company, 1952), p. 62.

[3] P. S. Epstein, *Textbook of Thermodynamics* (New York: John Wiley & Sons, Inc., 1937), p. 347.

[4] H. B. Callen, *Thermodynamics* (New York: John Wiley & Sons, Inc., 1960), p. 100.

mechanics provides the fundamental relation for a given system from an analysis based on the atomic or molecular interactions within the system. These molecular interactions will of course depend on the types of molecules present in the system and on the kind of environment that the system is exposed to.

This then, is what the remainder of the book is concerned with: we will investigate different kinds of molecules and different kinds of interactions between the molecules themselves, and between molecules and external forces such as are supplied by gravitation, and by electric and magnetic fields. In the next three chapters we shall develop some of the basic concepts of statistical mechanics which will be used as a foundation for the applications encountered in the ensuing chapters. In the remaining portion of the instant chapter we shall consider some of the principles and relations of thermodynamics, concluding with a description of the various kinds of particles encountered in nature, in terms of the types of statistical rules these particles are observed to obey.

The student will no doubt recall from his earlier encounters with the study of heat and thermodynamics two elementary quantities describing some of the properties of a substance: the volume coefficient of expansion[5]

$$\alpha(P, T) = \frac{1}{V}\left(\frac{\partial V}{\partial T}\right)_P \qquad (2\text{-}5)$$

and the isothermal compressibility[6]

$$\kappa_T(P, T) = -\frac{1}{V}\left(\frac{\partial V}{\partial P}\right)_T \qquad (2\text{-}6a)$$

The student also doubtless remembers that the number of possible independent variables in thermodynamics is so large that the subscript T is required in (2-6a) to remind us that the volume is being regarded as a function of pressure and temperature and that the *isothermal* compressibility is found from the slope of the volume along an isotherm, that is, over such a path that the independent variable T is constant. Now the constancy of the variable T does not imply that the entropy, say, remains constant. Thus it follows that, in general,

$$\left(\frac{\partial V}{\partial P}\right)_T \neq \left(\frac{\partial V}{\partial P}\right)_S \qquad (2\text{-}7)$$

and hence the adiabatic compressibility, defined by

$$\kappa_S(P, S) = -\frac{1}{V}\left(\frac{\partial V}{\partial P}\right)_S \qquad (2\text{-}6b)$$

[5]R. Resnick and D. Halliday, *Physics* (New York: John Wiley & Sons, Inc., 1966), Part I, Chap. 21.

[6]See Ref. 5, Chap. 22.

is not, in general, equivalent to the isothermal compressibility given by (2-6a).

In addition to the relation (2-7) and the chain rule of differentiation[7], which we find convenient to express as

$$\left(\frac{\partial \phi}{\partial u}\right)_\alpha \left(\frac{\partial u}{\partial v}\right)_\alpha \left(\frac{\partial v}{\partial w}\right)_\alpha \cdots \left(\frac{\partial y}{\partial z}\right)_\alpha \left(\frac{\partial z}{\partial \phi}\right)_\alpha = 1 \tag{2-8}$$

the cyclic relation, so named because it is found by the cyclic permutation of the parameters x, y, z in successive terms, given by

$$\left(\frac{\partial x}{\partial y}\right)_z \left(\frac{\partial y}{\partial z}\right)_x \left(\frac{\partial z}{\partial x}\right)_y = -1 \tag{2-9}$$

is frequently useful in obtaining various thermodynamic relations.

In addition to the five thermodynamic variables already mentioned: pressure, P; volume, V; temperature, T; internal energy U; and the entropy S; there are three more parameters frequently encountered in thermodynamics, which will be dealt with in some detail below: enthalpy, H; Helmholtz energy, A; and the Gibbs function, G.

In dealing with equilibrium thermodynamics it is a well established experimental fact that, except in discussing the singular cases involved with phase equilibria, any two of the above listed eight theromodynamic variables will uniquely determine the other six. This means that we can express any six dependent functions in terms of the two parameters chosen as the independent variables.

Of particular interest in comparing the results of various theoretical models depicting the atomic and molecular interactions of a substance with experimentally measured values are the (specific) heat capacities at constant volume and at constant pressure.

$$C_v = \left(\frac{\partial U}{\partial T}\right)_v \tag{2-10a}$$

and

$$C_p = \left(\frac{\partial H}{\partial T}\right)_p \tag{2-10b}$$

respectively. Thus if the internal energy of the system is known (or predicted) as a function of temperature from some theoretical model of the system, the theoretical value of the heat capacity at constant volume is readily obtained from (2-10a). It generally happens that it is theoretically easier to obtain the internal energy as a function of temperature than it is to express the enthalpy of the system as a function of temperature. On the other hand, it is experimentally more convenient to measure C_p than C_v. However the

[7]J. R. Britton, R. B. Kreigh, and L. W. Rutland, *University Mathematics* (San Francisco: W. H. Freeman and Co., 1965), Vol. I, Chap. 10.

combined first and second laws of thermodynamics (see below) provide a relation between C_p and C_v as follows:

$$C_p - C_v = \frac{\alpha^2 TV}{\kappa_T} \qquad (2\text{-}11)$$

where α and κ_T are given by (2-5) and (2-6a), respectively.

In all dealings with thermodynamic quantities we shall of course have to measure or express the various quantities appearing in the equations and expressions in a consistent set of units. For example, the first law of thermodynamics, which represents a statement of the principle of conservation of energy, asserts that the amount of heat, ΔQ, absorbed by the system under consideration from sources external to the system, goes into raising the internal energy of the system, ΔU, and into the amount of external work provided by the system, ΔW. The first law of thermodynamics, which we can write as

$$\Delta Q = \Delta U + \Delta W \qquad (2.12)$$

involves mechanical quantities ($\Delta U + \Delta W$) as well as thermal quantities (ΔQ). For historical reasons thermal and mechanical energies were, in the past, measured in different units and it was customary to introduce a conversion factor

$$J = 4{\cdot}186 \frac{\text{joule}}{\text{calorie}} \qquad (2\text{-}13)$$

called the *mechanical equivalent of heat*, into relations involving both mechanical energy and heat. The mechanical equivalent of heat is now recognized for what it is — merely a conversion factor, analogous to that used to convert ergs to joules; consequently we shall not include the factor J expressly in any of the equations or expressions to follow, and it will be incumbent upon the student to obtain consistency of units throughout his numerical calculations.

In interpreting the mathematical expression of the first law of thermodynamics we have taken ΔQ as positive when the system under consideration *absorbs* heat from its surroundings, and ΔW as positive when *the system does work on its* surroundings. This convention is not uniform throughout the literature, and to aid the student in identifying the convention used in (2-12), the process is depicted in Fig. 2-1 where the arrows indicate the direction of positive energy flow.

The student may remember his previous encounter with the second law of thermodynamics as a jejune experience, since the Kelvin–Planck, the Clausius, and Carathéodory statements are all presented as negative statements of impossible processes.[8] The second law of thermodynamics is

[8]M. W. Zemansky, *Heat and Thermodynamics*, 5th ed., (New York: McGraw-Hill Book Company, 1968), Chaps. 7 and 8.

inextricably involved with the concept of entropy which, we recall, is defined uniquely only for equilibrium states of the system, and when the system is in an equilibrium state, the entropy of the system, like the internal energy of the system, is a function only of the state of the system, and is completely independent of the past history of the system. The second law can then be thought of as defining the change in the entropy of the system when the system absorbs an amount of heat $đQ$, at the temperature T of the system, as the system moves reversibly from one to a neighboring equilibrium state,

$$dS = \frac{đQ}{T} \tag{2-14}$$

where the bar on the differential operator indicates that $đQ$ is not an exact differential, but rather depends on the path over which the system is taken when the heat is absorbed.

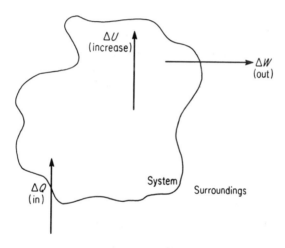

FIG. 2-1. The amount of heat ΔQ absorbed by the closed system results in work being done by the system and an increase in the internal energy of the system.

If we rewrite (2-12) in terms of infinitesimal changes in the state of the system as

$$dU = đQ - đW \tag{2-15}$$

where we have explicitly indicated by the bars in the differential operators that both the heat absorbed and the work done by the system depend on *how* the system changes, we note a striking similarity between the *mathematical forms* of the first and second laws of equilibrium thermodynamics. The first law tells us that although the quantity of heat absorbed and the amount of work done by the system in going from one to a neighboring equilibrium state each individually depend on the particular manner in which the system devolves, their difference is independent of the manner in which the system is taken from one state to the other.

The second law, as we have written it in (2-14), tells us that if the heat absorbed by the system is divided by the temperature of the system at which the heat is absorbed, the result is again a quantity which is independent of the manner in which the heat is supplied to the system. We shall return to this idea of exact differentials in the following section.

Let us now recall some of the relations between the various thermodynamic potentials: A, U, G, H and the quantities P, T, V, and S.

$$A = U - TS \tag{2-16}$$

$$H = U + PV \tag{2-17}$$

$$G = H - TS \tag{2-18}$$

We can gain some insight into the physical meaning of the thermodynamic potentials A, H, and G, by utilizing the first and second laws of thermodynamics for reversible processes. In a reversible isothermal transformation the total work done by the system is equal to the decrease in the Helmholtz energy A. To see this we express (2-16), for an infinitesimal transformation of the system, as

$$dA = dU - T\,dS - S\,dT \tag{2-19}$$

which, with the help of (2-14) and (2-15), becomes

$$dA = -\,\text{đ}W - S\,dT \tag{2-20}$$

and for reversible isothermal processes takes the form

$$\text{đ}W_T = -dA \tag{2-21}$$

as alleged. Thus if the system is mechanically isolated so that it performs no work, and the temperature of the system is kept constant, the Helmholtz energy does not change; and furthermore, the equilibrium state of the system will coincide with the state of minimum Helmholtz energy.

From (2-17) we can write

$$dH = dU + P\,dV + V\,dP \tag{2-22}$$

and if we assume that

$$\text{đ}W = P\,dV \tag{2-23}$$

we can substitute (2-15) into (2-22) to obtain

$$dH = \text{đ}Q + V\,dP \tag{2-24}$$

which, by the definition of heat capacity

$$C_P = \frac{dQ}{dT}\Big|_P = \left(\frac{\partial H}{\partial T}\right)_P$$

yields (2-10b). Thus the enthalpy of the system, which by (2-22) is a state function, possessing an exact differential, plays a role in isobaric processes which is identical to the role played in isothermal transformations by the internal energy.

To clarify the role of the Gibbs function we differentiate (2-18) to obtain

$$dG = dH - T\,dS - S\,dT \tag{2-25}$$

and substitute (2-24) into (2-25) which leads to

$$dG = dQ - T\,dS + V\,dP - S\,dT$$

which by the aid of (2-14) takes the form

$$dG = V\,dP - S\,dT \tag{2-26}$$

Hence in a reversible, isothermal, isobaric process the Gibbs energy is constant. Physically of course, a change of phase between solid and liquid or liquid and vapor, for example, occurs at constant temperature and constant pressure; thus the Gibbs function has the same value for any two phases of a substance in equilibrium (or in fact, for all three phases of a substance in equilibrium at the triple point).

EXAMPLE

Note that (2-26) has been derived under the assumption that *all* of the work done by the system is of the form (2-23). Scientists in general, and chemists in particular are often interested in the total work performed by a system less the expansion work, which we indicate by

$$dW' = dW - P\,dV \tag{2-23a}$$

If we wish to consider *only* the expansion work, dW' then is obviously zero. The student should show to his satisfaction that if (2-23a), rather than (2-23), is used to obtain the expression for dG, the result is

$$dG = -dW' + V\,dP - S\,dT \tag{2-26a}$$

rather than (2-26). From (2-26a) we see that in a reversible, isothermal, isobaric transformation, the net work (total, minus expansion work) done by the system is equal to the decrease in the Gibbs free energy, G, somewhat in analogy with (2-21)

$$dW' = -dG \tag{2-21a}$$

For a conservative system, possessing a potential energy U, we may identify the work done by the system as the negative change in the potential energy [see the discussion re (64) in App. III] of the system. Thus for a mass m in a uniform gravitational field, the gravitational potential energy is given by (1-115) as

$$U_g = mgz$$

and, from (63) of App. III, the electrostatic potential energy of a particle with charge q in an electrostatic field is

$$U_e = q\phi$$

Now from the mathematical form of (2-21a) we can attach a physical (chemical?) significance to another type of potential energy, commonly called the *chemical potential*, and denoted by μ

$$U_{\text{chem}} \equiv G = N\mu \tag{E1}$$

One can interpret gz as being the gravitational potential energy *per unit mass*, and ϕ as the electrostatic potential energy *per unit charge*. In the same manner, *the chemical potential, μ, is the Gibbs energy per particle* (the student should be cautioned that some authors represent μ as the Gibbs energy *per mole*)[9]; when the system traverses an isothermal and isobaric path. One can then define the chemical potential in terms of the Gibbs free energy as

$$\mu = \left(\frac{\partial G}{\partial N}\right)_{P,\,T} \tag{E2}$$

The chemical potential can be thought of as a quantitative measure of the tendency of a particle to escape from the system; since the particles, if they are not constrained, will move spontaneously to the state of lowest chemical potential. Consequently, for a system in equilibrium, the chemical potential must be constant throughout the entire system.

In our discussion we are considering the system to be composed of a single species of particle. The chemists are frequently interested in solutions or mixtures of several types of molecules N_1, N_2, ... For such a system there exists a separate chemical potential for each species of molecule and (E2) is modified to the form

$$\mu_i = \left(\frac{\partial G}{\partial N_i}\right)_{P,\,T,\,N_j}$$

where all particles other than class i are kept constant. Although we shall restrict our development to the system composed of one class of particles, the extension to a multicomponent system is clear.

[9]G. N. Lewis and M. Randall, *Thermodynamics*, 2nd ed. Rev. by K. S. Pitzer and L. Brewer (New York: McGraw-Hill Book Company, 1961), Chap. 14.

We now proceed to formulate another expression for μ, similar to (E2), in terms of the entropy of the system. We will consider the entropy to be a function of U, V, and N. The variability of N merely means that the system is "open" to the addition or expulsion of particles; whereas when N is assumed to be constant, the system is said to be "closed". We can then write

$$dS = \left(\frac{\partial S}{\partial U}\right)_{V,N} dU + \left(\frac{\partial S}{\partial V}\right)_{U,N} dV + \left(\frac{\partial S}{\partial N}\right)_{U,V} dN \qquad (E3)$$

From (2-28) we find

$$\left(\frac{\partial S}{\partial U}\right)_{V,N} = \frac{1}{T}$$

If in (2-9) we make substitutions

$$x \rightarrow S$$
$$y \rightarrow V$$
$$z \rightarrow U$$

we find that

$$\left(\frac{\partial S}{\partial V}\right)_U = \frac{-\left(\frac{\partial U}{\partial V}\right)_S}{\left(\frac{\partial U}{\partial S}\right)_V} = \frac{P}{T}$$

where the last substitutions are due to (2-28) and (2-29). Replacing the two terms on the r.h.s. of (E3) we find

$$dS = \frac{1}{T} dU + \frac{P\, dV}{T} + \left(\frac{\partial S}{\partial N}\right)_{U,V} dN \qquad (E4)$$

Now from (2-17) and (2-18) we have

$$G = U + PV - TS \qquad (2\text{-}18a)$$

which leads directly to

$$dG = dU + P\, dV - T\, dS + V\, dP - S\, dT$$

and, if the system is taken over an isobaric and isothermal path, we see that

$$dG\,|_{P,T} = dU + P\, dV - T\, dS = -T\left(\frac{\partial S}{\partial N}\right)_{U,V} dN$$

where the second equality results directly from (E4). From the definition of μ, given by (E2), we see that

$$\left(\frac{\partial G}{\partial N}\right)_{T,P} = -T\left(\frac{\partial S}{\partial N}\right)_{U,V} = \mu \qquad (E5)$$

We shall have occasion to make use of (E5) in Chap. 5 where we evaluate the absolute entropy of various systems.

Having recalled now the four thermodynamic potentials U, A, H, and G in terms of the parameters P, V, S, and T. We can invoke the first and second laws of thermodynamics to yield the last four parameters in terms of the derivatives of the first four potential energies, in analogy with Hamiltonian and Lagrangian mechanics.

Thus by expressing the external work done by the system as (2-23), and by substituting the second law of thermodynamics, (2-14), into (2-15), the first law of thermodynamics can be written as

$$dU = T\,dS - P\,dV \qquad (2\text{-}27)$$

from which follow the two relations

$$T = \left(\frac{\partial U}{\partial S}\right)_V \qquad (2\text{-}28)$$

and

$$P = -\left(\frac{\partial U}{\partial V}\right)_S \qquad (2\text{-}29)$$

Similarly, by substituting (2-23) into (2-20) we find

$$P = -\left(\frac{\partial A}{\partial V}\right)_T \qquad (2\text{-}30)$$

and

$$S = -\left(\frac{\partial A}{\partial T}\right)_V \qquad (2\text{-}31)$$

whereas substitution of (2-14) into (2-24) leads to

$$T = \left(\frac{\partial H}{\partial S}\right)_P \qquad (2\text{-}32)$$

and

$$V = \left(\frac{\partial H}{\partial P}\right)_S \qquad (2\text{-}33)$$

with (2-26) directly giving rise to

$$V = \left(\frac{\partial G}{\partial P}\right)_T \qquad (2\text{-}34)$$

and

$$S = -\left(\frac{\partial G}{\partial T}\right)_P \qquad (2\text{-}35)$$

We can now easily demonstratĕ the origin of (2-11), which was stated *supra* without proof. If the internal energy of the system is assumed to be a function of the volume and temperature [i.e., V and T are taken as the independent variables] we may express

$$dU = \left(\frac{\partial U}{\partial T}\right)_V dT + \left(\frac{\partial U}{\partial V}\right)_T dV \tag{2-36}$$

which, when substituted in to (2-27) leads to

$$dS = \frac{1}{T}\left(\frac{\partial U}{\partial T}\right)_V dT + \frac{1}{T}\left[P + \left(\frac{\partial U}{\partial V}\right)_T\right] dV \tag{2-37}$$

from which it follows that

$$\left(\frac{\partial S}{\partial V}\right)_T = \frac{1}{T}\left[P + \left(\frac{\partial U}{\partial V}\right)_T\right] \tag{2-38}$$

From (2-31) we see that

$$\left(\frac{\partial S}{\partial V}\right)_T = -\left[\frac{\partial}{\partial V}\left(\frac{\partial A}{\partial T}\right)_V\right]_T = -\frac{\partial^2 A}{\partial V \partial T} \tag{2-39}$$

and, assuming that the second derivative of the Helmholtz energy in (2-39) exists and is continuous,[10] it also follows that the order of differentiation is immaterial, so that

$$\frac{\partial^2 A}{\partial V \partial T} = \frac{\partial^2 A}{\partial T \partial V} \tag{2-40}$$

notwithstanding the relation (2-7), which applies to first derivatives. Hence, from (2-30) we find

$$\left(\frac{\partial P}{\partial T}\right)_V = -\left[\frac{\partial}{\partial T}\left(\frac{\partial A}{\partial V}\right)_T\right]_V = -\frac{\partial^2 A}{\partial T \partial V} \tag{2-41}$$

Since, by reason of (2-40), (2-41) and (2-39) are equivalent, we see that

$$\left(\frac{\partial P}{\partial T}\right)_V = \left(\frac{\partial S}{\partial V}\right)_T \tag{2-42}$$

Now (2-42) is the result of differentiating (2-30) and (2-31) and making use of (2-40). Similar relations result from applying this procedure to each of the pairs of equations: (2-28) and (2-29); (2-32) and (2-33); and (2-34) and (2-35); respectively

$$\left(\frac{\partial T}{\partial V}\right)_S = -\left(\frac{\partial P}{\partial S}\right)_V \tag{2-43}$$

[10]L. Brand, *Advanced Calculus* (New York: John Wiley & Sons, Inc., 1955), p. 163.

$$\left(\frac{\partial T}{\partial P}\right)_S = \left(\frac{\partial V}{\partial S}\right)_P \tag{2-44}$$

$$\left(\frac{\partial V}{\partial T}\right)_P = -\left(\frac{\partial S}{\partial P}\right)_T \tag{2-45}$$

The four relations (2-42) through (2-45) are referred to by some authors as the *Maxwell relations*, whereas other authors ascribe to equations (2-28) through (2-35) this appellation. We see that both sets of relations are inter-related through the generalized condition of (2-40), and so the particular name given to either set of relations is immaterial. ,

Returning to our derivation of (2-11), we see that (2-42) substituted into (2-38) leads to

$$\frac{1}{T}\left[P + \left(\frac{\partial U}{\partial V}\right)_T\right] = \left(\frac{\partial P}{\partial T}\right)_V \tag{2-46}$$

From (2-5) and (2-6a) we note that

$$\frac{\kappa_T}{\alpha} = -\left(\frac{\partial V}{\partial P}\right)_T \left(\frac{\partial T}{\partial V}\right)_P \tag{2-47a}$$

which, by the cyclic relation of (2-9), takes the form

$$\frac{\kappa_T}{\alpha} = \frac{1}{\left(\frac{\partial P}{\partial T}\right)_V} \tag{2-47b}$$

so that (2-46) becomes

$$\frac{1}{T}\left[P + \left(\frac{\partial U}{\partial V}\right)_T\right] = \frac{\alpha}{\kappa_T} \tag{2-48}$$

We now substitute (2-10a), (2-23), and (2-36) into the equation expressing the first law of thermodynamics, (2-15), to obtain

$$đQ = C_V \, dT + \left[P + \left(\frac{\partial U}{\partial V}\right)_T\right] dV \tag{2-49}$$

The heat capacity of a system at constant pressure is the rate of absorbing heat with temperature at constant pressure

$$đQ\Big|_P = C_P \, dT_P \tag{2-50}$$

and thus (2-49) takes the form

$$C_P - C_V = \left[P + \left(\frac{\partial U}{\partial V}\right)_T\right]\left(\frac{\partial V}{\partial T}\right)_P \tag{2-51}$$

which, with the aid of (2-5), takes the form

$$C_P - C_V = \alpha V \left[P + \left(\frac{\partial U}{\partial V} \right)_T \right] \tag{2-52}$$

Substitution of (2-48) into (2-52) leads directly to (2-11).

2-3   THERMODYNAMIC TEMPERATURE

When a simple thermodynamic system undergoes a quasi-static change such that the volume of the system increases by dV, the work dW done by the system is given by

$$dW = P \, dV \tag{2-23}$$

This is sometimes referred to as the mechanical work performed by the system. We note that the work is an extensive property of the system and is given as the product of an intensive parameter (the pressure) and an extensive parameter (dV). We also see that, in analogy with mechanics where we write the work as the product of a force and displacement,

$$dW = \mathbf{F} \cdot \mathbf{dx} \tag{2-53}$$

the pressure plays the part of a generalized force (the intensive parameter) and the volume assumes the role of a generalized coordinate (the extensive parameter). If we assume that the system possesses a magnetic dipole moment μ, and is placed in a magnetic field $\mathbf{B}$, the amount of work performed by the system in a quasi-static process would be given by

$$dW = P \, dV + \mathbf{B} \cdot \mathbf{d\mu} \tag{2-54}$$

(see Sec. 6-2), where $\mathbf{B}$ represents the (intensive) generalized force component and $\mathbf{d\mu}$ plays the part of the (extensive) generalized coordinate.

In the preceding section we noted that heat, like work, is not a state function of the system; yet it has to follow that, in a quasi-static process, we must be able to express dQ as a sum of products of intensive generalized forces with extensive generalized coordinates. Thus, for a thermodynamic system with n degrees of freedom, the heat absorbed by the system can be represented by

$$dQ = \sum_{k=1}^{n} y_k(x_1, x_2, \ldots, x_n) \, dx_k \tag{2-55}$$

where the x_i play the part of generalized coordinates and the y_i represent the generalized forces. If dQ, appearing in (2-55), were in fact an exact differential, it would be possible to write

$$dQ = \sum_{k=1}^{n} \frac{\partial Q}{\partial x_k} dx_k \tag{2-56}$$

In general it is found that (2-56) does not hold; however all is not lost, for frequently one can find an integrating factor $\lambda(x_1, x_2, \ldots, x_n)$ such that when (2-55) is multiplied by λ, the result is an exact differential $d\phi$, given by

$$d\phi(x_1, x_2, \ldots, x_n) = \lambda(x_1, x_2, \ldots, x_n)\, dQ \tag{2-57}$$

$$= \sum_{k=1}^{n} \lambda y_k \, dx_k \tag{2-58}$$

But in analogy with (2-56), if $d\phi$ is an exact differential, it must be possible to express it as

$$d\phi = \sum_{k=1}^{n} \frac{\partial \phi}{\partial x_k} dx_k \tag{2-59}$$

and by equating coefficients in the sums of (2-58) and (2-59) we can identify

$$\lambda y_k = \frac{\partial \phi}{\partial x_k} \tag{2-60}$$

Hence

$$\frac{\partial^2 \phi}{\partial x_j \cdot \partial x_k} = \frac{\partial(\lambda y_k)}{\partial x_j} \tag{2-61a}$$

and similarly

$$\frac{\partial^2 \phi}{\partial x_k \partial x_j} = \frac{\partial(\lambda y_j)}{\partial x_k} \tag{2-61b}$$

But it is well known[9] [cf. the discussion re (2-40)] that if $\partial\phi/\partial x_k \, (= \lambda y_k)$ and $\partial\phi/\partial x_j (= \lambda y_j)$ both exist [and here we have assumed that they do by reason of (2-55) and (2-59)], and if $\partial^2\phi/\partial x_j \, \partial x_k$ is continuous (and for most functions of interest to physicists and engineers this condition will be satisfied), then

$$\frac{\partial^2 \phi}{\partial x_j \, \partial x_k} = \frac{\partial^2 \phi}{\partial x_k \, \partial x_j} \tag{2-62}$$

and consequently,

$$\frac{\partial(\lambda y_j)}{\partial x_k} = \frac{\partial(\lambda y_k)}{\partial x_j} \qquad j, k = 1, 2, \ldots, n \tag{2-63}$$

The relation expressed by (2-63) is known as the reciprocity relation and is a statement of the necessary and sufficient condition that $d\phi$ be an exact differential.

For $n = 1$ or 2, an integrating factor always exists (although it may be difficult to determine), whereas for $n > 2$ there are imperfect differentials for which no integrating factor exists. On the other hand if [as we assumed in writing (2-55)] the heat $đQ$ is absorbed through a reversible process, there does exist an integrating factor, which we can identify as the reciprocal of the thermodynamic temperature. The function ϕ, in this event, becomes the entropy of the system,[11] S, as we can see by starting with the first law of thermodynamics and (2-23)

$$đQ = dU + P\,dV \tag{2-64a}$$

$$= \left(\frac{\partial U}{\partial T}\right)_V dT + \left[P + \left(\frac{\partial U}{\partial V}\right)_T\right] dV \tag{2-64b}$$

Assuming that the entropy exists and is a function of the temperature and volume we can make use of (2-38) to write

$$\frac{đQ}{T} = \frac{1}{T}\left(\frac{\partial U}{\partial T}\right)_V dT + \left(\frac{\partial S}{\partial V}\right)_T dV \tag{2-65}$$

Expressing the temperature on the r.h.s. of (2-65) by (2-28), and employing the cyclic relation (2-8), we find that (2-65) becomes (see Prob. 2-3)

$$\frac{đQ}{T} = \left(\frac{\partial S}{\partial T}\right)_V dT + \left(\frac{\partial S}{\partial V}\right)_T dV \tag{2-66}$$

which is the equivalent to the statement of the second law of thermodynamics, given by (2-14).

At this point the astute student may well point out that (2-66) is the result of *assuming* that the entropy function exists and has the properties of (2-28) and (2-38) *which were obtained from the relation (2-14)*, and hence we have done nothing more than exhibit the consistency of the relation (2-14). To such a charge no adequate defense can be presented. The authors hasten, however, to refer such a student to more thorough discussions concerning the interpretation of the reciprocal of the temperature as an integrating factor for $đQ$, which the student should find readily available.[12]

Although it is true that the absolute temperature can be identified with (the reciprocal of) an integrating factor of $đQ$, this fact is not sufficient to uniquely define the absolute temperature, since any differential expression

[11] A. Sommerfeld, *Lectures on Theoretical Physics*; Vol. V, Thermodynamics and Statistical Mechanics (New York: Academic Press, Inc., 1956), Chap. 1.

[12] See for example R. Weinstock, *American Journal of Physics* **35**, 566 (1967); M. W. Zemansky, *American Journal of Physics* **34**, 914 (1966), and references contained therein; A. B. Pippard, *Elements of Classical Thermodynamics* (London: Cambridge University Press, 1961), Chap. 4.

such as (2-55) which possesses an integrating factor will, in actuality, have an infinite number of integrating factors, which we can see in the following manner: let (2-57) be multiplied by any arbitrary function of ϕ, say $f(\phi)$, then since λ is an integrating factor of dQ, $\lambda f(\phi)$ will also be an integrating factor of $đQ$

$$\lambda f(\phi) \, đQ = f(\phi) \, d\phi$$
$$= d\psi \qquad (2\text{-}67)$$

where

$$\psi = \int f(\phi) \, d\phi \qquad (2\text{-}68)$$

But, among all such integrating factors, there will exist one which can be distinguished from all the others in the following manner (for a slightly different, but more detailed discussion of this procedure for determining the physical significance of the integrating factor, see the article by Zemansky in ref. 11): Consider several thermodynamic systems Σ, Σ', Σ'', ..., so arranged that they all are capable of exchanging heat reversibly with each other; when thermal equilibrium has been established among all the systems, the systems will then be all at the same temperature. Consequently, although each one of the systems Σ, Σ', Σ'', ..., will have an infinite number of different integrating factors, there will be one such integrating factor which is common to all the various systems. This one common integrating factor is then the reciprocal of the absolute temperature common to all the systems in thermal equilibrium, and is characterized by the two conditions:

(a) $1/T$ is the integrating factor of $đQ$ in a reversible transformation, and
(b) this integrating factor is the same for all systems in thermodynamic equilibrium with each other.

As an example of an application and interpretation of an integrating factor, let us consider a system performing only mechanical work as given by (2-23). For such a system we may write

$$đW = P \, dV + 0 \, dT \qquad (2\text{-}69)$$

We see that $đW$ is not a perfect differential since the reciprocity relation requires that for $đW$ to be an exact differential

$$\left(\frac{\partial P}{\partial T}\right)_V = \left(\frac{\partial 0}{\partial V}\right)_T \qquad (2\text{-}70a)$$

The r.h.s. of (2-70a) is, of course, zero, whereas the l.h.s. of (2-70a) is given by (2-47b), which generally is not zero.

If we multiply both sides of (2-69) by an integrating factor $\lambda(V, T)$, the reciprocity relation (2-63) is satisfied by

$$\left[\frac{\partial(\lambda P)}{\partial T}\right]_V = 0 = \lambda\frac{\alpha}{\kappa_T} + P\left(\frac{\partial\lambda}{\partial T}\right)_V \tag{2-70b}$$

which can be integrated to yield $\lambda(V, T)$ as

$$\ln\frac{\lambda}{\lambda_0} - \ln f(V) = -\int\frac{\alpha\,dT}{P\kappa_T} \tag{2-71}$$

or

$$\lambda = \lambda_0\,f(V)\,e^{-\int\frac{\alpha\,dT}{P\kappa_T}} \tag{2-72}$$

where $f(V)$ is an arbitrary function of the volume.

To be more specific, let the system under consideration be an ideal gas, whose equation of state is given (as we shall discover in Chap. 5) by

$$PV = nRT \tag{5-24}$$

The student can easily show (see Prob. 2-4) that for such a system

$$\alpha = 1/T \tag{2-73a}$$

and

$$\kappa_T = \frac{1}{P} \tag{2-73b}$$

so that (2-72) becomes

$$\lambda = \frac{\lambda_0\,f(V)}{T} \tag{2-74}$$

Now with the aid of (2-74) we can write (2-69) as

$$\lambda\,dW = \lambda_0\,f(V)\frac{P}{T}\,dV = \lambda_0\,f(V)\,nR\frac{dV}{V} \tag{2-75}$$

Inasmuch as $f(V)$ is an arbitrary function, we may express

$$f(V) = -\frac{V}{nR\lambda_0}\frac{dA}{dV} \tag{2-76}$$

where A is some new function which we now proceed to identify on physical grounds.

Since the coefficient of dT in (2-69) is zero, the equation would appear unchanged if the process of performing the work was conducted in an isothermal manner, for in this event it would be dT that was zero. But we saw in the preceding section, from (2-21), that in an isothermal process the amount of work done by any (arbitrary) system (not merely an ideal gas) is just the negative of the Helmholtz energy. If we substitute (2-76) into (2-74) we find

$$\lambda = -\frac{V}{nRT}\frac{dA}{dV} = -\frac{1}{P}\left(\frac{\partial A}{\partial V}\right)_T \qquad (2\text{-}77)$$

in terms of our isothermal interpretation and the equation of state for our system. But from (2-30) we see that the r.h.s. of (2-77) is unity and hence (2-75) becomes

$$\lambda \, đW = đW = -dA \qquad (2\text{-}78)$$

were we have used (2-76) in the r.h.s. of (2-75). Since (2-78) is identical to (2-21) we interpret the quantity A as the Helmholtz energy and we see that for an isothermal process the integrating factor is just unity.

2-4 PERFECT GAS

The term perfect gas has frequently been used with different meanings, and consequently there has resulted some degree of confusion which holds over until the present time. We shall attempt to avoid this ambiguity by modifying the term with a precise statement of the properties which we, at any given time, attribute to the gas. In particular we shall be interested in (ignoring) the effects of *cohesion* and *covolume* in a real gas. We shall speak of cohesion as the phenomenon of intermolecular forces holding matter together. It is an interaction between adjacent parts of the matter and acts throughout the interior of the substance composing the matter. The term *covolume* is used to designate the correction applied to the volume of the gas to account for the effect of the volume of the molecules comprising the gas, although this term is not strictly the molecular volume itself.

It used to be thought (prior to the discovery of the significance of Planck's constant, h) that when a gas has its molecules sufficiently far removed from each other on the average, so that the effects arising from cohesion and covolume could be neglected:

(a) that it would obey the law of Boyle-Mariotte – that at a given temperature

$$PV = \text{constant} \qquad (2\text{-}79)$$

(b) that the product (2-79) would define a thermodynamic temperature scale – that is, that the gas would follow the law of *Gay-Lussac* (Charles' law):

$$\frac{PV}{T} = \text{const} \qquad (2\text{-}80)$$

(c)   and that the gas would obey Joule's law — that its internal energy
      would be a function only of the temperature:

$$U = U(T) \tag{2-81}$$

We now know that this is not the case. A gas in which the effects of cohesion
and covolume can be ignored in general does not obey the laws of Boyle-
Mariotte, Gay-Lussac, or Joule; and in order for the gas without cohesion
and covolume to obey these three laws it is necessary that the gas obey a
supplementary condition, which requires the introduction of the constant h;
the gas must be *nondegenerate*. When we say the gas is nondegenerate, we
mean that the gas is adequately described (insofar as agreement with experiments are concerned) by the application of classical or Maxwell-Boltzmann-
Planck statistics (*cf.* Sec. 3-2). This condition will prevail when the density
of particles in the gas system is much less than the number of states (per unit
volume of the system) which are accessible or available for occupation by
the particles (see the discussion in Sec. 5-3 A *infra*). This topic of degeneracy
will be pursued in the following section of the instant chapter, wherein it will
be alleged that the classical statistics is a limiting approximation to the two
forms of quantum statistics which becomes valid when the probability of a
quantum state being occupied by a particle of the system becomes small.

We now represent our gas without cohesion and covolume as being
composed of molecules, whose volume may be neglected, which on the
average are far removed from one another. We shall suppose that the
molecules are enclosed in a rectangular box limited by six partitions located
at

$$
\begin{aligned}
x_1 &= 0 & x_2 &= a \\
y_1 &= 0 & y_2 &= b \\
z_1 &= 0 & z_2 &= c
\end{aligned}
\tag{2-82}
$$

as shown in Fig. 2-2.

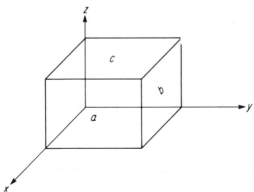

FIG. 2-2. Box of dimensions $a \times b \times c$ enclosing a
gas without cohesion and covolume.

The forces acting on a molecule are of two kinds: internal forces due to, and exchanged with, the other molecules, and external forces transmitted to the molecule from the walls of the box.

One can define the virial of Clausius by[13]

$$\frac{1}{T}\int_0^T \sum \mathbf{F}_i \cdot \mathbf{r}_i \, dt = \frac{1}{T}\int_0^T \sum m_i \, \mathbf{r}_i \cdot \ddot{\mathbf{r}}_i \, dt, \tag{2-83}$$

where the sum is to be taken over all the molecules of the gas, and the integrals provide the time average over a very long time T. The quantity in the sum on the right-hand side of (2-83) can be rearranged as

$$m_i \mathbf{r}_i \cdot \ddot{\mathbf{r}}_i = m_i \frac{d}{dt}(\mathbf{r}_i \cdot \mathbf{v}_i) - m_i v_i^2$$

$$= m_i \frac{d}{dt}\left[\frac{d}{dt}\left(\frac{1}{2}r_i^2\right)\right] - 2\varepsilon_{k_i}$$

$$m_i \mathbf{r}_i \cdot \ddot{\mathbf{r}}_i = \frac{1}{2}\frac{d^2}{dt^2}(m_i r_i^2) - 2\varepsilon_{k_i} \tag{2-84}$$

where the velocity of the molecule has been written as

$$\mathbf{v}_i \equiv \dot{\mathbf{r}}_i$$

and ε_{k_i} is the kinetic energy of the ith molecule.

We recognize the moment of inertia of the system as

$$I = \sum m_i r_i^2 \tag{2-85}$$

and the total kinetic energy of the system as

$$E_k = \sum \varepsilon_{k_i} \tag{2-86}$$

in terms of which we can express the virial of Clausius as

$$\frac{1}{T}\int_0^T \sum \mathbf{F}_i \cdot \mathbf{r}_i \, dt = \frac{1}{2T}\int_0^T d\left(\frac{dI}{dt}\right) - \frac{2}{T}\int_0^T E_k \, dt \tag{2-87}$$

The first integral on the r.h.s. of (2-87) is perfect and the remaining two integrals are just the time averages of the integrands, so we can write (2-87) as

$$\langle \sum \mathbf{F}_i \cdot \mathbf{r}_i \rangle_t = \frac{1}{2T}\left[\left(\frac{dI}{dt}\right)_T - \left(\frac{dI}{dt}\right)_0\right] - 2\langle E_k \rangle_t \tag{2-88}$$

[13]H. Goldstein, *Classical Mechanics* (Reading, Mass.: Addison-Wesley Publishing Company, 1950), p. 70.

Now if the gas is in an equilibrium steady state, the time rate of change of the moment of inertia of the system will be of sensibly the same value at time T and at time O, and will at least display no secular change with T. Consequently, the first term on the r.h.s. of (2-88) is effectively null, and we have

$$\langle \Sigma \mathbf{F}_i \cdot \mathbf{r}_i \rangle_t = -2\langle E_k \rangle_t \tag{2-89}$$

Eq. (2-89) is a statement of the theorem of Clausius, who called the expression on the l.h.s. *the virial*.

Let us calculate the virial to our gas enclosed by the (imaginary) geometrical boundaries shown in Fig. 2-2. The forces in the virial are, as we mentioned earlier, made up of the forces of interaction between the molecules and the stresses across the physical or geometrical boundary. The internal force on molecule i due to collision with molecule j is $\mathbf{F}_{ij}$, and from Newton's third law, molecule j receives a force of $\mathbf{F}_{ji} = -\mathbf{F}_{ij}$ as a result of the collision. These two forces appear in the virial as

$$\mathbf{F}_{ij} \cdot \mathbf{r}_i + \mathbf{F}_{ji} \qquad \mathbf{F}_{ij} \cdot (\mathbf{r}_i - \mathbf{r}_j) \tag{2-90}$$

On impact, $\mathbf{F}_{ij}$ may be quite large, but, since we have ignored the volumes occupied by the molecules, the two radii $\mathbf{r}_i$ and $\mathbf{r}_j$ are equal, and the virial on impact is null. At some distance between the molecules, $\mathbf{r}_i \neq \mathbf{r}_j$, but $\mathbf{F}_{ij} = 0$, since we have neglected the cohesion forces between molecules of the gas. Consequently, a gas without cohesion and covolume has a zero internal virial.

The other contribution to the virial is due to the stresses across the geometrical (or even physical for that matter) boundary in Fig. 2-2. The stress (force per unit area of the boundary) is what we call the pressure. In the absence of surface tension or external force fields we require the pressures on any boundary or across any internal surface of the gas to be always equal. The hydrostatic pressure, P, will be equal to the (negative of the) tensile force per unit area since the shearing stresses will all be zero[14]. Thus the force components will be given by $-\alpha P\, dS$, $-\beta P\, dS$, and $-\gamma P\, dS$, where α, β, γ are the direction cosines of the outward normal to the surface vector $\mathbf{dS} = \hat{n}\, dS$, and are given by $\alpha = \hat{i} \cdot \hat{n}$, $\beta = \hat{j} \cdot \hat{n}$, $\gamma = \hat{k} \cdot \hat{n}$, where $\hat{i}, \hat{j}, \hat{k}$ are the conventional unit vectors along the x, y, and z axes, respectively. The virial then takes the form

$$\langle \Sigma \mathbf{F}_i \cdot \mathbf{r}_i \rangle_t = \langle -P \iint \mathbf{r} \cdot d\mathbf{S} \rangle_t$$

$$= \langle -P \iiint \nabla \cdot \mathbf{r}\, dV \rangle_t \tag{2-91}$$

[14]F. W. Constant, *Theoretical Physics* (Reading, Mass.: Addison-Wesley Publishing Company, 1954), Vol. 1, Chap. 11.

where the right-hand side of (2-91) follows as an immediate consequence of the divergence theorem. Since $\nabla \cdot \mathbf{r} = 3 = $ constant, we see that

$$\langle \Sigma \mathbf{F}_i \cdot \mathbf{r}_i \rangle_t = \langle - P3V \rangle_t$$

$$- 2\langle E_k \rangle_t = - 3PV \tag{2-92}$$

Eq. 2-92 is valid in general for any gas [however; see the discussion in Chap. 9 *re* (9-17) describing a photon gas]. In particular (2-92) can be applied to a monatomic gas. We define a monatomic gas by the condition that it possesses no other energy than its kinetic energy of translation. In (2-92) we can denote the total energy of the molecules in the system by U, where

$$U \equiv \langle E_k \rangle_t \tag{2-93}$$

and then we have as the relation to be obeyed by a gas system composed of monatomic molecules without cohesion and covolume:

$$PV = \frac{2}{3} U \tag{2-94}$$

The total internal energy of such a system is then equal to the time average of the system kinetic energy (of translation) and is constant.

Thus far we have considered only the mechanical aspects of such a model for the gas system. We can now use (2-94) in the differential form of the first law of thermodynamics, (2-15):

$$đQ = dU + đW \tag{2-95}$$

If we assume that the system is capable only of mechanical work through an expansion, then

$$đW = P \, dV \tag{2-23}$$

After differentiating (2-94) and incorporating (2-23) in (2-95), we see that

$$đQ = \frac{3}{2}(P \, dV + V \, dP) + P \, dV$$

$$= \frac{5}{2} P \, dV + \frac{3}{2} V \, dP$$

$$= PV \left[\frac{5}{2} \frac{dV}{V} + \frac{3}{2} \frac{dP}{P} \right]$$

$$= PV \, d \left[\ln V^{5/2} P^{3/2} \right] \tag{2-96}$$

One of the two conditions which the absolute temperature is required to satisfy, discussed near the end of Sec. 2-3, is that its reciprocal must be an integrating factor for the heat reversibly absorbed by the monatomic gas system. Thus, from the second law of thermodynamics

$$dS = \frac{\text{đ}Q}{T} = \frac{PV}{T} d[\ln(V^{5/2} P^{3/2})] \qquad (2\text{-}97)$$

If (2-97) is to be an exact differential it will be necessary that the quantity PV/T be a function of $V^{5/2} P^{3/2}$, or $V^5 P^3$, or some other combination consistent with the logarithmic term in (2-97). Thus we can express

$$\frac{PV}{T} = F(V^5 P^3) = F\left(\frac{V^3 P^3}{T^3} V^2 T^3\right)$$

$$= F\left[\left(\frac{PV}{T}\right)^3 V^2 T^3\right]$$

$$= G(V^2 T^3)$$

or

$$\frac{PV}{T} = f(V T^{3/2}) \qquad (2\text{-}98)$$

From (2-98) we see that, in general, PV/T is not a constant, and thus a monatomic gas without cohesion and covolume follows neither the law of Boyle-Mariotte (2-79), nor that of Gay Lussac, (2-80). Also from (2-94) and (2-98) we find

$$U = \frac{3}{2} T f(V T^{3/2}) \qquad (2\text{-}99)$$

and so, in general, such a gas system does not obey Joule's law, (2-81), either since, from (2-99) the internal energy is a function of V as well as T.

If we inquire as to the conditions under which the monatomic gas without cohesion and covolume *will* obey the law of Boyle-Mariotte (and we shall denote such a gas as a Mariotte gas), that is to say, if $T = $ constant then $PV = $ constant, we find, from (2-98),

$$\frac{PV}{T} = \frac{\text{const}}{\text{const}} = f(V T^{3/2}) \qquad (2\text{-}100)$$

and since the ratio of two constants is a constant we have

$$f(V T^{3/2}) = \text{const} = b \qquad (2\text{-}101)$$

and thus

$$PV = b T \qquad (2\text{-}102)$$

But (2-102) is just an expression of Charles' law and so a Mariotte gas is also a Gay-Lussac gas. Furthermore, a Mariotte gas also obeys Joule's law, since (2-99) and (2-101) may be combined to yield

$$U = \frac{3}{2}bT \tag{2-103}$$

which is equivalent to the condition expressed by (2-81).

We can express (2-97) in the form

$$dS = \frac{3}{2}\frac{PV}{T}d\left[\ln\left(PV^{5/3}\right)\right] \tag{2-104}$$

and, from the same reasoning that led to (2-98), we see that there must be a functional relation between PV/T and $PV^{5/3}$. Thus when (2-104) is integrated we may express S as a function of $PV^{5/3}$

$$S = \Phi\left(PV^{5/3}\right) \tag{2-105}$$

For a reversible adiabatic process the entropy of the system is constant, and the equation to be satisfied by a monatomic gas having a null internal virial will be, for such a process,

$$PV^{5/3} = \frac{PV}{T}V^{2/3}T = \text{const} \tag{2-106}$$

But, from the functional relation between PV/T and $PV^{5/3}$ implied by (2-104), S is also a function of PV/T, and so not only must $PV^{5/3}$ be constant along a system adiabat, but also PV/T must be constant along this path. This requires (2-106) to be expressible as

$$V^{2/3}T = \text{const} \tag{2-107}$$

By taking the natural logarithm of both sides of (2-107) we can write

$$VT^{3/2} = \text{const} \tag{2-108}$$

which must be obeyed by the system in a reversibly adiabatic process. We can express the equation of an adiabat in several other ways which are equivalent to equations (2-106) through (2-108).

$$\frac{PV}{T}\frac{T}{P}T^{3/2} = \text{const}$$

but we have already seen that PV/T is constant if S is constant, so

$$\frac{T^{5/2}}{P} = \text{const} \tag{2-109}$$

and in a manner analogous to that used in obtaining (2-108), we can write

$$\frac{T}{P^{2/5}} = \text{const} \tag{2-110}$$

Equations (2-107) and (2-108) show that it is not possible to obtain a temperature of $T = 0$ (the so-called absolute zero temperature) by a finite adiabatic expansion, since as T approaches zero it would be necessary for V to tend toward infinity. The equations (2-106) through (2-110) are all valid for any reversible adiabatic process undergone by a monatomic gas without cohesion and covolume, whether or not the gas obeys the laws of Boyle-Mariotte, Gay-Lussac, and Joule.

We can incorporate some of the results of this section into (2-14) and (2-67) which then leads to

$$\frac{đQ}{Tf(S)} = \frac{dS}{f(S)} = \text{an exact differential} \tag{2-111}$$

where $f(S)$ is an arbitrary function of the entropy. In particular, we can define a new function (of the absolute temperature T, and the entropy S) as

$$\theta = Tf(S) \tag{2-112}$$

which, of course, is still quite arbitrary, since $f(S)$ is assumed to be arbitrary.

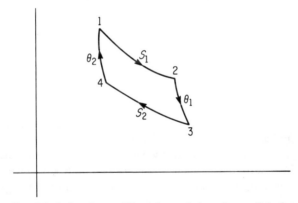

Fig. 2-3. A closed reversible cycle consisting of two adiabatic arcs, S_1 and S_2, and two lines of constant θ, θ_1, and θ_2.

Thus, in terms of the new function θ, we can express (2-111) as

$$\frac{đQ}{\theta} = \text{an exact differential} \tag{2-113}$$

which is equivalent to the condition that the integral of $đQ/\theta$ should vanish when the system executes a closed reversible cycle:

$$\oint \frac{đQ}{\theta} = 0 \tag{2-114}$$

Let us now consider a special type of closed reversible cycle, formed by two adiabatic arcs, S_1 and S_2, and two lines representing constant values of θ, θ_1, and θ_2, as shown in Fig. 2-3, where the unlabeled axes may by symbolically taken as any two of the triplet of numbers, (P, V, T):

$$\oint \frac{dQ}{\theta} = \int_1^2 \frac{dQ}{\theta} + \frac{1}{\theta_1} \int_2^3 dQ + \int_3^4 \frac{dQ}{\theta} + \frac{1}{\theta_2} \int_4^1 dQ$$

$$0 = \frac{Q_1}{\theta_1} + \frac{Q_2}{\theta_2} \qquad\qquad (2\text{-}115)$$

The integrals between the limits of $(1, 2)$ and $(3, 4)$, representing the two adiabatic portions of the cycle, vanish identically, since no heat is gained or lost by the system over this portion of the cycle. The quantities Q_1 and Q_2 in (2-115) represent the amounts of heat absorbed by the system at each of the constant values of θ_1 and θ_2, respectively.

We now define a pseudo-Carnot cycle by taking $f(S)$ to be of the form given by (2-98) in (2-112)

$$\theta = Tf(S) = T\chi(V\,T^{3/2}) \qquad\qquad (2\text{-}116)$$

where χ is any arbitrary function. In particular we shall take

$$\chi(V\,T^{3/2}) = (V\,T^{3/2})^{-2/3}$$

$$= V^{-2/3}\,T^{-1} \qquad\qquad (2\text{-}117)$$

so that

$$\theta = V^{-2/3} \qquad\qquad (2\text{-}118)$$

From our choice of θ, we see that the portion of the curve in Fig. 2-3 corresponding to $\theta = $ constant is equivalent to $V = $ constant. The Otto cycle thus formed (sometimes called the cycle of Beau de Rochas) will now consist of two lines at constant volume and two adiabats. Equation (2-115) can be rewritten as

$$Q_1 V_1^{2/3} + Q_2 V_2^{2/3} = 0 \qquad\qquad (2\text{-}119)$$

In (2-119) the terms V_1 and V_2 will always be positive, and by our convention, Q_1 and Q_2 will be positive when the heat flows *into* the system; thus (2-119) tells us that when the system is taken through a closed reversible cycle, *some* heat must flow *out of*, and be lost by the system. For the remainder of this chapter let us agree to change our sign convention so that the heat *given up by the system* at $V_1 = $ const, will be counted as positive. This change in sign convention will allow us to write (2-119) as

$$\frac{Q_1}{Q_2} = \left(\frac{V_2}{V_1}\right)^{2/3} \qquad\qquad (2\text{-}120)$$

The thermodynamic efficiency of any engine, operating in a cycle, is given by

$$\eta = \frac{\text{work output of engine}}{\text{heat input to engine}} \qquad (2\text{-}121)$$

With our sign convention, the work output from an Otto cycle engine as given by the first law of thermodynamics (remember that the system suffers no net change in internal energy in traversing any number of complete cycles) is just

$$\Delta W = Q_2 - Q_1 \qquad (2\text{-}122)$$

and Q_2 is the heat input to the engine. Hence the thermodynamic efficiency of an ideal internal combustion engine, operating with such a gas as we have been discussing (i.e., one which does not obey the laws of Boyle, Charles, or Joule) will be given by

$$\eta = 1 - \frac{Q_1}{Q_2} \qquad (2\text{-}123)$$

$$= 1 - \left(\frac{V_2}{V_1}\right)^{2/3}$$

$$= 1 - \frac{1}{r^{2/3}} \qquad (2\text{-}124)$$

where

$$r = \frac{V_1}{V_2} \qquad (2\text{-}125)$$

is the common compression ratio often quoted in automobile sales literature. The student should notice that (2-124) is the same result one obtains from using a monatomic gas which obeys the classical laws [see Sec. 7-4 of Ref. 8, where for a monatomic ideal gas $\gamma = C_p/C_v = 5/3$]. Eq. 2-124 is also obtained when the gas system is taken quasistatically through the Joule cycle (see Prob. 2-7) and this is true independent of any consideration of degeneracy.

In Fig. 2-4 the system of adiabatic lines, in the V-T plane, is represented by the generic relation

$$VT^{3/2} = \text{const} \qquad (2\text{-}126)$$

in accord with (2-98) which implies that

$$S = \phi(VT^{3/2}) \qquad (2\text{-}127)$$

The function ϕ, appearing in (2-127), is still unknown and one can only note the isentropic differences between the curves of Fig. 2-4 by marking on each one of them the value of the entropy. If we consider the infinitesimal path between points A and B, shown in Fig. 2-4, along which the temperature is increased by dT and the volume is held constant, then

$$dQ_{AB} = CdT \qquad \qquad (2\text{-}128)$$

and

$$dS_{AB} = \frac{CdT}{T} \qquad \qquad (2\text{-}129)$$

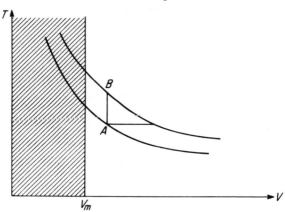

FIG. 2-4. Systems of adiabats lying in the V-T plane.

The quantity C, appearing in (2-128) and (2-129), is of course the heat capacity of the system at constant volume, and from a postulate attributed to Duhem[15], $C > 0$; that is, it is necessary to furnish heat to the system in order to raise the temperature at constant volume. Thus $dS_{AB} > 0$ and the entropy increases with increasing temperature (at constant volume) and when $VT^{3/2}$ increases the ϕ of (2-127) is also an increasing function.

It should also be noted that our original hypothesis, which was that the cohesion and covolume could be ignored, is only valid for sufficiently large values of the volume of the system of molecules, for example $V > V_m$. This means that the cross-hatched region in Fig. 2-4 should be excluded from consideration when applying our results to actual physical systems.

2-5 PERFECT GASES AND REAL PARTICLES

We now conclude this chapter with a preview of coming attractions in the form of information that will be obtainable from an analysis of thermo-

[15]P. Duhem, *Le Potential Thermodynamic et Ses Applications* (Paris: Chevalier et Riviera, 1886), p. 33.

dynamic systems based on the techniques developed from statistical mechanics. The properties of the perfect gas discussed in the preceding section were derived from the virial of Clausius for a system of noninteracting gas molecules (no cohesion forces between the molecules) which obeyed Newton's second law [$\mathbf{F}_i = m_i \ddot{\mathbf{r}}_i$ in (2-83)]. No mention was made of statistics per se, and the entire development was along the lines of what is traditionally thought of as kinetic theory and thermodynamics. Historically, this was the manner in which the theory of the perfect gas developed. In Sec. 5-2 we will see that the equation of state for the gas without cohesion and covolume is obtained when the molecules of the gas are distinguishable so that we can keep track of which particles we have assigned to particular energy states representing the gas system.

In the last half-century however, experimental results have shown us that particles of a given genus on the atomic and nuclear level are indistinguishable and thus cannot be labeled for identification purposes. Hence all electrons, or all protons, or all photons behave in exactly the same way (of course any electron can be distinguished from any proton or any photon) and there is no way to number the various electrons, say, as we would pool balls. Not only have we learned that all atomic particles of a given class are identical, but furthermore all classes of particles can be dichotomized according to the spin angular momentum of the particle (see Sec. 11-1).

All particles found in nature possess spin angular momentum, usually called *spin* for short, which is either an integer or an odd half-integer multiple of Planck's constant divided by twice pi. This last quantity is generally denoted by

$$\hbar \equiv \frac{h}{2\pi} = 1.0545 \times 10^{-27} \text{ erg-sec} \tag{2-130}$$

and is pronounced "*h*-bar" where h is Planck's constant. Those particles whose intrinsic spin angular momentum is an integer multiple of $\hbar$, are said to possess integer spin and are called *bosons*. The term boson arises from the fact that such particles (having integer spin) obey the statistics of Bose-Einstein, which is discussed at length in the following chapters. Table 2-1 lists several examples of particles obeying Bose-Einstein statistics. Particles having odd half-integer spin obey the statistics of Fermi-Dirac, which is also discussed at greater length in the succeeding chapters, and are known as *fermions*. Examples of fermions are also given in Table 2-1.

From Table 2-1 we note that both protons and neutrons obey Fermi-Dirac statistics, since they each have spin $1/2\,\hbar$, yet a composite particle consisting of an even number of these fermions behaves like a boson, e.g., He^4, B^{10}, N^{14}, O^{16}. On the other hand, a composite particle made up of an odd number of fermions is again a fermion, e.g., He^3, B^{11}, N^{15}, and O^{17}. These observations are consistent with the general rule enunciated above that all particles, whether or not they are composites, which have integral

Table 2-1. Spin characteristics of particles found in nature

Particle or element	Symbol	Spin (in units of $\hbar$)
BOSONS		
Photon	γ	1
Pi meson	π	0
Helium $-$ 4 nucleus	He^4	0
Boron $-$ 10 nucleus	B^{10}	3
Nitrogen $-$ 14 nucleus	N^{14}	1
Oxygen $-$ 16 nucleus	O^{16}	0
FERMIONS		
Electron	e	1/2
Muon	μ	1/2
Proton	p	1/2
Neutron	n	1/2
Helium $-$ 3 nucleus	He^3	1/2
Boron $-$ 11 nucleus	B^{11}	3/2
Nitrogen $-$ 15 nucleus	N^{15}	1/2
Oxygen $-$ 17 nucleus	O^{17}	5/2

spin obey Bose-Einstein statistics and all particles having odd half-integral spin are fermions.

A gas composed of bosons will be shown (in a later chapter) to have values of internal energy, entropy, and pressure, all of which vanish when the absolute temperature goes to zero. Expressing

$$X = VT^{3/2} \tag{2-131}$$

we shall show in a later chapter that for large values of X, the equation of state of a boson gas may be written as

$$PV = RT\left[1 - \frac{Nh^3}{16(m\pi k)^{3/2}}\frac{1}{X} + \cdots\right] \tag{2-132}$$

where R is the universal gas constant, k and h are Boltzmann's and Planck's constants, respectively, and N is the number of particles, each having a mass m. For values of X sufficiently large that the second term in (2-132) can be neglected, the boson gas will obey the three laws of Mariotte, Gay-Lussac, and Joule. One then says that the gas is nondegenerate and it can serve as a gas thermometer in the classical sense.

A gas composed of fermions, at a finite volume, has zero entropy at $T = 0$, but the pressure and internal energy do not vanish at zero temperature. The equation of state for the Fermi gas may be expressed, for large values of X, as

$$PV = RT\left[1 + \frac{Nh^3}{16(m\pi k)^{3/2}}\frac{1}{X} + \cdots\right] \tag{2-133}$$

in analogy with (2-132). Again, when X is sufficiently large the Fermi gas becomes non degenerate, the equation of state reduces to

$$PV = RT$$

which is of the form (2-102), and the gas also obeys the three classical gas laws and can be used as a gas thermometer.

The statement that the Fermi or Bose gas becomes nondegenerate means that a gas composed of either fermions or bosons will, under certain conditions, obey the three classical, perfect gas laws derived in the preceding section. From (2-132) and (2-133) these conditions will occur when X in (2-131) is large. This means that at high temperatures or when the volume occupied by the molecules is large the perfect gas laws will be obeyed by the gas composed of real particles. But these conditions are the conditions for dilute gases, which were the conditions assumed in our analysis in Sec. 2-4.

Another way of considering this situation leads us to realize that at high temperatures the thermal energy of the gas molecules will be large, which means that the number of allowed energy states for the system becomes large. Thus we see that as the number of available quantum energy states increases, with the number of molecules available to fill these states remaining constant, the probability of a particular quantum state being occupied by a molecule of the system becomes very small. This is just the condition in which the gas system behaves as a classical gas, and the gas is then said to be nondegenerate.

PROBLEMS

2-1. Verify the veracity of (2-28) through (2-35).

2-2. Derive (2-11) using the procedure developed in Sec. 2-2 and supplying any steps which are missing or not intuitively obvious to you.

2-3. Obtain (2-66) by the method outlined in the text and demonstrate its equivalence to (2-14).

2-4. From the equation of state for an ideal gas, (5-24), and the defining equations for the volume coefficient of expansion, (2-5), and the isothermal compressibility, (2-6a), obtain equations (2-73a) and (2-73b) and substitute these results into (2-72) to obtain (2-74).

2-5. Starting with (2-97) justify (2-98).

2-6. Obtain (2-108) from (2-107).

2-7. The Joule cycle is defined by a closed path consisting of two adiabats S_1 and S_2, connected by two isobars (lines of constant pressure) P_1 and P_2. Depict the Joule cycle on a P-V diagram and on a P-S diagram. By a proper choice of $\chi(S)$ (and it will be a proper choice for this cycle if $\theta = $ constant implies $P = $ constant) show that (2-124) is obeyed for the Joule cycle when the working substance is a monatomic gas without cohesion and covolume.

2-8. Obtain (2-124) and make appropriate plots for a monatomic gas without cohesion and covolume taken around a Carnot cycle (which consists of two adiabats and two isotherms).

2-9. (a) Show that the integral of the imperfect differential

$$dV = y\,dx - x\,dy$$

depends on both the path of integration and the end points of integration. (b) Show that the perfect differential

$$dV = (xy^2 - x)\,dx + (x^2y + y)\,dy$$

depends only on the end points of integration and is independent of path.

2-10. Determine whether

$$dV = (y - x^2y^2)\,dx - (x + 1)\,dy$$

is an exact differential. If it is not an exact differential, find an integrating factor that will make it an exact differential.

2-11. (a) Apply the virial theorem to a central force whose potential is proportional to r^n for a single particle, and express the virial in terms of the potential energy. (b) Apply the results of part (a) to the one dimensional harmonic oscillator.

2-12. The Joule cycle of Prob. 2-7 and the Otto cycle are idealized versions of the gas turbine and the four stroke gasoline engine respectively. Explain the operation of each with reference to their respective P-V diagram.

2-13. What would be the increase in efficiency of an engine if its compression ratio is increased from $7:1$ to $9:1$? In a real engine would you expect the efficiency to be greater or less than that calculated from the Otto cycle with the ideal gas fuel? Why?

3 Statistical Interpretation of Macroscopic Equilibrium States

3-1 INTRODUCTION

The material discussed in this section will apply equally well to systems in which quantum statistics must be used as to those systems which can be adequately described by classical or prequantum mechanical statistics. This material will be applicable to any system of molecules which is devoid of interaction energy between the molecules.

We assume that the energy of any molecule is composed of the sum of its kinetic energy (of translation, vibration, or rotation) and of its potential energy corresponding, for example, to its internal parameters ($1/2\kappa x^2$ in the case of a diatomic molecule viewed as a vibrator), and also any potential energy arising from bodies external to the collection of molecules (as from the effects of a gravitational field or the orientational potential energy due to a magnetic field), but in all cases we exclude any mutual interaction energy. Thus under these conditions the total internal energy of the system is the sum of the energies of the molecules comprising the system (a system without interaction of its constituents).

We assume that each molecule may be found in either a definite number (as in the quantum theory) or in an indefinite number (forming a continuous series) of states. We will consider the case of discrete states and treat the classical case by passing to the continuous limit. We shall classify these states according to the energy associated with the states and they will be designated as energy levels. It will frequently happen that for a given energy there may correspond several different (g, for example) states, and then the energy level is said to be g-fold degenerate. A postulate, following naturally from Liouville's theorem, will later lead us to assign to these states an equal a priori probability of being occupied.

We further suppose that we have a very large number N of these molecules (N is of the order of Avogadro's number, for example) and that there are various different ways of distributing these molecules among the given energy levels. Each of these possible distributions of the molecules corresponds to one macroscopic state. One basic hypothesis in this material is that the macroscopic equilibrium state which is observed the most often (and for practical purposes, it will be found to be observed so much more often than the others, that it will be the only macroscopic equilibrium state which is observed, aside from small fluctuations) is that one which is such that the number of distributions of the molecules corresponding to it is a maximum. In other words, in practice we assume that the most probable macroscopic state of the system is that one which is observed.

The task of estimating the observed macroscopic state is then equivalent to counting the total number W of corresponding distributions. In order to accurately count the number of distributions, we must first know the rules of the game. We must know, for example, if the molecules are distinguishable or not, if an arbitrary number of molecules can be put into each state, or if the number is fixed. To each of the possible different rules of the game there will correspond a different set of statistics, and we must inquire of experiment to show us which rules are valid (and under what conditions they are valid). We shall build on the foundations laid in Chapter 1, treating our molecules as the balls (numbered or not according to rules) and our (energy) states as the boxes, having an equal a priori probability for the presence of a ball in each box (as is presumed to be the case in the game of roulette).

3-2 MAXWELL-BOLTZMANN-PLANCK STATISTICS

For this game the rules are that the balls are to be distinguishable and numbered, and each box (energy level) is capable of holding any number of balls from zero (the level is then empty) to all N of them. Let n_i represent the number of molecules having energy w_i. We first assume that the total number of molecules, N, is given, and that the total energy of the system, U, is given. Then

$$\Sigma n_i = N \qquad (3\text{-}1)$$

and

$$\Sigma n_i w_i = U \qquad (3\text{-}2)$$

In (3-1) and (3-2) the sum is to be taken over all possible energy levels which are consistent with the configuration of the system, and the first equation is equivalent to (1-85).

The number of arrangements of these N molecules corresponding to the distribution with n_1 molecules in the level with energy w_1, n_2 in the level having energy w_2, ..., is, of course, given by equation (1-84). However, if the level w_i is g_i-fold degenerate, it will be necessary, in each level, to distribute the n_i molecules with energy w_i into g_i boxes (in all possible ways). Since the rules for the Maxwell-Boltzman-Planck game allow each of the g_i boxes to hold any number of molecules, we find from (1-89) that the energy level associated with w_i will have $(g_i)^{n_i}$ possible arrangements. Thus the total number of ways of distributing the N molecules will be given by

$$W = N! \frac{\Pi(g_i)^{n_i}}{\Pi n_i!} \tag{3-3}$$

We now suppose that the number of molecules is so large that each of the terms in (3-3) containing factorials can be replaced by the stirling formula of (1-30). Furthermore, by this assumption, we ignore the quantity $1/2$ in comparison with n_i and N. Thus (3-3) becomes (see Prob. 3-1)

$$\ln W = N \ln N + \sum n_i \ln \left(\frac{g_i}{n_i} \right) \tag{3-4}$$

In the following material it will be convenient to deal with the quantity

$$W' \equiv \frac{W}{N!} = \frac{\Pi(g_i)^{n_i}}{\Pi n_i!} \tag{3-5}$$

obtained by dividing the total number of arrangements of the N molecules by $N!$. The particles obeying the resulting statistics are frequently called[1] "corrected boltzons" and we shall see later that by adopting W' in lieu of W, the absolute entropy thus calculated will be the same for all three statistics (Maxwell-Boltzmann-Planck, Fermi-Dirac, and Bose-Einstein) in the case of weak degeneracy. The student will recall from Sec. 1-3 that the effect of dividing (3-3) by $N!$ is to remove the distinguishability between particles which is inherent in the Maxwell-Boltzmann-Planck statistics. Thus the "corrected boltzons" are ordinary boltzons which have lost their identity, so that all corrected boltzons look alike. In Sec. 2-5 we found that all fundamental particles in nature of a given genus are indistinguishable and hence the corrected Maxwell-Boltzmann-Planck statistics ought to give a better description of the behavior of such particles, in dilute systems, than the classical statistics. If the particles are truly distinguishable one, of course, must use W and not W' to describe the system.

We note that (1-30) [cf. also (1-190)] leads to

$$\ln (N!) \simeq \left(N + \frac{1}{2} \right) \ln N - N + \frac{1}{2} \ln 2\pi \tag{3-6}$$

---

[1] N. Davidson, *Statistical Mechanics* (New York: McGraw-Hill Book Company, 1962), Chap. 6.

which, under the approximation that $N \gg 1/2$, leads to

$$\ln(N!) \simeq N \ln N - N \tag{3-7}$$

since the $\ln 2\pi$ is only about 1.84. Thus

$$\ln W' = \ln W - \ln N!$$

or

$$\ln W' = \sum n_i \left(1 + \ln \frac{g_i}{n_i}\right) \tag{3-8}$$

(see Prob. 3-2).

Since W and W' differ only by a constant, they will take their maximum values simultaneously (although the maximum values, themselves, will differ). Also the quantity W, and its natural logarithm will take their (different) maximum values under the same conditions. Thus we can now look for the maximum of $\ln W$, given by (3-4).

$$\delta \ln W = \delta(N \ln N) + \sum \ln\left(\frac{g_i}{n_i}\right)\delta n_i + \sum n_i \delta[\ln g_i - \ln n_i] \tag{3-9}$$

$$\delta \ln W = \sum \ln\left(\frac{g_i}{n_i}\right)\delta n_i - \sum \delta n_i \tag{3-10}$$

Equation (3-10) follows from (3-9) since the total number of molecules, N, and the degeneracy of each level are both constants and not subject to variation, as is the number of molecules in each energy level, n_i. Also from (3-1) we see that

$$\sum \delta n_i = \delta N = 0 \tag{3-11}$$

so that the variation in the total number of arrangements of the N molecules becomes

$$\delta \ln W = \sum \ln\left(\frac{g_i}{n_i}\right)\delta n_i \tag{3-12}$$

In addition to the conditions expressed by (3-11) and (3-12), we can take the variation of (3-2) to obtain

$$\delta U = \delta \sum w_i n_i = 0$$

or

$$\sum w_i \delta n_i = 0 \tag{3-13}$$

Since the variation in the natural logarithm of the total number of arrangements of the N molecules distributed through the allowed energy levels, in the total number of molecules to be distributed, and in the total energy of the system, all vanish separately, any linear combination of them, expressed by equations (3-11), (3-12), and (3-13), will still vanish. It is customary to take the linear combination in the following manner: multiply (3-11) by $\ln \alpha$, (3-12) by unity, and (3-13) by $-\beta$, and then add. This recipe leads to

$$\sum \left[\ln\left(\frac{g_i}{n_i}\right) + \ln \alpha - \beta w_i \right] \delta n_i = 0 \tag{3-14}$$

The (presently unknown) quantities α and β are called "Langrange Multipliers",[2] and since (3-14) must hold for arbitrary n_i, we find that the coefficients of the n_i must all vanish separately:

$$\ln \frac{g_i}{n_i} + \ln \alpha - \beta w_i = 0 \tag{3-15}$$

or

$$n_i = \alpha g_i e^{-\beta w_i} \tag{3-16}$$

[The student may recognize that although (3-14) holds for arbitrary n_i, the n_i are restricted by (3-1) and (3-2) and thus are not independent. Consequently two of the equations represented by (3-15) are only valid because of the presence of the Lagrangian multipliers, α and β, which are forced to assume the values which make these two equations identically zero. The number of words devoted by the authors to this aspect of the utility of Lagrange undetermined multipliers should *not* be construed as an indication of its importance[2].] The distribution of (3-16) is called the Maxwell-Boltzmann-Planck distribution or the canonical distribution, and it is valid if the series of levels is discrete (quantum conditions) or continuous (classical conditions).

3-3   BOSE-EINSTEIN STATISTICS

For this game we suppose that the particles are indistinguishable, and that there is no limit to the number of molecules in each state. As before, let n_i be the number of molecules having energy w_i. If the ith energy level is g_i-fold degenerate, the n_i particles will have to be distributed into g_i boxes such that any box may have any or all of the molecules. The number of corresponding arrangements is given by (1-91), which can be written in the nomenclature of this chapter as

$$W_i = \frac{(n_i + g_i - 1)!}{n_i!(g_i - 1)!} \tag{3-17}$$

[2]M. L. Boas, *Mathematical Methods in the Physical Sciences* (New York: John Wiley & Sons, Inc., 1966), p. 145.

The total number of arrangements over all energy levels can be expressed as

$$W = \Pi \frac{(n_i + g_i - 1)!}{n_i!(g_i - 1)!} \qquad (3\text{-}18)$$

There is no need to permute the order of the different energy levels, as any permutation reproduces the same arrangement as the original, since the molecules have been assumed to be indistinguishable. With the use of (3-17) we can express (3-18) in the form

$$\ln W = \Sigma[(n_i + g_i)\ln(n_i + g_i) - n_i \ln n_i - g_i \ln g_i] \qquad (3\text{-}19)$$

if we assume that both g_i and n_i are much greater than unity. The g_i are presumed constant and thus the variation in the thermodynamic probability is found from

$$\delta \ln W = \Sigma \delta n_i \ln \left(1 + \frac{g_i}{n_i}\right) = 0 \qquad (3\text{-}20)$$

Following the recipe suggested in the previous section, we can obtain an equation analogous to (3-14) in the form

$$\Sigma \left[\ln \left(1 + \frac{g_i}{n_i}\right) + \ln \alpha - \beta w_i \right] \delta n_i = 0 \qquad (3\text{-}21)$$

which, due to the independence of the δn_i, requires

$$\ln \alpha \left(1 + \frac{g_i}{n_i}\right) = \beta w_i \qquad (3\text{-}22)$$

Eq. 3-22 can easily (see Prob. 3-4) be solved to yield

$$n_i = \alpha g_i \frac{e^{-\beta w_i}}{1 - \alpha e^{-\beta w_i}} \qquad (3\text{-}23)$$

This distribution, for particles obeying the Bose-Einstein statistics, differs from the canonical distribution of (3-16) by the term in the denominator. Thus, whenever the second term in the denominator can be neglected compared to unity, the Bose-Einstein distribution function will approach, asymptotically, the Maxwell-Boltzmann-Planck distribution function of (3-16).

3-4 FERMI-DIRAC STATISTICS

The rules for this game require the molecules to be indistinguishable, but the Pauli exclusion principle (see Sec. 11-1 *infra*) is invoked so that only one molecule can be put into each state; otherwise the state is to be left empty. These rules were exactly the rules that led to (1-97b) which, in the nomenclature of this section, can be written as the number of arrangements in which n_i molecules can be distributed among the g_i states in the level associated with energy w_i:

$$W_i = C(g_i)_{n_i} = \frac{g_i!}{n_i!(g_i - n_i)!} \tag{3-24}$$

where the rules of the game require that

$$n_i \leq g_i \tag{3-25}$$

Again, the total number of arrangements for the system will be given by the product of (3-24) over all energy levels:

$$W = \Pi \frac{g_i!}{n_i!(g_i - n_i)!} \tag{3-26}$$

The sentence immediately following (3-18) is equally applicable to (3-26), which can be rewritten with the use of (3-7) as

$$\ln W = \Sigma[g_i \ln g_i - n_i \ln n_i - (g_i - n_i) \ln (g_i - n_i)] \tag{3-27}$$

The by now familiar recipe leading to (3-14) and (3-21) leads, in this section, to (see Prob. 3-5).

$$\Sigma\left[\ln \left(\frac{g_i}{n_i} - 1\right) + \ln \alpha - \beta w_i\right]\delta n_i = 0 \tag{3-28}$$

which, in turn, directly leads to

$$n_i = \alpha g_i \frac{e^{-\beta w_i}}{1 + \alpha e^{-\beta w_i}} \tag{3-29}$$

The Fermi-Dirac distribution function differs from the Bose-Einstein distribution function, (3-23), only by the sign of the second term in the denominator, and thus also tends toward the canonical distribution function when this term is small compared to unity.

3-5 SUMMARY

A. Maxwell-Boltzmann-Planck statistics:

$$\ln W = N \ln N + \Sigma n_i \ln \left(\frac{g_i}{n_i}\right) \tag{3-4}$$

$$n_i = \alpha g_i \, e^{-\beta w_i} \tag{3-16}$$

$$\ln\left(\frac{g_i}{n_i}\right) = \beta w_i - \ln\alpha \tag{3-15a}$$

$$U = \Sigma n_i w_i \tag{3-2}$$

$$N = \Sigma n_i \tag{3-1}$$

$$W' = \frac{W}{N!} \tag{3-5}$$

$$\ln W = N\ln\left(\frac{N}{\alpha}\right) + \beta U \tag{3-30}$$

$$\ln W' = N\ln\left(\frac{e}{\alpha}\right) + \beta U \tag{3-31}$$

B. Bose-Einstein Statistics:

$$\ln W = \Sigma g_i \ln\left(1 + \frac{n_i}{g_i}\right) + \Sigma n_i \ln\left(1 + \frac{g_i}{n_i}\right) \tag{3-19a}$$

$$n_i = \frac{\alpha g_i}{e^{\beta w_i} - \alpha} \tag{3-23a}$$

$$1 + \frac{n_i}{g_i} = \frac{1}{1 - \alpha e^{-\beta w_i}}$$

$$1 + \frac{g_i}{n_i} = \frac{e^{\beta w_i}}{\alpha}$$

$$\ln W = -N\ln\alpha + \beta U - \Sigma g_i \ln\left(1 - \alpha e^{-\beta w_i}\right) \tag{3-32}$$

C. Fermi-Dirac statistics:

$$\ln W = \Sigma n_i \ln\left(\frac{g_i}{n_i} - 1\right) - \Sigma g_i \ln\left(1 - \frac{n_i}{g_i}\right) \tag{3-27a}$$

$$n_i = \frac{\alpha g_i}{e^{\beta w_i} + \alpha} \tag{3-29a}$$

$$\frac{g_i}{n_i} - 1 = \frac{e^{\beta w_i}}{\alpha}$$

$$1 - \frac{n_i}{g_i} = \frac{1}{1 + \alpha e^{-\beta w_i}}$$

$$\ln W = -N\ln\alpha + \beta U + \Sigma g_i \ln\left(1 + \alpha e^{-\beta w_i}\right) \tag{3-33}$$

PROBLEMS

3-1. Use (1-30) to approximate the terms $N!$ and $n_i!$ in (3-3). Take the natural logarithm of the resulting expression and use (3-1) to eliminate two terms. Finally ignore $1/2$ compared to N and n_i and obtain (3-4).

3-2. (a) By subtracting (3-7) from (3-4) and using (3-1) obtain (3-8). (b) By using the definition of W' in (3-5) obtain (3-8) by means of the method suggested in Prob. 3-1.

3-3. Starting with (3-8), find the variation in $\ln W'$ corresponding to (3-12). Using this result and the two equations (3-11) and (3-13), find the distribution applicable to corrected boltzons, in terms of the Lagrange undetermined multipliers, α and β. Contrast your result to (3-16), and make any appropriate comments.

3-4. Obtain (3-23) from (3-22).

3-5. (a) Obtain (3-28) from (3-27) with the use of (3-11) and (3-13). (b) Obtain (3-29) from (3-28).

3-6. For a nondegenerate isolated system with relative energy levels 0, 1, 2, 3, 4 which has 5 particles and a total energy of 4 (arbitrary units) find the possible distributions and the number of arrangements for each distribution with Boltzmann's statistics.

3-7. An isolated system has four energy levels of relative value 0, 1, 2, 3 and consists of four particles. The energy levels 0 and 1 are twofold-degenerate and the energy levels 2 and 3 are threefold-degenerate where the system has a total energy of 3 (arbitrary units).

(a) Find the possible distributions of particles for each of the three statistics.
(b) Calculate the number of arrangements for each distribution for the three statistics.

3-8. Find the dimensions of a rectangle which maximizes its area, xy, by means of Lagrange multipliers if

$$x + y = 20$$

3-9. Show that

$$\ln p! \approx p \ln p - p + \tfrac{1}{2} \ln 2\pi p \qquad (3\text{-}6)$$

and if p is large that

$$\ln p! \approx p \ln p - p \qquad (3\text{-}7)$$

Use these two approximations to evaluate $\ln(10!)$ and compare the results.

3-10. From equations (3-23) and (3-29) it is seen that

$$\alpha \exp(-\beta w_i) \ll 1$$

implies

$$\frac{n_i}{g_i} \ll 1$$

Show that in this limit

$$W_{\text{Bose-Einstein}} \approx W_{\text{Fermi-Dirac}} \approx \frac{W_{\text{Maxwell-Boltzmann-Planck}}}{N!}$$

where $W_{\text{Maxwell-Boltzmann-Planck}}$ is given by (3-3).

4 | *Interpretation of Thermodynamic Equilibrium*

4-1 THE LAGRANGE MULTIPLIERS α AND β

The distribution functions developed in the preceding chapter are not completely determined, since they are expressed in terms of the Lagrange undetermined multipliers α and β. Thus the problem of describing the distribution of the molecules among the allowed energy levels of the system such that the macroscopically observed state results, is reduced to the problem of interpreting (and consequently evaluating) the constants α and β.

Let us first turn our attention to the constant β. We would like to show that if two systems σ_1 and σ_2 are capable of exchanging energy between each other (the sum of their energies being constant), and if we assume that thermodynamic equilibrium is realized when the number of arrangements is a maximum for the collection of the systems, then the constant β will be the same for σ_1 and σ_2.

This theorem will be valid even if σ_1 and σ_2 obey statistics of different kinds (one of the three discussed in Chap. 3, or even other statistics). For example σ_1 might be a system of bosons and σ_2 a system of fermions, β would be the same for σ_1 and σ_2.

We shall designate the parameters describing σ_1 by latin letters, and those describing σ_2 by Greek letters. Let w_i be the energy of the molecules in the ith level of σ_1 and ε_1 the corresponding energy in σ_2; then the number of arrangements for a given distribution among the levels of σ_1 will be a particular function

$$W_1 = f(n_1, n_2, \cdots, n_i, \cdots) \tag{4-1}$$

and that for σ_2 will be

$$W_2 = \phi(v_1, v_2, \cdots, v_i, \cdots) \tag{4-2}$$

The total number of arrangements covering the ensemble of the two systems σ_1 and σ_2 will then be given as the product of (4-1) and (4-2)

$$W = f(n_1, \cdots, n_i, \cdots,) \ \phi(v_1, \cdots, v_i, \cdots) \tag{4-3}$$

or

$$\ln W = \ln f + \ln \phi \tag{4-4}$$

We can now set

$$F = \ln f \tag{4-5a}$$

$$\Phi = \ln \phi \tag{4-5b}$$

and

$$U = \Sigma n_i w_i + \Sigma v_i \varepsilon_i \tag{4-6}$$

We now vary the number of particles in the various energy levels of the two systems, n_i and v_i:

$$\delta \ln W = \Sigma \frac{\partial F}{\partial n_i} \delta n_i + \Sigma \frac{\partial \Phi}{\partial v_i} \delta v_i = 0 \tag{4-7}$$

$$\Sigma \delta n_i = 0 \tag{4-8a}$$

$$\Sigma \delta v_i = 0 \tag{4-8b}$$

$$\Sigma w_i \, \delta n_i + \Sigma \varepsilon_i \, \delta v_i = 0 \tag{4-9}$$

and use our standard recipe of Chap. 3, by which we multiply (4-8a) and (4-8b) by $\ln \alpha_1$ and $\ln \alpha_2$, respectively, (4-9) by $-\beta$, and add equations (4-7) through (4-9) to obtain

$$\Sigma \left[\frac{\partial F}{\partial n_i} + \ln \alpha_1 - \beta w_i \right] \delta n_i + \Sigma \left[\frac{\partial \Phi}{\partial v_i} + \ln \alpha_2 - \beta \varepsilon_i \right] \delta v_i = 0 \tag{4-10}$$

The distribution over σ_1 and σ_2, respectively will then be

$$\frac{\partial F}{\partial n_i} = -\ln \alpha_1 + \beta w_i$$

$$\tag{4-11}$$

$$\frac{\partial \Phi}{\partial v_i} = -\ln \alpha_2 + \beta \varepsilon_i$$

Equation 4-3 is a result of the assumption that σ_1 and σ_2 are independent subsystems of the ensemble composed of the collection of σ_1 and σ_2. Since both σ_1 and σ_2 are such that the conditions, under which their separate thermodynamic probabilities (e^F and e^Φ) are each maximized, viz, equations (4-11), are of the identical form for the maximization of the ensemble thermodynamic probability, it follows[1] that β is a characteristic of the ensemble, containing both σ_1 and σ_2, as a whole. It then has the same value in both σ_1 and σ_2 (as it has throughout the collective system containing both σ_1 and σ_2), which were assumed to be arbitrary systems. Thus β is a quantity which is the same between arbitrary systems which are compelled to devolve (with w_i and g_i being constant) such that the sum of their energies is constant. The only thermodynamic function which possesses this property is the temperature. We then set

$$\beta = \beta_{(T)} \qquad (4\text{-}12)$$

and it only remains to specify the nature of the function $\beta_{(T)}$ by taking under consideration a particular system.

Before we get down to specifics, however, a few more general comments are in order. In the development above, we assumed that the system attained equilibrium when the thermodynamic probability W reached its maximum value. Let us now suppose that the conditions applied to the system are modified by an infinitesimal amount (U changes by δU, α by $\delta\alpha$, β by $\delta\beta$, g_i by δg_i, and w_i by δw_i) subject to the restraint that $\delta N = 0$ (the system is assumed to be closed). We suppose that the energy levels may be displaced and that the number of states associated with a given level may change. In order that this infinitesimal change in the conditions surrounding the system be reversible, it may be necessary to wait a rather long time so that, under the new conditions, the modified distribution of particles among the microstates will still correspond to a (new) maximum of W (i.e., it will be necessary to wait a sufficient time for the molecules to redistribute themselves among the new energy levels of the system). Of course, when this modification has been achieved, n_i will be replaced by its new value of $n_i + \delta n_i$. The study of this reversible change in the system will lead to a more physical interpretation of the quantities α and β.

We now recall some of the reasoning which led Boltzmann to his formulation of the relation between the entropy of the system and the thermodynamic probability of the system. An isolated system σ, may occupy any of various (constant) energy states. We can classify these states by means of their increasing W (the number of ways of realizing a given energy state)

$$W_1 < W_2 \quad \cdots \quad < \quad W_n$$
$$E_1 \quad E_2 \quad \cdots \quad \quad E_n \qquad (4\text{-}13)$$

The spontaneous evolution of the system will be such that the system

---

[1]For a more detailed discussion of this point see G. H. Wannier, *Statistical Physics* (New York: John Wiley & Sons, Inc., 1966), Sec. 4-1; E. Schrodinger, *Statistical Thermodynamics* 2nd ed. (London: Cambridge University Press, 1952), Chap. 2.

passes into the more probable states. Furthermore, this evolution will proceed in the direction of increasing entropy

$$S_1 < S_2 < \quad \cdots \quad < S_n \tag{4-14}$$

The realization of the existence of relations (4-13) and (4-14) suggested to Boltzmann that there must also exist a relation (which he supposed to be universal and independent of the nature of σ) between S and W.

$$S = S(W) \tag{4-15}$$

To determine the form of this functional relation, let us take two isolated and entirely independent systems σ_1 and σ_2. The probability of finding the ensemble of the two systems with σ_1 in state E_1, having an associated probability W_1, and σ_2 in E_2, with W_2, is, according to (4-3)

$$W = W_1 W_2 \tag{4-16}$$

The entropy of the ensemble, which is a sum of integrals, is the sum of the system entropies

$$S = S_1 + S_2 \tag{4-17}$$

Since S is additive and W is multiplicative, if there is to be a relation between them, it can only be such that

$$S_1 = k \ln W_1$$

$$S_2 = k \ln W_2$$

$$S_1 + S_2 = k \ln W_1 W_2$$

$$S = k \ln W. \tag{4-18}$$

We can now recover the Boltzmann relation of (4-18) by a more direct route in each of the three statistics discussed in Chap. 3.

4-2 MAXWELL-BOLTZMANN-PLANCK STATISTICS

Let us now make use of some of the formulas which were collected in the last section of the preceding chapter. By holding N constant, while varying the other parameters in (3-30), we obtain

$$\delta \ln W_m = -\frac{N}{\alpha} \delta\alpha + \beta\delta U + U\delta\beta \tag{4-19}$$

The Maxwell-Boltzmann-Planck distribution function is given by

$$n_i = \alpha g_i e^{-\beta w_i} \tag{3-16}$$

which leads to

$$N = \alpha \Sigma g_i \, e^{-\beta w_i} \tag{4-20}$$

The condition that N be constant can be expressed by

$$0 = \delta\alpha\Sigma g_i \, e^{-\beta w_i} + \alpha\Sigma\delta g_i \, e^{-\beta w_i} - \alpha\Sigma g_i \, e^{-\beta w_i}[\beta\delta w_i + w_i\,\delta\beta] \tag{4-21}$$

By substituting (3-16) and (4-20) into (4-21) we can write

$$0 = \frac{N}{\alpha}\delta\alpha + \Sigma\frac{\delta g_i}{g_i}n_i - \beta\Sigma n_i\delta w_i - U\delta\beta \tag{4-22}$$

By adding (4-19) and (4-22) we find that

$$\delta \ln W_m = \beta\left\{\delta U + \sum n_i\left[\frac{\delta g_i}{\beta g_i} - \delta w_i\right]\right\} \tag{4-23}$$

Let us now define

$$\delta\tau \equiv \sum\left[\frac{1}{\beta}\frac{\delta g_i}{g_i} - \delta w_i\right]n_i \tag{4-24}$$

so that (4-23) becomes

$$\delta \ln W_m = \beta(\delta U + \delta\tau) \tag{4-25}$$

We will endeavor to show, in the following chapter, that the quantity $\delta\tau$ defined by (4-24) has the properties ascribed to the external work performed by the system, not only in the case where the system is taken to be a collection of gas molecules, but for arbitrary systems. If we accept for the moment the allegation that

$$\delta\tau = \text{variation in the external work of the system} \tag{4-26}$$

Then, from (2-15) we can write

$$\delta U + \delta\tau = \delta Q \tag{4-27}$$

or

$$\delta \ln W_m = \beta\delta Q \tag{4-28}$$

The left-hand side of (4-28) is given by (4-19), which is an exact (variational) differential, and thus the quantity $\beta\delta Q$ must also be an exact differential. We have shown in the preceding section that β is a function of the absolute temperature [cf. (4-12)], and is the same for all systems in thermodynamic equilibrium with each other. This last condition is equivalent to condition (b) in Sec. 2-3, if we view $\beta_{(T)}$ as being an integrating factor of δQ. But from condition (a) in Sec. 2-3, the integrating factor of δQ in a reversible transformation is (apart from constant factors) the reciprocal of the thermodynamic temperature. Thus we are led to the conclusion that

$$\beta_{(T)} = \frac{\text{const}}{T}$$

where it is customary to take the constant such that β is expressed as

$$\beta = \frac{1}{kT} \tag{4-29}$$

Eq. 4-29 is the culmination of our endeavor to answer the question "What is β?" It still remains for us to verify that $\delta\tau$ (at least in the case of a gas) is the external work, and once that trifle is subdued, the student should have only one remaining question: "What is β?" Upon reexamination of (4-29), we see that the functional temperature dependence of (4-12) has been determined; but we still haven't evaluated β, because we have not determined the multiplicative constant k. Both of these matters will be taken up again in the following chapter. For the present we content ourselves with developing thermodynamic relations in terms of k (and the other Lagrange multiplier α).

From (2-14), (4-29), and (4-28), we can write

$$\delta k \ln W_m = \frac{\delta Q}{T} = \delta S$$

which can be integrated to yield

$$S = k \ln W_m + \text{const} \tag{4-30}$$

We notice that (4-30) is brought into direct agreement with (4-18) by taking the integration constant to be null. Thus we designate the resulting function

$$S = k \ln W_m \tag{4-31}$$

by the name "absolute entropy," which can be written as

$$S = Nk \ln \frac{N}{\alpha} + \frac{U}{T} \tag{4-32}$$

by means of (3-30). The Helmholtz energy can be expressed, from (2-16), as

$$A = -NkT \ln \frac{N}{\alpha} \tag{4-33}$$

From (3-31) we find the entropy and Helmholtz energy, applicable to a system of corrected boltzons, to be

$$S' = Nk \ln \left(\frac{e}{\alpha}\right) + \frac{U}{T} \tag{4-34}$$

and

$$A' = - NkT \ln\left(\frac{e}{\alpha}\right) \qquad (4\text{-}35)$$

respectively.

We now proceed to develop analogous expressions for the two quantum systems discussed in Chap. 3.

4-3 BOSE-EINSTEIN STATISTICS

By proceeding in the manner of the preceding section, and with the use of (3-32), we can write

$$\delta \ln W_m = - N\frac{\delta\alpha}{\alpha} + \beta\delta U + U\delta\beta - \Sigma\, \delta g_i \ln(1 - \alpha e^{-\beta w_i})$$

$$- \Sigma g_i \frac{- \delta\alpha e^{-\beta w_i} - \alpha e^{-\beta w_i}(-\beta\delta w_i - w_i\delta\beta)}{1 - \alpha e^{-\beta w_i}} \qquad (4\text{-}36)$$

The last term in (4-36) can perhaps be analyzed most efficaciously by decomposing it into three terms, each of which can be attacked separately. First we consider

$$+ \Sigma g_i \frac{e^{-\beta w_i}}{1 - \alpha e^{-\beta w_i}} \delta\alpha = \Sigma \frac{g_i\, \delta\alpha}{e^{\beta w_i} - \alpha}$$

$$= \Sigma n_i \frac{\delta\alpha}{\alpha}$$

$$= N\frac{\delta\alpha}{\alpha} \qquad (4\text{-}37a)$$

where we have used (3-1) and (3-23a).

Second, we write

$$- \alpha\beta\Sigma \frac{g_i e^{-\beta w_i}\,\delta w_i}{1 - \alpha e^{-\beta w_i}} = - \beta\Sigma \frac{\alpha g_i}{e^{\beta w_i} - \alpha}\delta w_i$$

$$= - \beta\Sigma n_i\,\delta w_i \qquad (4\text{-}37b)$$

And lastly,

$$- \Sigma \frac{\alpha g_i\, e^{-\beta w_i}\, w_i\delta\beta}{1 - \alpha e^{-\beta w_i}} = - \delta\beta\Sigma n_i\, w_i$$

$$= - U\delta\beta \qquad (4\text{-}37c)$$

Substituting (4-37) into (4-36) leads to

$$\delta \ln W_m = \beta \delta U - \beta \Sigma n_i \, \delta w_i - \Sigma \delta g_i \ln (1 - \alpha e^{-\beta w_i}) \qquad (4\text{-}38)$$

Again, we can identify the external work of the system (which we will verify in the following chapter) as

$$\delta \tau = - \Sigma \left[\frac{\delta g_i}{\beta} \ln (1 - \alpha e^{-\beta w_i}) + n_i \, \delta w_i \right] \qquad (4\text{-}39)$$

so that (4-38) becomes

$$\delta \ln W_m = \beta [\delta U + \delta \tau] \qquad (4\text{-}40)$$

which is exactly of the form of (4-25) for the Maxwell-Boltzmann-Planck system.

From (3-2) we can write

$$\delta U = \Sigma n_i \, \delta w_i + \Sigma w_i \, \delta n_i \qquad (4\text{-}41)$$

which, when combined with (4-39) and (4-40), leads to

$$\delta Q = \Sigma \left[w_i \, \delta n_i - \frac{1}{\beta} \delta g_i \ln (1 - \alpha e^{-\beta w_i}) \right] \qquad (4\text{-}42)$$

We can also write (4-40) in the form

$$\delta k \ln W_m = \frac{\delta Q}{T} = \delta S$$

which, again, leads to the absolute entropy in the form

$$S = k \ln W_m$$

$$S = - Nk \ln \alpha + \frac{U}{T} - k \Sigma g_i \ln (1 - \alpha e^{-\beta w_i}) \qquad (4\text{-}43)$$

and

$$A = U - TS$$

$$A = NkT \ln \alpha + kT \Sigma g_i \ln (1 - \alpha e^{-\beta w_i}) \qquad (4\text{-}44)$$

where use has been made of (3-32).

4-4 FERMI-DIRAC STATISTICS

We follow the procedure of the preceding section by taking the variation in $\ln W_m$ of (3-33):

$$\delta \ln W_m = -N\frac{\delta\alpha}{\alpha} + \beta\delta U + U\delta\beta + \Sigma\delta g_i \ln (1 + \alpha e^{-\beta w_i})$$

$$+ \Sigma g_i \frac{e^{-\beta w_i}[\delta\alpha - \alpha(\beta\delta w_i + w_i\delta\beta)]}{1 + \alpha e^{-\beta w_i}} \qquad (4\text{-}45)$$

As before, we attack the last term in (4-45) by decomposing it into three parts, the first of which can be written as

$$\Sigma \frac{g_i e^{-\beta w_i}\delta\alpha}{1 + \alpha e^{-\beta w_i}} = \frac{\delta\alpha}{\alpha}\Sigma n_i = N\frac{\delta\alpha}{\alpha} \qquad (4\text{-}46a)$$

The second term takes the form

$$-\Sigma \frac{\alpha g_i e^{-\beta w_i}}{1 + \alpha e^{-\beta w_i}}\beta\delta w_i = -\beta\Sigma n_i \,\delta w_i \qquad (4\text{-}46b)$$

and the third part may be expressed as

$$-\Sigma \frac{\alpha g_i e^{-\beta w_i}}{1 + \alpha e^{-\beta w_i}}w_i\delta\beta = -\delta\beta\Sigma n_i w_i = -U\delta\beta \qquad (4\text{-}46c)$$

Substitution of (4-46) into (4-45) leads to

$$\delta \ln W_m = \beta\delta U + \Sigma[\delta g_i \ln (1 + \alpha e^{-\beta w_i}) - \beta n_i \,\delta w_i] \qquad (4\text{-}47)$$

which we write as

$$\delta \ln W_m = \beta[\delta U + \delta\tau] \qquad (4\text{-}48)$$

where we (in the following chapter) identify the external work as

$$\delta\tau = \Sigma\left[\frac{1}{\beta}\delta g_i \ln (1 + \alpha e^{-\beta w_i}) - n_i \,\delta w_i\right] \qquad (4\text{-}49)$$

With the aid of (4-41) we can express

$$\delta Q = \Sigma\left[w_i \,\delta n_i + \frac{1}{\beta}\delta g_i \ln (1 + \alpha e^{-\beta w_i})\right] \qquad (4\text{-}50)$$

in analogy with (4-42). The absolute entropy is again given by (4-31) which we write as

$$S = -Nk \ln \alpha + \frac{U}{T} + k\Sigma g_i \ln (1 + \alpha e^{-\beta w_i}) \qquad (4\text{-}51)$$

and

$$A = NkT \ln \alpha - kT\Sigma g_i \ln (1 + \alpha e^{-\beta w_i}) \qquad (4\text{-}52)$$

It remains for us to show that the significance which we have given to $\delta\tau$, as being the external work of the system, is admissible as well as determining the constant k. This will be done in the following chapter.

PROBLEMS

4-1. Obtain the expression, analogous to (4-24), for the external work applicable to a system of corrected boltzons, and contrast your result to (4-24) with any appropriate comments.

4-2. The sum over states is called the partition function [cf. (7-16) *infra*]. For Maxwell-Boltzmann-Planck statistics show that

$$n_i = \frac{N}{Z} g_i \exp(-\beta w_i)$$

and that

$$S = Nk \ln Z + \frac{U}{T}$$

where $Z = \Sigma g_i \exp(-\beta w_i)$ is the partition function.

4-3. What is the partition function for a system of three particles which obey Maxwell-Boltzmann-Planck statistics and which has nondegenerate energy levels $E_1 = 1$ and $E_2 = 2$ (arbitrary units). (*Hint:* See Prob. 4-2.)

4-4. Consider a system with N particles which obey Maxwell-Boltzmann-Planck statistics and find the Helmholtz free energy of the system if the particles can occupy n possible energy levels where $W_1 = W_2 = \cdots = W_n$.

4-5. For a system which obeys Bose-Einstein statistics, all the particles will go into the lowest energy level at the temperature of absolute zero. How many arrangements will the system have at $T = 0$ if the system has N particles and each energy level has a degeneracy of 10? If each energy level has a degeneracy of 1?

4-6. At the temperature of absolute zero, particles which obey Fermi-Dirac statistics will go to the lowest possible energy configuration.

$$g_L = L + 3 \quad \text{for} \quad L = 0, 1, 2, \ldots$$

What is the number of possible arrangements at $T = 0$ (a) if there are 3 particles? (b) if there are 12 particles? (c) if there are 15 particles?

5 | Definition of States Having Equal A Priori Probability

5-1 INTRODUCTION

All of the results obtained in the preceding chapter can be shown to be independent of the manner in which the states of equal a priori probability (among which the N molecules are distributed) are chosen. This is so because of the postulate suggested by the Liouville theorem. Suppose that someone tells us that an incompressible fluid (say, water) occupies a certain volume, and, without telling us any more, asks us to define the volume required such that there is an equal probability of finding a single molecule within that volume. We would reply (having read Sec. 1-4) that, if we divide the total volume occupied by the incompressible fluid, into N equal volumes $\Delta\tau$, the a priori probability of finding a molecule in each of the volume elements ought to be the same.

The phase points move throughout the phase space as the molecules of an incompressible fluid, with each molecule being represented by a phase point. This was the point of view we took in Sec. 1-4, and consistent with this philosophy, we now set up the following postulate: **The domains having equal volume in the phase space describing the subsystems of an ensemble (p_i, q_i) all have equal a priori probabilities of occupation by the subsystems.** In other words, the subsystems of an ensemble describing an isolated thermodynamic system (in which $N = $ const, $U = $ const, and the volume $V = $ const) are distributed uniformly (i.e., with equal a priori probability) over the possible microstates consistent with the constant (prespecified) values of N, V, and U.

We now partition the phase space into elements of equal, but arbitrary, phase volume

$$\Delta\tau = \int \ldots \int dp_1 \, dp_2 \, \cdots \, dp_\pi \, dq_1 \, dq_2 \, \cdots \, dq_\pi \qquad (5\text{-}1)$$

where π is the number of degrees of freedom associated with the system.

By our postulate, we conclude that the states corresponding to the presence of a phase point in any one of the $\Delta\tau$ is the same as for any other volume element. The phase points are then distributed such that the resulting thermodynamic probability is a maximum.

The classical statistics of Maxwell-Boltzmann required that the volumes $\Delta\tau$ be taken to be infinitesimal after the calculation of the maximum thermodynamic probability has been performed:

$$\Delta\tau \rightarrow d\tau = dp_1 \cdots dp_\pi \, dq_1 \cdots dq_\pi \qquad (5\text{-}2)$$

Under the quantum statistics, associated with the names of Planck, Bose, and Fermi, it is assumed that the phase volume of (5-1) is equal to h^π, where h is Planck's constant:

$$\Delta\tau = h^\pi = \int \cdots \int dp_1 \cdots dp_\pi \, dq_1 \cdots dq_\pi \qquad (5\text{-}3)$$

The condition expressed by (5-3) is frequently termed the *Bohr-Sommerfeld quantization rule.*

Let us suppose that the gas is enclosed in a container having a volume V. Then

$$\iiint dq_1 \, dq_2 \, dq_3 = \iiint dx \, dy \, dz = V \qquad (5\text{-}4)$$

and

$$\iiint dp_1 \, dp_2 \, dp_3 = \iiint dp_x \, dp_y \, dp_z = \frac{h^3}{V} \qquad (5\text{-}5)$$

The kinetic energy of a molecule of mass m can be written as

$$\varepsilon_k = \frac{p^2}{2m} \qquad (5\text{-}6)$$

from which we see that the states of constant energy can be represented in a three-dimensional momentum space by the surface of a sphere having a radius equal to the magnitude of the momentum:

$$p = |\mathbf{p}| = \sqrt{p_x^2 + p_y^2 + p_z^2} \qquad (5\text{-}7)$$

It proves to be more convenient to consider the number of states corresponding to molecules with momentum between p and $p + dp$, than the number of states with energy between ε_k and $\varepsilon_k + d\varepsilon_k$; although the relation between energy and momentum given by (5-6) still persists. From our postulate, the number of states corresponding to momentum in the range between p and $p + dp$ is proportional to the volume between two concentric spheres of radius p and $p + dp$. This volume can be written, to first order in dp (see Prob. 5-1) as

$$4\pi p^2 \, dp \qquad (5\text{-}8)$$

The number of states corresponding to the range in momentum from p to $p + dp$ (which we have called the *degeneracy factor*) is just the ratio of the volume between the concentric spheres, given by (5-8), to the size of one cell in the momentum space, which is given by (5-5):

$$g(p) = \frac{4\pi p^2 \, dp}{\left(\dfrac{h^3}{V}\right)} = \frac{V}{h^3} 4\pi p^2 \, dp \tag{5-9}$$

At this point let us pause to reflect on what has occurred behind the barrage of verbiage and the smokescreen of equations. The energies w_i associated with the ensemble energy level number i has been assumed, by (5-6), to be entirely kinetic (which is certainly consistent with a description of a gas without cohesion). For a molecule with a specified m, the (kinetic) energy is determined by the magnitude of the molecular momentum. In recognition of this fact, we relabel the energy levels of the ensemble, calling them momentum levels, and the degeneracy in the energy representation (the number of states corresponding to a given energy) will be the same in the momentum representation. We then look to the number of molecules with momentum between p and $p + dp$, rather than the number with a momentum of exactly p (which would correspond to an energy of exactly w_i). This means that instead of summing over discrete energy states we shall have to integrate over the continuous momentum interval. Consequently, we have anticipated this development by replacing the discrete index i on the degeneracy factor by the continuous label p in (5-9).

We now rewrite the discrete energy distribution functions summarized in Sec. 3-5 in terms of the continuous momentum parameter as:

(a) *Maxwell-Boltzmann-Planck*

$$n_i = \alpha g_i e^{-\beta w_i} \Rightarrow dn = \frac{\alpha V}{h^3} 4\pi p^2 e^{-(\beta p^2/2m)} \, dp \tag{5-10}$$

(b) *Bose-Einstein*

$$n_i = \frac{\alpha g_i}{e^{\beta w_i} - \alpha} \Rightarrow dn = \frac{\dfrac{\alpha V}{h^3} 4\pi p^2 \, dp}{e^{\beta p^2/2m} - \alpha} \tag{5-11}$$

(c) *Fermi-Dirac*

$$n_i = \frac{\alpha g_i}{e^{\beta w_i} + \alpha} \Rightarrow dn = \frac{\dfrac{\alpha V}{h^3} 4\pi p^2 \, dp}{e^{\beta p^2/2m} + \alpha} \tag{5-12}$$

5-2   APPLICATION TO A GAS WITHOUT COHESION AND COVOLUME

In this section we shall consider the volume and the temperature to be variables of interest, so that from (5-9) we can write

$$\frac{dg}{g} = \frac{dV}{V} \tag{5-13}$$

In terms of these variables, the expressions for the external work performed by the system which we wrote in the preceding chapter will have to reduce to the form

$$\delta\tau = P\delta V \tag{5-14}$$

Equation (2-94) gives us a workable relation between P and V

$$PV = \frac{2}{3}U \tag{2-94}$$

A. *Maxwell-Boltzmann-Planck Statistics*

From (4-24) we have an expression for a quantity which was alleged to be the external work performed by the system

$$\delta\tau = \frac{1}{\beta} \sum n_i \frac{\delta g_i}{g_i} - \sum n_i \delta w_i \tag{4-24}$$

The energies of the individual levels of the system, $w_i = p^2/2m$, are not subject to variation, since in this section we are only permitting T and V to vary. Thus (4-24) takes the form

$$\delta\tau = \frac{1}{\beta} \sum n_i \frac{\delta V}{V}$$

$$= \frac{N}{\beta} \frac{\delta V}{V} \tag{5-15}$$

when (5-13) and (3-1) are incorporated. The internal energy of the system is described by (3-2) in terms of the discrete energy distribution function, which can be expressed in terms of the continuous momentum parameter and (5-10) as

$$U = \sum n_i w_i \tag{3-2}$$

$$= \int_{p=0}^{\infty} \frac{p^2}{2m} \, dn \tag{5-16a}$$

$$= \frac{4\pi \alpha V}{2mh^3} \int_0^{\infty} p^4 e^{-(\beta p^2/2m)} \, dp \tag{5-16b}$$

The total number of particles in the system is similarly given by (3-1) which can be expressed as

$$N = \Sigma n_i \qquad (3\text{-}1)$$

$$= \int_{p=0}^{\infty} dn \qquad (5\text{-}17a)$$

$$= \frac{4\pi\alpha V}{h^3} \int_0^{\infty} p^2 e^{-(\beta p^2/2m)} dp \qquad (5\text{-}17b)$$

The integrals appearing in (5-16b) and (5-17b) can be expressed in terms of the gamma function discussed in Chap. 1 with the result that

$$N = \frac{2\pi\alpha V}{h^3} \left(\frac{2m}{\beta}\right)^{3/2} \Gamma(3/2) \qquad (5\text{-}18)$$

and

$$U = \frac{2\pi\alpha V}{\beta h^3} \left(\frac{2m}{\beta}\right)^{3/2} \Gamma(5/2) \qquad (5\text{-}19)$$

By using the recursion relation of (1-2) we can write (5-19) in the form

$$U = \frac{3}{2}\frac{N}{\beta} \qquad (5\text{-}20)$$

which when substituted into (5-15), leads to

$$\delta\tau = \frac{2}{3} U \frac{\delta V}{V} \qquad (5\text{-}21)$$

Now, by substituting (2-94) into (5-21) we find

$$\delta\tau = P\delta V \qquad (5\text{-}14)$$

which is the external work done by the system as foretold in the preceding chapter.

Furthermore, by combining (2-94) and (5-20) we find that

$$PV = NkT \qquad (5\text{-}22)$$

and

$$U = \frac{3}{2} NkT \qquad (5\text{-}23)$$

Thus our gas without cohesion and covolume obeys the laws of Boyle-Mariotte, Gay-Lussac, and Joule, discussed in Sec. 2-3. The generally accepted equation of state of an ideal gas is written[1]

$$PV = nRT \tag{5-24}$$

where n describes the number of moles of the gas and $R = 8\cdot317$ joule/ (gm-mole $- K°$) is the universal gas constant. We see that the gas without cohesion and covolume will obey the ideal gas law if the constant k is chosen such that

$$k = \frac{nR}{N} = \frac{R}{N_0} \tag{5-25}$$

where the number of moles of the gas has been written as the ratio of the number of molecules to Avogadro's number, N_0. As the astute student has no doubt already surmised, k is the well-known Boltzmann constant. Thus we see that a gas without cohesion which obeys the statistics of Boltzmann or Planck, follows the three classical gas laws of Boyle, Charles, and Joule. Hence one can utilize this gas as a thermometer yielding a thermodynamic scale.

B. *Bose-Einstein Statistics*

We now will endeavor to show that the quantity $\delta\tau$, defined by (4-39), represents the system external work. As in the classical case, the energy associated with the system levels will not vary, so that (4-39) takes the form

$$\delta\tau = -\frac{1}{\beta} \Sigma\, \delta g_i \ln\left(1 - \alpha e^{-\beta w_i}\right) \tag{5-26}$$

We now substitute (5-13) into (5-26) and then make the transition from the sum over discrete energy states to the integral over the continuous momentum range suggested by (5-9)

$$\delta\tau = -\frac{1}{\beta}\Sigma\frac{\delta V}{V}\, g_i \ln\left(1 - \alpha e^{-\beta w_i}\right)$$

$$= \frac{-4\pi\delta V}{\beta h^3}\int_0^\infty p^2\, dp \ln\left(1 - \alpha e^{-\beta p^2/2m}\right)$$

$$= -\frac{4\pi\delta V}{3\beta h^3}\left(\frac{2m}{\beta}\right)^{3/2} J \tag{5-27}$$

$$J = \int_0^\infty \ln\left(1 - \alpha e^{-x^2}\right) d\,(x^3)$$

$$= \left[x^3 \ln\left(1 - \alpha e^{-x^2}\right)\right]\Big|_0^\infty - 2\alpha\int_0^\infty \frac{x^4 e^{-x^2}\, dx}{1 - \alpha e^{-x^2}} \tag{5-28}$$

[1]R. T. Weidner and R. L. Sells, *Elementary Modern Physics* (Boston: Allyn and Bacon, Inc., 1960), Chap. 1.

The integrated part of (5-28) vanishes at both limits (see Prob. 5-3) and we can identify the integral with the internal energy of the system. From (3-2), (3-23), (5-6), and (5-9) we can write

$$U = \frac{4\pi\alpha V}{\beta h^3}\left(\frac{2m}{\beta}\right)^{3/2}\int_0^\infty \frac{x^4 e^{-x^2}\,dx}{1 - \alpha e^{-x^2}} \qquad (5\text{-}29)$$

and by combining (5-29) with (5-27) and (5-28) we find

$$\delta\tau = +\frac{2}{3}\frac{\delta V}{V}U \qquad (5\text{-}21a)$$

which is the very same result we obtained from the classical case. An analysis analogous to that case leads us to conclude that $\delta\tau$ is the external work performed by the system and that k is still Boltzmann's constant.

C. *Fermi-Dirac Statistics*

Again, under the assumption that the temperature and volume are the only thermodynamic variables, and that the energy of the various system levels does not change, we have, from (4-49),

$$\delta\tau = \frac{1}{\beta}\Sigma\delta g_i \ln\left(1 + \alpha e^{-\beta w_i}\right)$$

$$= \frac{1}{\beta}\Sigma\frac{\delta V}{V}g_i \ln\left(1 + \alpha e^{-\beta w_i}\right)$$

$$= \frac{4\pi\delta V}{\beta h^3}\int_0^\infty p^2 dp \ln\left[1 + \alpha e^{-\beta(p^2/2m)}\right] \qquad (5\text{-}30)$$

We can express (5-30) in the form of (5-27) by letting

$$K = \int_0^\infty \ln\left(1 + \alpha e^{-x^2}\right)d(x^3) \qquad (5\text{-}31)$$

so that

$$d\tau = \frac{4\pi\delta V}{3\beta h^3}\left(\frac{2m}{\beta}\right)^{3/2}K \qquad (5\text{-}32)$$

We can integrate (5-31) by parts to obtain

$$K = \frac{\beta h^3}{2\pi V}\left(\frac{\beta}{2m}\right)^{3/2}U \qquad (5\text{-}33)$$

(see Prob. 5-5), which, when substituted back into (5-32) leads to the relation of (5-21). Thus a gas without cohesion and covolume, obeying any of the three statistics we have been discussing will obey the ideal gas law of (5-24) and in all cases we find that the undetermined constant, associated with the Lagrange multiplier β, is the well-known Boltzmann constant.

5-3 CALCULATION OF THE ABSOLUTE ENTROPY

A. *Maxwell-Boltzmann-Planck Statistics*

The absolute entropy of a system of corrected boltzons is given by (4-34), which we express as

$$S' = Nk[1 - \ln \alpha] + \frac{U'}{T} \tag{5-34}$$

From the results of Prob. 3-3 and the development leading to (5-20) we note that the internal energy has the same value for a system of boltzons, given by (5-20), as for a system of corrected boltzons having the same number of particles and at the same temperature. Consequently, we can write

$$\frac{U'}{T} = \frac{3}{2} Nk \tag{5-35}$$

as an equation of state for the corrected boltzon gas without cohesion and covolume. For such a system we then find

$$S' = Nk[5/2 - \ln \alpha] \tag{5-36}$$

$$A' = U' - TS' = NkT[\ln \alpha - 1] \tag{5-37}$$

and

$$G' = U' + PV - TS' = NkT \ln \alpha \tag{5-38}$$

where we have used (5-22) to evaluate the Gibbs free energy.

We now recall the relation of (5-18) which can be written as

$$N = \alpha V \left(\frac{2\pi mkT}{h^2} \right)^{3/2} \tag{5-39}$$

with the help of (1-2), (1-27), and (1-28). We now see that, for our classical gas without cohesion and covolume, (5-39) may be solved for the second Lagrange undetermined multiplier, which we express as

$$\alpha = \frac{N/V}{N_c} \tag{5-40}$$

where we have written

$$N_c = \left(\frac{2\pi mkT}{h^2} \right)^{3/2} = \frac{1}{\Lambda^3} \tag{5-41}$$

The quantity N_c is generally referred to as *the effective density of states*, and represents the number of states available to the particles per unit volume of the gas[2]. From the discussion at the end of Sec. 2-5 we see that the gas will be nondegenerate if the number of states (per unit volume) available to the particles is much greater than the number of particles [divided by the volume occupied by the gas] in the system. Mathematically, we can represent this condition as

$$N_c \gg N/V \qquad (5\text{-}42\text{a})$$

which is formally equivalent to the condition

$$\alpha \ll 1 \qquad (5\text{-}42\text{b})$$

Whenever the requirements of (5-42) are met the gas will be suitably represented by the classical statistics and the quantum distribution functions (5-11) and (5-12), reduce to the classical distribution function of (5-10) (also cf. the discussion at the ends of Sec. 3-3 and 3-4). If our system contains a mole of gas, say, then

$$\frac{N}{V} = 6.025 \times 10^{23} \frac{\text{atoms}}{\text{gm-mole}} \times \frac{1 \text{ gm-mole}}{22.4 \times 10^3 \text{cm}^3} = 2.69 \times 10^{19} \frac{\text{atoms}}{\text{cm}^3}$$

at standard temperature and pressure. If we take $m = 25$ amu for the molecules at $300°K$, we find $N_c \simeq 1.16 \times 10^{26}$ atoms/cm³, which is indeed much greater than N/V. Thus we see why the atoms of most gases at ordinary temperatures and pressures may be treated classically with valid results. Except at *very low* temperatures, or when m is *very small* (of the order of the mass of an electron), or for very large values of N/V (very dense gases near the liquifaction point) we find that the conditions of (5-42) are obeyed and the gas without cohesion and covolume will be nondegenerate.

The quantity Λ in (5-41) is known as *the thermal de Broglie wavelength*. The reason for this appellation can be readily discerned if we recall that the ordinary de Broglie wavelength is written as

$$\lambda = \frac{h}{p} = \frac{h}{\sqrt{2m\varepsilon_K}} \qquad (5\text{-}43)$$

for a free particle whose energy is all kinetic. The similarity between λ and Λ becomes more apparent if we write

$$\Lambda = \frac{h}{\sqrt{2m(\pi kT)}} \qquad (5\text{-}44)$$

In the ensuing chapter it is shown that the thermal energy of a particle obeying classical statistics is $1/2kT$ times the number of degrees of freedom

---

[2]E. Spenke, *Electronic Semiconductors* (New York: McGraw-Hill Book Company, 1958), Chap. 8.

which the particle possesses. Thus (5-44) would represent the de Broglie wavelength of a free, classical particle having 2π degrees of freedom. The two quantities λ and Λ, are certainly of the same order of magnitude, and in fact, if in (5-43) we let

$$\varepsilon_K = 3/2kT \tag{5-45}$$

as intimated by (6-8) for a monatomic molecule, we see that

$$\frac{\Lambda}{\lambda} = \sqrt{\frac{3}{2\pi}} = 0.69... \tag{5-46}$$

whereas, for a molecule possessing six degrees of freedom, the ratio becomes 0.98... (see Prob. 5-7).

We can substitute (5-40) into (5-36) to obtain

$$S' = Nk\left[\frac{5}{2} + \ln\frac{(2\pi mkT)^{3/2}V}{Nh^3}\right] \tag{5-47}$$

which, however, is not in the form of the fundamental relation for a gas without cohesion and covolume, obeying classical statistics. Recall from Sec. 2-2 that the fundamental relation for the system is the relation which expresses the entropy of the system as a function of the extensive parameters needed to completely specify the system. We can put (5-47) in the form of the fundamental relation by making use of the equation of state given by (5-35). Let

$$\begin{aligned}
S_0' &= Nk\left[\frac{5}{2} - \ln\alpha_0\right] \\
&= Nk\left[\frac{5}{2} + \ln\frac{(2\pi mkT_0)^{3/2}V_0}{N_0h^3}\right]
\end{aligned} \tag{5-48}$$

be the entropy of the system at some different state of the system represented by N_0, V_0, T_0. (Notice that N_0 is *not* Avogadro's number as used here.) Then we find that

$$S' - S_0' = Nk\ln\left[\left(\frac{T}{T_0}\right)^{3/2}\left(\frac{V}{V_0}\right)\left(\frac{N_0}{N}\right)\right]$$

or

$$S' = S_0' + Nk\ln\left[\left(\frac{V}{V_0}\right)\left(\frac{U}{U_0}\right)^{3/2}\left(\frac{N_0}{N}\right)^{5/2}\right] \tag{5-49}$$

The expression (5-49) is the desired fundamental relation for our gas system composed of corrected boltzons without cohesion and covolume. If the reference entropy S_0' is known, (5-49) contains all possible thermodynamic information which is knowable about the system.

B. *Bose-Einstein Statistics*

We now proceed to evaluate the absolute entropy for a system of bosons without cohesion and covolume, taking as our starting point (4-43), which we express as

$$S = \frac{U}{T} - Nk \ln \alpha - J_1 \tag{5-50}$$

where we have written

$$J_1 = k\Sigma g_i \ln (1 - \alpha e^{-\beta w_i})$$

$$= k \int_0^\infty \frac{4\pi V}{h^3} p^2 dp \ln (1 - e^{-\beta p^2/2m})$$

$$= \frac{4kN_cV}{3\sqrt{\pi}} J \tag{5-51}$$

with J given by (5-28). By combining (5-28) and (5-29) we can write

$$J = -\frac{\beta\sqrt{\pi}}{2VN_c} U \tag{5-52}$$

which when substituted into (5-51) leads to

$$J_1 = -\frac{2}{3}\frac{U}{T} \tag{5-53}$$

Hence the absolute entropy takes the form

$$S = \frac{5}{3}\frac{U}{T} - Nk \ln \alpha \tag{5-54}$$

which if combined with (5-35) is in agreement with the result of (5-36). We also find that the Gibbs free energy is the same as (5-38) when use is made of (2-94).

C. Fermi-Dirac Statistics

The absolute entropy for a system composed of fermions is given by (4-51), which we write here as

$$S = \frac{U}{T} - Nk \ln \alpha + K_1 \tag{5-55}$$

where we have set

$$K_1 = k\Sigma g_i \ln (1 + \alpha e^{-\beta w_i})$$

$$= k \int_0^\infty \frac{4\pi V}{h^3} p^2 dp \ln (1 + \alpha e^{-\beta p^2/2m})$$

$$K_1 = \frac{4kN_cV}{3\sqrt{\pi}} K \tag{5-56}$$

and where K is defined by (5-31). We find that K is evaluated by (5-33), which takes the form

$$K = \frac{\beta\sqrt{\pi}}{2N_c V} U \qquad (5\text{-}57)$$

and when substituted into (5-56) leads to

$$K_1 = \frac{2}{3}\frac{U}{T} \qquad (5\text{-}58)$$

When (5-58) is inserted in (5-55) we find the absolute entropy for the fermion system to be of the same form as previously encountered in the boson and corrected boltzon systems, and given by (5-54).

We conclude this section (and chapter) with the observation that the expression for the absolute entropy is given by (5-54) or (5-36) for a gas system without cohesion and covolume, irrespective of the type of statistics that the individual constitutents of the system obey; that is whether they are corrected boltzons, bosons, or fermions, so long as the condition (5-42) is valid.

We also observe that the Gibbs potential

$$G = NkT \ln \alpha \qquad (5\text{-}59)$$

is of the same form for all three statistics, and that α has the same significance in all three cases, and may be expressed as

$$\alpha = e^{G/NkT} \qquad (5\text{-}60)$$

from inversion of (5-59), or as

$$\alpha = e^{\mu/kT} \qquad (5\text{-}61)$$

in terms of the chemical potential when use is made of (E2) in Chap. 2. For a system of corrected boltzons α is also given by (5-40) which may be incorporated into (5-61) to yield an expression for the chemical potential of such a system in terms of N, V, T. Since we have obtained the fundamental relation for the corrected boltzon system we can also obtain an expression for μ from (5-49) and (E5) in Chap. 2 (see Prob. 5-8).

PROBLEMS

5-1. Write the exact volume between two concentric spheres of radius p and $p + dp$, and obtain (5-8) as a first-order approximation.

5-2. Let $x = \beta p^2/2m$ and use (1-1) to obtain (5-18) and (5-19) from (5-16b) and (5-17b).

5-3. Using L'Hospital's rule (or any other suitable method of your choice) verify that the first term on the r.h.s. of (5-28) vanishes.

5-4. Verify that the internal energy of a system of bosons is given by (5-29) and obtain (5-21a).

5-5. With the aid of (5-16) and (5-12) obtain (5-33) from (5-31).

5-6. Evaluate the effective density of states N_c, given by (5-41), in units of cm^{-3} in the c.g.s. system and show that the Lagrange undetermined multiplier α, of (5-40) is consequently dimensionless. Take the mass to be that of (a) an electron, and (b) a proton, at room temperature.

5-7. Show that for a molecule having six degrees of freedom (d.o.f.) the ratio of (5-44) to (5-43) becomes

$$\frac{\Lambda}{\lambda} = 0.98 \ldots$$

5-8. (a) Obtain an expression for the chemical potential of a system of corrected boltzons from the fundamental relation, (5-49) and (E5) of Chap. 2. (b) Show that this result is equivalent to the expression obtained for $\mu - \mu_0$ by equating (5-61) and (5-40) and subtracting a reference chemical potential analogous to (5-48). (c) Evaluate μ_0 in terms of kT.

5-9. Find the partition function (sum over states – see Prob. 4-2) for a classical ideal gas.

5-10. Write the Fermi-Dirac distribution function in terms of the chemical potential.

5-11. Show that for the Bose-Einstein statistics

$$\lim_{T \to 0} \frac{N_j}{N_0} = 0$$

where N_0 is the number of particles in the ground state at $T = 0$ and where $j > 0$. Assume that $\alpha \to 1$ as $T \to 0$.

5-12. If the chemical potential, $\mu \gg kT$, for a perfect Fermi gas, show that

$$\mu = \frac{3^{2/3}h^2}{8\pi^{2/3}m} \left(\frac{N}{V}\right)^{2/3}$$

Use the approximations that

$$\exp(w - \mu)\beta \simeq 0 \text{ for } w < \mu \text{ and } \exp(w - \mu)\beta = \infty \text{ for } w > \mu$$

and include a factor of 2 to take into account spin. [*Hint*: see (13-43) *infra*.]

5-13. What is the entropy of a system of N particles at $T = 0$ which obey Bose-Einstein statistics if all the particles are in the ground state with a degeneracy of: (a) $g_0 = 100$? (b) $g_0 = 1$?

6 | *Classical Statistics — Applications*

6-1 THE MAXWELL GAS

The classical statistics are those which assume the canonical distribution of Boltzmann for the energy levels of the system. We have seen in Chap. 3 that the Boltzmann factor, $\alpha g_i e^{-\beta w_i}$, where β is given by (4-29), is common to all three statistics that we have discussed. Thus for the Maxwell gas we have the momentum distribution function for the system given by (5-10).

It is customary, when considering classical kinetic theory, to take the absolute value of the molecules' velocity as a variable in place of the momentum of the molecule.

$$v = |\mathbf{v}| = \left| \frac{\mathbf{p}}{m} \right| \tag{6-1}$$

The velocity distribution function is then found from (5-10) and (6-1) as

$$dn = Be^{-\beta mv^2/2} v^2 \, dv \tag{6-2}$$

where

$$B = N \sqrt{\frac{2}{\pi}} \left(\frac{m}{kT} \right)^{3/2} \tag{6-3}$$

is a constant (see Prob. 6-1). In general we shall not need the evaluation of the constant B appearing in the velocity distribution function of (6-2). As an example we can use (6-2) to calculate the average value of the velocity squared, which is given by

$$\langle v^2 \rangle = \frac{\int v^2 \, dn}{\int dn} \tag{6.4a}$$

$$\langle v^2 \rangle = \frac{\int_0^\infty e^{-\beta m v^2/2} v^4 \, dv}{\int_0^\infty e^{-\beta m v^2/2} v^2 \, dv}$$

$$= \frac{2}{\beta m} \frac{\int_0^\infty e^{-x} x^{3/2} \, dx}{\int_0^\infty e^{-x} x^{1/2} \, dx} \tag{6-4b}$$

where we have taken

$$x = \frac{1}{2} \beta m v^2 \tag{6-5}$$

as the substituted variable in (6-4b). From (1-1) and (1-2) we can write

$$\langle v^2 \rangle = \frac{3}{\beta m} \tag{6-6}$$

which leads to the following expression for the average kinetic energy of a single molecule of the Maxwell gas

$$\frac{m \langle v^2 \rangle}{2} = \frac{3}{2} kT \tag{6-7}$$

The total internal energy of a monatomic gas is just the sum of the molecular kinetic energies of translation [see Eq. 2-93] and is given by

$$U = N \frac{m \langle v^2 \rangle}{2}$$

$$= \frac{3}{2} NkT \tag{6-8}$$

The average molecular speed (not velocity, which is a vector quantity) is given by

$$\langle |\mathbf{v}| \rangle \equiv \langle v \rangle = \frac{\int v \, dn}{\int dn}$$

$$= \frac{\int_0^\infty e^{-(\beta m v^2)/2} v^3 \, dv}{\int_0^\infty e^{-(\beta m v^2)/2} v^2 \, dv}$$

$$\langle v \rangle = \left(\frac{2}{\beta m}\right)^{1/2} \frac{\displaystyle\int_0^\infty e^{-x}x\,dx}{\displaystyle\int_0^\infty e^{-x}x^{1/2}\,dx}$$

$$\langle v \rangle = \sqrt{\frac{8\,kT}{m\pi}} \tag{6-9}$$

By comparing (6-6) and (6-9) we see that the average speed is less than the root-mean-square speed, and in fact the two are related by

$$\frac{\langle v \rangle}{\sqrt{\langle v^2 \rangle}} = \sqrt{\frac{8}{3\pi}} = 0.9213 \dots \tag{6-10}$$

From symmetry arguments and the principle of equipartition of energy (see Sec. 6-2) we should expect that the value of the mean square of any component of the velocity of a molecule should be one third of the result of (6-6). To demonstrate that our intuition is correct we need to go back to our discussion, in Sec. 5-1, of the continuous momentum distribution function and the evaluation of the density of states [i.e., the degeneracy factor $g(p)$].

From our fundamental postulate in that section, we can see that the momentum and velocity distribution functions applicable to classical statistics can be written as

$$dn(p) = A_p e^{-\beta p^2/2m}\, dp_x\, dp_y\, dp_z\, dx\, dy\, dz \tag{6-11a}$$

and

$$dn(v) = A_v e^{-(\beta m v^2)/2}\, d\dot{x}\, d\dot{y}\, d\dot{z}\, dx\, dy\, dz \tag{6-11b}$$

respectively, where

$$p^2 = p_x^2 + p_y^2 + p_z^2 \tag{6-12a}$$

and

$$v^2 = \dot{x}^2 + \dot{y}^2 + \dot{z}^2 \tag{6-12b}$$

The constants A_p and A_v, appearing in (6-11), can easily be determined by normalization (see Prob. 6-2) but, like the constant in (6-2), generally do not need to be evaluated explicitly. We can now utilize (6-11b) to calculate the mean square of the x-component (say) of the molecular velocity

$$\langle \dot{x}^2 \rangle = \frac{\displaystyle\int\!\!\int\!\!\int\!\!\int\!\!\int\!\!\int_0^\infty \dot{x}^2 e^{-\beta m(\dot{x}^2 + \dot{y}^2 + \dot{z}^2)/2}\, d\dot{x}\, d\dot{y}\, d\dot{z}\, dx\, dy\, dz}{\displaystyle\int\!\!\int\!\!\int\!\!\int\!\!\int\!\!\int_0^\infty e^{-\beta m(\dot{x}^2 + \dot{y}^2 + \dot{z}^2)/2}\, d\dot{x}\, d\dot{y}\, d\dot{z}\, dx\, dy\, dz} \tag{6-13}$$

The sextuple integrals, appearing in the numerator and denominator of (6-13) can be written as the product of six simple integrals, which, with the exception of the integral over $\dot{x}$, are of the same form in the numerator and denominator, with the result that (6-13) takes the form

$$\langle \dot{x}^2 \rangle = \frac{\displaystyle\int_0^\infty e^{-(\beta m \dot{x}^2)/2}\, \dot{x}^2\, d\dot{x}}{\displaystyle\int_0^\infty e^{-(\beta m \dot{x}^2)/2}\, d\dot{x}}$$

$$= \frac{2}{\beta m} \frac{(I_2/2)}{(I_1/2)} \tag{6-14}$$

where I_1 and I_2 are given by (1-26) and (1-27), respectively. Thus, we see that our intuition was indeed correct, and

$$\langle \dot{x}^2 \rangle = \langle \dot{y}^2 \rangle = \langle \dot{z}^2 \rangle = \frac{1}{\beta m} = \frac{1}{3} \langle v^2 \rangle \tag{6-15}$$

The specific heat capacity at constant volume of any thermodynamic system can be expressed as

$$c_v = \frac{1}{n}\left(\frac{\partial U}{\partial T}\right)_V \tag{6-16}$$

For a system composed of the monatomic Maxwell gas, whose internal energy is given by (6-8), we find (by recalling that $NR = nr$, where n is the number of moles in the system.

$$c_v = \frac{1}{n}\frac{\partial}{\partial T}\left(\frac{3}{2} nRT\right)$$

$$c_v = \frac{3}{2} R \tag{6-17}$$

From the calculation leading to (6-15) we see that each of the three degrees of freedom associated with the point molecule contributes $R/2$ to the specific heat capacity. One can then speak of the molar specific heat capacity per molecular degree of freedom as being

$$\frac{R}{2} = 4.158 \quad \text{joule/gm-mole-deg} \tag{6-18a}$$

$$= 0.993 \quad \text{cal/gm-mole-deg} \tag{6-18b}$$

where (6-18b) follows from (6-18a) by means of (2-13). This is a particular example of the more general theorem of the equipartition of energy to be discussed in the following section of the current chapter.

6-2 EQUIPARTITION OF ENERGY

In general a molecule of any gas typically to be found in the laboratory will possess not only kinetic energy of translation, but also kinetic energy of rotation, and of internal vibration. In addition there may be some potential energy due to internal deformation or a potential energy arising from external forces. In the preceding section all of these additional energy terms were neglected because the molecule was considered to be a (mathematical) point.

The specification of the state of an arbitrary molecule can be effected in terms of the $2f$ parameters appearing in the Lagrangian formulation of (1-98), where f is the number of degrees of freedom (d.o.f.) available to the molecule. Of these f d.o.f., three will be needed to locate the center of mass of the molecule; some will be required to specify the orientation of the molecule in a Galilean reference system, and others will be used to describe the internal deformation.

The kinetic energy of the molecule is a quadratic function of the generalized velocities, as given by (1-99). By means of a principal axis transformation,[1]

$$Q_i = \sum_{j=1}^{f} a_{ij} q_j \tag{6-19}$$

in which Q_i is seen to be a function of all f of the q_i, the kinetic energy can be put in a form containing no cross-products of the velocities, $\dot{q}_j \dot{q}_k$. In this case, (1-99) becomes

$$\varepsilon_K (Q_j, \dot{Q}_j) = \sum_{i=1}^{f} G_{ii} (Q_j) \dot{Q}_i^2 \tag{6-20}$$

The coordinates Q_j, where $j = 1, 2, \ldots, f$, are orthogonal parameters representing a point in an f-dimensional (generally non-Euclidean) hyperspace. The kinetic energy given by (1-99) is of the form of what is called in books on tensor analysis *the square of the element of arc velocity*, with A_{mn} in (1-99) taking the role of the metric tensor [G_{ii} in the orthogonal frame of (6-20)]. The whole field of mechanics can be constructed in the framework of tensors but unfortunately, this fascinating vignette would lead us astray from our announced goal of investigating the equipartition of energy.[2] The corresponding conjugate momentum is given by (1-100) and (1-98), which reduces to

$$P_i = \frac{\partial \varepsilon_K}{\partial \dot{Q}_i} = 2 G_{ii} \dot{Q}_i \tag{6-21}$$

---

[1]A. Kyrala, *Theoretical Physics: Applications of Vectors, Matrices, Tensors, and Quaternions* (Philadelphia: W. B. Saunders Company, 1967), Sec. 3-9.

[2]See for example I. S. Sokolnikoff, *Tensor Analysis*, 2nd ed. (New York: John Wiley & Sons, Inc., 1964), Sec. 43 and Chap. 4.

and the kinetic energy can then be expressed in terms of the coordinates and momenta as

$$\varepsilon_K = \sum_{i=1}^{f} \frac{P_i^2}{4G_{ii}}$$

$$\varepsilon_K = \sum_{i=1}^{f} A_i P_i^2 \tag{6-22}$$

where

$$A_i = (4G_{ii})^{-1} \tag{6-23}$$

Note that the quantity $2G_{ii}$ in (6-21) can be interpreted as an effective mass* or a generalized mass, and (6-21) is thereby brought into the cartesian form of (1-106). Although this analogy is often useful, it must not be taken too literally. As we have already seen, the P_i need not have units of kgm-m/sec and the $\dot{Q}_i$ may be expressed in units other than m/sec so that the "effective mass" might not have units of kgm.

The potential energy of the molecule can be written in terms of the Q_i, by means of the principal axis transformation of (6-19), as

$$\varepsilon_p = \varepsilon_p(Q_i) \quad i = 1,2,...,f \tag{6-24}$$

and the canonical distribution then becomes

$$dn(P) = B_P e^{-\beta[\Sigma A_i P_i^2 + \varepsilon_p(Q_i)]} dP_1 \cdots dP_f dQ_1 \cdots dQ_f, \tag{6-25}$$

in analogy with (6-11a), although it is to be noted that in the latter distribution function, which describes a system without cohesion, the potential energy is identically zero. Thus the presence of the potential energy term in the Boltzmann factor is seen to be identified with the presence of intermolecular forces (i.e., cohesion) among the molecules of the ensemble. More will be said about this at the end of this section.

We now proceed to calculate the average value of $A_1 P_1^2$:

$$\langle A_1 P_1^2 \rangle = \frac{\int \cdots \int A_1 P_1^2 e^{-\beta A_1 P_1^2} \cdots e^{-\beta A_f P_f^2} dP_1 \cdots dP_f e^{-\beta \varepsilon_p} dQ_1 \cdots dQ_f}{\int \cdots \int e^{-\beta A_1 P_1^2} \cdots e^{-\beta A_f P_f^2} dP_1 \cdots dP_f e^{-\beta \varepsilon_p} dQ_1 \cdots dQ_f} \tag{6-26}$$

In (6-26) the A_i are all functions of the Q_j and it is no longer possible to separate (6-26) as a product of integrals as was done with (6-13). The integrals

---

*See Chap. 9 of Ref. 3 for a discussion of effective masses which may even be *negative*!

now must be evaluated successively. Integrating first of all over dP_1, the other terms $P_2 \cdots P_f Q_1 \cdots Q_f$ are to be treated as constants.

$$\int_0^\infty A_1 P_1^2 \, e^{-\beta A_1 P_1^2} \, dP_1 = \frac{1}{(\beta^{3/2})(A_1^{1/2})} \int_0^\infty x^2 e^{-x^2} \, dx$$

$$= \frac{(I_2/2)}{(\beta^{3/2})(A_1^{1/2})} \tag{6-27}$$

where I_2 is given by (1-27). The denominator can also be integrated over P_1 with the result that

$$\int_0^\infty e^{-\beta A_1 P_1^2} \, dP_1 = \frac{1}{\sqrt{\beta A_1}} \int_0^\infty e^{-x^2} \, dx$$

$$= \frac{(I_1/2)}{\sqrt{\beta A_1}} \tag{6-28}$$

with I_1 given by (1-25). Upon substitution of (6-27) and (6-28) into (6-26), we find

$$\langle A_1 P_1^2 \rangle$$

$$= \frac{I_2}{I_1 \beta} \frac{\int \cdots \int A_1^{-1/2} e^{-\beta A_2 P_2^2} \cdots e^{-A_f P_f^2} \, dP_2 \cdots dP_f e^{-\beta \varepsilon_p} \, dQ_1 \cdots dQ_f}{\int \cdots \int A_1^{-1/2} e^{-\beta A_2 P_2^2} \cdots e^{-\beta A_f P_f^2} \, dP_2 \cdots dP_f e^{-\beta \varepsilon_p} \, dQ_1 \cdots dQ^f}$$

$$\langle A_1 P_1^2 \rangle = \frac{1}{2\beta} \tag{6-29}$$

since the (nonseparable) integrals in the numerator and denominator are identical and thus cancel, and the ratio of I_2/I_1 has been substituted from (1-28).

Eq. 6-29 represents the average value of the contribution of one (particular) degree of freedom to the kinetic energy; and it can easily be seen that all d.o.f. will contribute the same amount and in the very same way. Thus the total contribution of one d.o.f., from all N molecules, to the total ensemble energy will be

$$U/\text{d.o.f.} = \frac{1}{2} NkT \tag{6-30a}$$

$$= \frac{1}{2} nRT \tag{6-30b}$$

and the contribution to the specific heat capacity of one d.o.f. (from the kinetic energy) will be $R/2$. The theorem of the equipartition of energy can then be stated as: **the contribution of the kinetic energy of the molecules in the system to the molar specific heat capacity of the system is given by**

$$c_v = f\frac{R}{2} \tag{6-31}$$

where f is the number of d.o.f. of the molecule. It can be seen that (6-17) is indeed a special case of (6-31).

In general, when the potential energy of the molecule is of an arbitrary form, there is no unique way to determine its contribution to the specific heat capacity, but when the potential energy can be expressed as a linear combination of the squares of the parameters Q_i,

$$\varepsilon_p(Q_i) = \sum_{i=1}^{t} B_i Q_i^2 \tag{6-32}$$

then each one of the terms in (6-32) will contribute $R/2$ to the molar specific heat capacity (see Prob. 6-3) in the same way as the terms of (6-22). The potential energy function of (6-32) is easily recognized to represent harmonic vibrations and is found to (at least approximately) describe the vibrations of a diatomic molecule and those of the atoms in a solid crystal.

We shall conclude this section by investigating two examples of non-quadratic potential energy: the gravitational potential energy, and the potential energy associated with paramagnetic molecules in an external magnetic field.

From (1-115), (6-11), and (6-25) we see that the canonical distribution function for a molecule of mass m in a gravitational field parallel to the z-axis of our (rectangular cartesian) coordinate system can be written as

$$dn(v) = A_v e^{-\beta m[(\dot{x}^2 + \dot{y}^2 + \dot{z}^2)/2 + gz]}\, d\dot{x}\, d\dot{y}\, d\dot{z}\, dx\, dy\, dz \tag{6-33}$$

From (6-33) we can evaluate

$$\left\langle \frac{m\dot{x}^2}{2} \right\rangle = \frac{kT}{2} \tag{6-34}$$

which is independent of z, and of course, analogous relations hold for the y and z components of the velocity. Inasmuch as the velocities and co-ordinates are assumed to be independent parameters, we can lump them together into the normalization constant, and express the number of molecules to be found in a column of cross-sectional area A_z at a height between z and $z + dz$ as

$$dn_{(z)} = Be^{-\beta mgz}\, dz \tag{6-35}$$

This formula may be identified with the surveying formula of Laplace, which is usually written in the form

$$dP = -\rho g dz \tag{6-36}$$

which expresses the change in atmospheric pressure with altitude. The density, ρ, of an ideal gas can be expressed in terms of the molecular mass, M, of the gas molecules as

$$\rho = \frac{Nm}{V} = \frac{nM}{\left(\dfrac{nRT}{P}\right)}$$

$$\rho = \frac{MP}{RT} = \frac{mP}{kT} \tag{6-37}$$

By substitution of (6-37) into (6-36) we have

$$\frac{dP}{P} = -\frac{mg}{kT}\,dz \tag{6-38}$$

which can be integrated to yield

$$P = P_0 e^{-(mg/kT)z} \tag{6-39}$$

Eq. 6-39, which was obtained from, and, of course, is equivalent to (6-36) is frequently referred to as the *law of atmospheres*, or as the barometric formula. It is perhaps one of the simplest examples of the Maxwell-Boltzmann-Planck distribution law.*

The equation of state of our Maxwell gas [as can be seen from (2-94) and (6-8)] is given by

$$N = \frac{PV}{kT} = \frac{P_0 V}{kT}\, e^{-(mg/kT)z} \tag{6-40}$$

which can be expressed, for our closed isothermal system (N, V, T all constant) as

$$dN = -\frac{P_0 V mg}{(kT)^2}\, e^{-(mg/kT)z}\,dz$$

$$dN_{(z)} = -Ce^{-(mg/kT)z}\,dz \tag{6-41}$$

Comparison between (6-41) and (6-35) indicate that the two representations of the number of molecules to be found between z and $z + dz$ are the same if

$$\beta = \frac{1}{kT} \tag{6-42}$$

which is in agreement with (4-29).

The distribution of particles with increasing altitude as given by (6-41) is an isothermal distribution, and is in agreement with observation at high altitudes (i.e., in the stratosphere). At lower altitudes (e.g., in the troposphere)

*This illustration is pursued further in H. J. G. Hayman, *Statistical Thermodynamics* (New York: Elsevier Publishing Company, 1967), p. 1.

rising and falling air currents stir up the atmosphere resulting in the adiabatic displacement of air masses. Thus the specific entropy, rather than the temperature, is the quantity which reaches equilibrium in these regions. In general a truly thermodynamic equilibrium situation is not attained; however, if the ebullient sources should disappear, thermodynamic equilibrium would be established from the troposphere to the surface of the earth. The contribution to the specific heat capacity for the case of an infinitely high atmosphere can be obtained from

$$\langle mgz \rangle = \frac{\displaystyle\int_0^\infty mgz\, e^{-\beta mgz}\, dz}{\displaystyle\int_0^\infty e^{-\beta mgz}\, dz} \tag{6-43a}$$

$$= \frac{1}{\beta} \tag{6-43b}$$

where the integrals are easily evaluated by (1-1),

$$U_{\text{grav}} = N \langle mgz \rangle = NkT \tag{6-44}$$

and

$$c_v = R \tag{6-45}$$

in contrast to (6-31). One can calculate as an exercise (see Prob. 6-4) the specific heat capacity to be expected from an atmosphere of finite height.

We now turn our attention to the Langevin description of paramagnetic atoms and molecules. Paramagnetic molecules possess a permanent magnetic dipole moment μ and are relatively free to orient that moment in any direction. In the absence of an external magnetic field, **B**, the orientation of the dipole moments of the N molecules in the system will be random in nature. But when the external field is applied to the system, there will be a torque, which is opposed by the disruptive influence of thermal agitation, on the molecule tending to align the moment parallel to the field, this results in a positive susceptibility, which in general is strongly temperature dependent.

Let θ be the angle between the direction of the magnetic moment of the molecule and the direction of the external magnetic field. The work required to bring the magnetic dipole moment into a position where it is parallel to the external field from one where the relative angle between them is θ, is given by

$$W = \int_{\theta}^{0} \boldsymbol{\tau} \cdot d\boldsymbol{\theta} = \int_{\theta}^{0} \boldsymbol{\mu} \times \mathbf{B} \cdot d\boldsymbol{\theta}$$

$$= \int_{\theta}^{0} \mu B \sin \theta \, d\theta$$

$$= -\mu B + \mu B \cos \theta \tag{6-46}$$

For a conservative field the work done is the negative change in potential energy of the system. It is customary to absorb the angle independent term of (6-46) into the definition of the potential energy, which may then be written

$$\varepsilon_p = -\boldsymbol{\mu} \cdot \mathbf{B} = -\mu B \cos \theta \tag{6-47}$$

The orientation of the molecular magnetic dipole moment can most easily be defined in terms of a system of spherical polar coordinates (θ, ϕ) with $\mathbf{B}$ taken along the polar axis, as shown in Fig. 6-1.

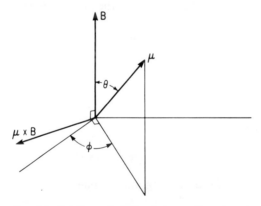

FIG. 6-1. Relative orientation between the external magnetic field B, and the molecular magnetic dipole moment.

In spherical polar coordinates, the velocity of the center of mass of the molecule is given by

$$\mathbf{v} = \dot{r}\,\hat{\mathbf{r}} + r\dot{\theta}\,\hat{\boldsymbol{\theta}} + r \sin \theta\,\dot{\phi}\,\hat{\boldsymbol{\phi}} \tag{6-48}$$

where $\hat{\mathbf{r}}$, $\hat{\boldsymbol{\theta}}$, and $\hat{\boldsymbol{\phi}}$ are unit vectors in the respective mutually orthogonal directions. The kinetic energy of the molecule can be written as the sum of the kinetic energy of translation of the center of mass of the molecule plus the kinetic energy of rotation about the center of mass, both of which can be expressed in terms of the velocity of the form (6-48). However, we are now interested only in the potential energy contribution, since the kinetic energy contribution to the specific heat capacity is given by (6-31) (with $f = 5$ for a diatomic molecule undergoing only translation and rotation). All of the magnetic dipoles do not point in the direction of the external magnetic field [in spite of the fact that this is the condition for minimum energy as given by (6-47)], since the thermal energy of the system results in the (nearly) random orientation of μ relative to **B**. On the other hand, the existence of **B** causes the dipoles to tend to align parallel to **B**; consequently the purely random orientation, which would prevail if **B** = 0, must be weighted by a factor containing the energy ε_p required to turn a dipole through the angle θ. This "weighting factor" is nothing more than the Boltzmann factor.

$$e^{-\beta\varepsilon_p} = e^{\mu B \cos \theta / kT} \tag{6-49}$$

If the distributions of dipole moments were perfectly random, as would occur in the absence of an external magnetic field, then the number of dipoles oriented at an angle between θ and $\theta + d\theta$ with respect to **B**, which is directed along the z-axis in Fig. 6-1, would be proportional to the area of a strip of width $d\theta$ and length $1 \sin \theta \, 2\pi$ on the surface of a sphere, centered at the origin and of unit radius. Writing the proportionality (normalization) constant as A and incorporating the weighting factor of (6-49), we have the angular distribution of molecules possessing permanent magnetic dipoles as

$$dn(\theta) = Ae^{\mu B \cos \theta / kT} \, d \, (\cos \theta) \tag{6-50}$$

(See Prob. 6-5.)

The contribution of the potential energy of the system to the total internal energy is given by

$$U_B = N\langle -\mu B \cos \theta \rangle$$
$$= -N \mu B \langle \cos \theta \rangle \tag{6-51}$$

The magnetization M describing the magnetic state of the material is equivalent to the magnetic dipole moment per unit volume of the material. For a paramagnetic substance with a random orientation of the molecular dipole moments (**B** = 0) the net magnetization of the system vanishes. The presence of the external field will cause the dipoles to tend to align parallel to **B**, and the net magnetization will then be parallel to **B** as well. Since the component of each dipole in the direction of **B** is $\mu \cos \theta$, the net component of magnetization will be given by

$$M = \left\langle \frac{N\mu \cos \theta}{V} \right\rangle$$
$$= \frac{N\mu}{V} \langle \cos \theta \rangle \tag{6-52}$$

From (6-51) and (6-52) we see that by evaluating $\langle \cos \theta \rangle$ we can immediately write the potential energy contribution to the molar specific heat capacity and the magnetic susceptibility of a paramagnetic system. Thus we write

$$\langle \cos \theta \rangle = \frac{\int \cos \theta \, dn}{\int dn}$$

$$= \frac{\int_0^\pi \cos \theta \, e^{\mu B \cos \theta / kT} \, d(\cos \theta)}{\int_0^\pi e^{\mu B \cos \theta / kT} \, d(\cos \theta)}$$

$$\langle \cos \theta \rangle = \coth a - \frac{1}{a} \qquad (6\text{-}53)$$

where

$$a = \frac{\mu B}{kT} \qquad (6\text{-}54)$$

(See Prob. 6-6.)

The r.h.s. of (6-53) is known as the *Langevin function*, commonly written as

$$L(x) = \coth x - \frac{1}{x} \qquad (6\text{-}55)$$

(See Prob. 6-7.) For weak fields or high temperatures

$$a \ll 1 \qquad (6\text{-}56)$$

and accordingly,

$$L(a) \simeq \frac{a}{3} \left[1 - \frac{a^2}{15} + \cdots \right] \qquad (6\text{-}57)$$

(See Prob. 6-8.) Hence, to first order in a, we see that

$$\langle \cos \theta \rangle \simeq \frac{\mu B}{3kT} \qquad (6\text{-}58)$$

Thus the contribution to the system internal energy is

$$U = \frac{-nR\mu^2 B^2}{3k^2 T} \qquad (6\text{-}59)$$

which, in contrast to the cases considered *supra*, represents a decrease in the system energy. The contribution to the molar specific heat capacity is easily seen to be

$$c_v = \frac{R}{3} \left(\frac{\mu B}{kT} \right)^2 \qquad (6\text{-}60)$$

which is subject to the restriction of (6-56), but at any rate is not constant. The magnetization induced in the system can be written as

$$M = \frac{N}{V} \mu L(a) \qquad (6\text{-}61)$$

where in the region of validity of (6-56) we have

$$\mathbf{M} = \frac{N^* \mu^2}{3kT} \mathbf{B} \qquad (6\text{-}62)$$

The expression of (6-62) has been written vectorially to indicate that $\mathbf{M}$ and $\mathbf{B}$ are in the same direction. The magnetic field $\mathbf{B}$ and the magnetic intensity $\mathbf{H}$, are related for isotropic conditions by

$$\mathbf{B} = \mu_0 K_m \mathbf{H} \qquad (6\text{-}63)$$

where K_m is the specific permeability of the substance and $\mu_0 = 4\pi \times 10^{-7}$ henry/m is the permeability of empty space. The magnetic susceptibility, which is given by the ratio of M to H, may then be expressed as

$$\chi_m = \frac{M}{H} = \left| \frac{N^* \mu^2 \mu_0 K_m}{3kT} \right. \qquad (6\text{-}64)$$

and where the density of molecules has been written as

$$N^* = N/V \qquad (6\text{-}65)$$

The relation of (6-64) whereby the magnetic susceptibility of a paramagnetic arrangement of dipoles varies inversely with the absolute temperature, is known as the *Curie law*, and is experimentally verified at elevated temperatures, which by (6-56) is the region where (6-64) should be valid.[3] A quantum-mechanical description of the phenomenon modifies the results somewhat and leads to the *Curie-Weiss law*, in which the susceptibility takes the form

$$\chi_m = \frac{C}{T - \Theta} \qquad (6\text{-}66)$$

where C is a constant and Θ is a characteristic temperature of the material.

Langevin has extended these results to the interpretation of the Cotton-Mouton effect, which is the magnetic birefringence analogue of the Kerr electro-optic effect.[4] This effect is observed in liquids placed in a transverse magnetic field and is attributed to the aligning of the (either permanent or induced) magnetic dipole moments of the anisotropic molecules.

[3] The material of this example is covered in nearly all books dealing with solid state physics; see for example C. Kittel, *Introduction to Solid State Physics*, 3rd ed. (New York: John Wiley & Sons, Inc., 1966), Chap. 14.

[4] F. A. Jenkins and H. E. White, *Fundamentals of Optics*, 3rd ed. (New York: McGraw-Hill Book Company, 1957), Chap. 29.

Similarly, the Debye theory of dielectrics is based on the identical model for the orientation of electric dipoles in an impressed electric field.

6-3   SIMPLE SOLIDS AND NONMONATOMIC GASES

A molecule, whether it be monatomic, diatomic, or polyatomic, when considered as a body of finite size, ought always to have three degrees of freedom of orientation, leading, from (6-31), to a molar specific heat capacity at constant volume of $3R/2$ for these three degrees of orientational freedom. In addition there should be three degrees of translational freedom so that the minimum value of c_v should be $6R/2$.

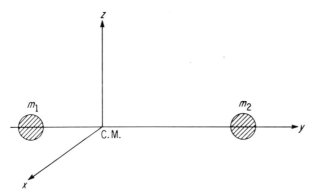

Fig. 6-2. A diatomic molecule viewed as a rigid rotator.

Experimental results for the polyatomic gas indicate that c_v is greater than $3R$; however, for the diatomic gases it appears that c_v is closer to $5R/2$, and for the monatomic gases c_v is found to be $3R/2$.

Before the work of Planck, these divergences between the predictions based on the equipartition principle and the results of experiments, were "explained" by saying that the monatomic molecules behaved as perfectly smooth spheres. The collisions between two such spheres thus did not give rise to any torque capable of modifying the orientation of the sphere; the degrees of freedom of translation were not exchangeable with those of orientation; and any elevation of the temperature would not modify the behavior of the molecules, which could thus not be distinguished from that to be expected of geometrical points; by this mechanism of assumptions the embarrassing conclusions foisted by the arguments of the preceding section were avoided.

For the diatomic molecules, it was argued that each atom is to be considered as a perfectly smooth ball, and the two atoms are to be assumed to be connected, in the form of a "dumbbell," as shown in Fig. 6-2, where for convenience we have we have taken the line connecting the two atoms along the y-axis, and the origin at the center of mass of the molecule. By assuming the distance between the atoms to be constant, the motion of the diatomic molecule about its center of mass can be analyzed as a "rigid rotator" by means of classical mechanics. Thus viewed, the diatomic molecule can be seen to have two degrees of freedom of rotation about the center of mass (rotation about the x- and z-axes), since the kinetic energy of rotation about the y-axis is assumed to be negligible compared to that for the other two axes. These two degrees of freedom of rotation of the diatomic molecule, when combined with the three degrees of freedom of translation of the center of mass, are just sufficient to give agreement with experiment.

Both for the monatomic and the diatomic molecule, when analyzed from the viewpoint of classical statistics, it has to be postulated that one or more degrees of freedom do not participate in the equipartition of energy. This solution to the problem is unsatisfactory from at least two points of view:

1. If there were even a very small amount of internal friction, the equipartition of energy would eventually be established and this would manifest itself in the measurement of c_v, as it would take a rather long time before all the degrees of freedom participated. Thus in the measurement of c_v, one would observe the thermodynamic equilibrium with the three translational degrees of freedom appearing quite rapidly, and the other degrees of freedom entering much more slowly. There is no experimental evidence for such an effect.

2. Experiments show that the two degrees of rotational freedom associated with a diatomic gas at room temperature do not contribute to the molar specific heat capacity at low temperatures (these gases are then said to be degenerate). For H_2 at room temperature $c_v = 5R/2$ while at low temperatures $c_v = 3R/2$ as is to be expected from a monatomic gas, although the molecule is still diatomic at the low temperature. The classical theory does not yield results which are compatible with these experimental results. The explanation of these difficulties has been satisfactorily given only after the introduction of Planck's constant, h. The fact that at room temperature, three degrees of freedom for a monatomic gas and one degree of freedom for a diatomic gas, do not enter into the equipartition of energy, can be explained on the basis of the negligible moment of inertia for the corresponding degree of freedom when considered from a quantum-mechanical point of view.

In the above description of the diatomic molecule as a rigid rotator, no allowance was made for the possibility that the two atoms might vibrate relative to the center of mass of the molecule along the line connecting the two atoms. We now replace the massless, rigid rod connecting the two atoms in our model of the diatomic molecule by a potential energy function ε_p. If r_0 is the separation distance between the atoms when the molecule is in an equilibrium configuration, and r is the separation distance after the molecule has suffered a change in its internal energy (perhaps by collision with another molecule), then the relative change in position of one atom with respect to the other can be described in terms of

$$\delta = r - r_0 \tag{6-67}$$

The potential energy function can be expressed in terms of δ as

$$\varepsilon_p(\delta) = \varepsilon_p(r_0) + \left.\frac{\partial \varepsilon_p}{\partial r}\right|_{r_0} \delta + \frac{1}{2}\left.\frac{\partial^2 \varepsilon_p}{\partial r^2}\right|_{r_0} \delta^2 + \cdots \tag{6-68}$$

by means of a simple Taylor expansion. The first term on the r.h.s. of (6-68) is a constant representing the potential energy of the molecule in its equilibrium configuration and can be absorbed by choosing our zero reference of potential at $\delta = 0$. The attractive force between the atoms is given by $-\partial \varepsilon_p/\partial r$, and this vanishes by definition, at the equilibrium configuration. Consequently, the lowest order term in δ occurring in the potential energy is quadratic, and we can write, to lowest order

$$\varepsilon_p = b\delta^2 \tag{6-69}$$

The total energy of the molecule can then be written as

$$w = \varepsilon_k + b\delta^2 \tag{6-70}$$

where the kinetic energy term

$$\varepsilon_k = \frac{(m_1 + m_2)}{2}(\dot{x}^2 + \dot{y}^2 + \dot{z}^2) + \frac{I}{2}(\dot{\theta}^2 + \sin^2\theta\dot{\phi}^2) + \frac{\mu}{2}\dot{\delta}^2 \tag{6-71}$$

contains three translational terms, two rotational terms, and a term representing the kinetic energy of vibration (I is the moment of inertia of the molecule about the center of mass, and μ is the reduced mass). Since all the terms in w are quadratic, each and every one will contribute $kT/2$ to the system energy per molecule and $R/2$ to the molar specific heat capacity (as shown in Prob. 6-3). Thus we see that the molar specific heat capacity at constant volume for a system composed of diatomic molecules capable of translation, rotation, and vibration ought to be $7R/2$. In reality, at ordinary temperature, experiments yield values of $5R/2$, but at higher temperature this value tends toward $7R/2$ as predicted from classical analysis.

This disagreement between the experimental results and theory has only been resolved by means of quantum statistics, which indicate that at ordinary temperatures the two terms arising from vibration (potential and kinetic energy contributions) are unexcited and do not contribute to the heat capacity of the system.

For a simple solid crystal, the atoms are assumed to be placed on the lattice points much in the manner of the knots on a seine. The potential energy function, due to all the other atoms at their lattice sites, which influences the motion of a given atom ought to be a function of the co-ordinates x, y, and z, representing the atom's departure from equilibrium. The potential energy can be expanded in a manner analogous to that of (6-68):

$$\varepsilon_p(x, y, z) = a_0 + [Ax + By + Cz] + [ax^2 + by^2 + cz^2$$
$$+ 2dxy + 2exz + 2fyz] + \cdots \qquad (6\text{-}72)$$

where we can choose our zero reference of potential at

$$x = y = z = 0 = a_0 \qquad (6\text{-}73)$$

Similarly, the x-component of the force acting on the atom under consideration is given by

$$-F_x = A + 2(ax + dy + ez) + \cdots \qquad (6\text{-}74)$$

and since the equilibrium configuration occurs at

$$x = y = z = 0 = F_x = F_y = F_z$$

it follows that

$$A = B = C = 0 \qquad (6\text{-}75)$$

and the lowest order terms appearing in the potential energy are those in the second square bracket of (6-72). These terms are precisely of the form which lend themselves to the principal axis transformation of (6-19), and so the potential energy function for the atom in a simple solid crystal may then be expressed as

$$\varepsilon_p = \frac{k_1 x^2}{2} + \frac{k_2 y^2}{2} + \frac{k_3 z^2}{2} \qquad (6\text{-}76)$$

and the kinetic energy is of the form

$$\varepsilon_x = \frac{m\dot{x}^2}{2} + \frac{m\dot{y}^2}{2} + \frac{m\dot{z}^2}{2} \qquad (6\text{-}77)$$

where we have used the same symbols, x, y, z, to represent the transformed coordinates in the principal axis representation; this should cause no confusion to the student who has read Sec. 6-2.

Once again we see that all the terms in the kinetic and potential energy can be expressed in the form of (6-20) and (6-32) so that the total contribution to the molar specific heat capacity at constant volume for such a model of the solid should be

$$c_v = \frac{6R}{2} = 5.958 \text{ cal/gm-mole-deg} \qquad (6\text{-}78)$$

The quantities k_1, k_2, k_3 appearing in (6-76) can be interpreted as spring constants for vibrational modes of the internal energy of the simple solid system. These quantities ought to depend on the lattice dimensions of the crystal, and one can suppose that when the temperature of the crystal is raised the lattice spacing, and consequently the k_1, k_2, k_3, are prevented from changing by applying an external pressure on the crystal of the proper magnitude. Indeed, when the specific heat capacity of a solid is being measured it is generally measured at constant pressure rather than at constant volume, for reasons of experimental convenience. But the ratio of the specific heat capacity at constant pressure to that at constant volume is the same as the ratio of the isothermal to adiabatic compressibility of the system[5]

$$\frac{c_p}{c_v} \equiv \gamma = \frac{\kappa_T}{\kappa_S} \tag{6-79}$$

where

$$\kappa_{T,S} = -\frac{1}{V}\left(\frac{\partial V}{\partial P}\right)_{T,S} \tag{6-80}$$

is the compressibility. For most simple solids, it is observed experimentally that γ is in the vicinity of 1.1 and thus, from (6-78) and (6-79)

$$c_p = 6.55 \text{ cal/gm-mole-deg} \tag{6-81}$$

This relation of (6-81) is the classical value of the law of Dulong and Petit, which is generally verified by experiment at ordinary temperatures (although one notable exception is diamond). But even here the classical theory is insufficient to account for all the experimental results:

1. At low temperatures the specific heat capacity of all substances tends towards zero as the absolute temperature tends toward zero. This is not predicted from the classical analysis.
2. The specific heat capacity of a metal and an insulating crystal are observed to be roughly the same value. But there is ample experimental evidence to support the hypothesis that in a metal there exist free (conduction) electrons which form an electronic gas which ought to undergo translational motion. Thus in the metal, in addition to the six vibrational degrees of freedom associated with the positive ions (neutral atoms in the case of an insulator) about their lattice sites, and which should also be present for an insulator, there should be an additional three degrees of electronic translational freedom not found in insulators. Hence the classical theory predicts $c_v = 9R/2$ for metals, and $6R/2$ for insulators. As mentioned above, this difference is not confirmed by experiment.

[5]See, for example, M. W. Zemansky, *Heat and Thermodynamics* (New York: McGraw-Hill Book Company, 1957), Chap. 13.

It is remarkable that a single hypothesis, introducing the constant h, reconciles all these difficulties. This hypothesis is the basis of the two following chapters.

PROBLEMS

6-1. Verify equation (6-3) by integrating (6-2).

6-2. Evaluate A_p and A_v in (6-11) and demonstrate the dimensional correctness of your result.

6-3. Calculate the average value of $B_1 Q_1^2$ and show that the contribution of the potential energy function of (6-32) to the molar specific heat capacity of the system for which (6-32) is valid is given by

$$c_v = t \frac{R}{2}$$

6-4. Obtain the specific heat capacity for a gas of finite height, y, in an external gravitational field, by replacing the upper limit of the integrals in (6-43a) by y.

6-5. From the discussion in the text, deduce (6-50).

6-6. Verify (6-53).

6-7. Make a sketch of the Langevin function $L(x)$ as a function of x. Determine the behavior as $x \to 0$ and $x \to \infty$ and relate these limits to an appropriate fact situation by means of (6-54).

6-8. Verify (6-57) and obtain the next term in the series.

6-9. Show that the fluctuations in the velocity of a Maxwellian gas is

$$\langle (\Delta v)^2 \rangle = \langle (v - \langle \bar{v} \rangle)^2 \rangle = \frac{kT}{m} \left(3 - \frac{8}{\pi} \right)$$

[*Hint*: make use of the equations (6-6) and (6-9)].

6-10. If the molecules of a gas emit light at a frequency v, what will be the average range of frequencies an observer will see due to the thermal motion of the gas? [*Hint*: consider the Doppler shift, $v = v_0(1 + v/c)$ and evaluate Δv].

6-11. A Maxwellian gas is in a container which is surrounded by a vacuum. If the container has a pinhole in it, how many molecules with velocity v pass thru the hole per unit area per unit time? What is the physical significance of this quantity?

6-12. If a gas of molecules, each having mass m, is in a container which rotates at an angular velocity ω, what is the density of the gas as a function of radius?

6-13. What is the average kinetic and the average potential energy of a one-dimensional harmonic oscillator? What is the average total energy of a three-dimensional harmonic oscillator?

7 | Planck Representation of a Blackbody

7-1 INTRODUCTION

Historically, it was by the way of explaining the difficulties born in the classical theory of the radiation emitted (or absorbed) by a blackbody that Planck introduced the constant, h, which bears his name. By definition, a blackbody is one whose surface has the property of absorbing all the radiation incident upon it, i.e., none of the radiation incident on the blackbody is reflected by the blackbody. In addition to Planck, the other classical physicists, at the turn of the present century, assumed that the absorption (or emission) of the radiation incident on the solid (whether it was a "perfect" blackbody, or not) was effected through the molecules of the solid by means of a mechanism which could be mathematically analyzed as simple harmonic oscillators.[1] Planck proposed that the phase space representing the motion of these harmonic oscillators should not be divided into infinitesimal elements, but rather that the lower limit of divisibility should be cells of finite size h^π, where π is the number of degrees of freedom of the system [see the discussion in Sec. 5-1 leading to (5-3).] Let us consider a simple harmonic oscillator having a single degree of freedom (the molecule may be capable of motion in only one dimension determined by the relative orientation of the electric field vector of the incident radiation and the molecular electric dipole moment, for example) x; the energy of the oscillator is then given by

$$\varepsilon = \frac{p^2}{2m} + \frac{Kx^2}{2} \tag{7-1}$$

---

[1] See almost any text on atomic physics; for example, R. M. Eisberg, *Fundamentals of Modern Physics* (New York: John Wiley & Sons, Inc., 1961), Chap. 2.

where

$$p = m\dot{x} \tag{7-2a}$$

$$x = A \cos(\omega t + \delta) \tag{7-2b}$$

and

$$\omega = \sqrt{\frac{K}{m}} \tag{7-2c}$$

with δ representing an arbitrary phase factor.

For the one dimensional simple harmonic oscillator the corresponding phase space will have two dimensions and the surfaces of equal energy are, by (7-1), ellipses in the p-x plane as shown in Fig. 7-1 (see also Prob. 1-12):

$$a = \sqrt{\frac{2\varepsilon}{K}} \tag{7-3a}$$

$$b = \sqrt{2m\varepsilon} \tag{7-3b}$$

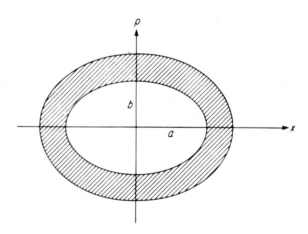

FIG. 7-1. Trajectories of constant energy in phase space representing a one-dimensional simple harmonic oscillator.

These ellipses are called *phase orbits*, since the phase point, representing the motion of the oscillator, will make one complete traversal of the elliptical path during one complete vibration of the oscillator, so long as ε in (7-1) remains constant. From a classical analysis, two neighboring phase orbits may be arbitrarily close, arising from the fact that classical oscillators may possess energies throughout a continuous range. The phase integral of the system,[2] which geometrically represents the area in phase space enclosed by the phase orbit, for a given (constant) energy can be written as

$$\oint p \, dx = nh + \text{const}$$

where $\oint$ is the phase integral, n is any integer, and h is Planck's constant. Classically, the constant appearing in (7-4) may be completely arbitrary (except for dimensions, of course, which must be those of action, the same as h; e.g., erg-sec) reflecting the fact that the energy in (7-1) may take any value. In the theory of Planck and Bohr it is assumed that the constant is null; this assumption is basic to the general formulation of the quantum condition. When the Planck hypothesis is applied to (7-4), the result is that

$$\oint p \, dx = nh \qquad (7\text{-}5)$$

and consequently we conclude that not all phase states are available to our system, but that only those states occur for which the value of the phase integral is an integer multiple of Planck's constant. Now if the two ellipses of Fig. 7-1 are neighboring, we see that the smaller ellipse will obey the condition (7-5) and the larger ellipse will obey (7-5) with n replaced by $n + 1$; and hence the area of phase space between two allowed, adjacent phase orbits will be h, independent of n. Thus we see that Planck's hypothesis has the effect of dividing the phase space into cells of equal size, and from our fundamental postulate of Sec. 5-1, all energy states of the system thus have equal a priori probabilities.

A more sophisticated analysis, based upon the postulates of quantum mechanics leads to the conclusion that the constant of (7-4) has the value of $h/2$. Thus the phase integral becomes

$$\oint p \, dx = (n + 1/2)h \qquad (7\text{-}6)$$

and the essential features of the theory based on the Planck hypothesis are preserved.

In general then, we can write the phase integral in the form

$$\oint p \, dx = \oint m\dot{x}\dot{x} \, dt = \oint 2\varepsilon_k \, dt$$

or

$$2\oint \varepsilon_k \, dt = sh \qquad (7\text{-}7)$$

where, for a one-dimensional simple harmonic oscillator, s is any integer n, based on the Planck hypothesis, and $s = n + \frac{1}{2}$ from a quantum-mechanical

[2]See, for example, G. Joos, *Theoretical Physics*, 3rd ed. (New York: Hafner Publishing Company, 1958), Chap. 6.

analysis. From (7-2) we write (7-7) in the form

$$\oint 2\varepsilon_k \, dt = \oint m A^2 \omega^2 \sin^2 (\omega t + \delta) \, dt$$

$$= m\omega^2 A^2 \int_0^T \sin^2 (\omega t + \delta) \, dt$$

$$\oint 2\varepsilon_k \, dt = m\omega^2 A^2 \frac{T}{2} \tag{7-8}$$

where T, of course, is the period of oscillation.

Furthermore,

$$\oint 2\varepsilon_p \, dt = \oint K x^2 \, dt$$

$$= K A^2 \frac{T}{2} \tag{7-9}$$

(See Prob. 7-1). And from (7-2c), (7-8), and (7-9), we see that

$$\oint 2\varepsilon_k \, dt = \oint 2\varepsilon_p \, dt = \frac{1}{2} \oint 2\varepsilon \, dt \tag{7-10}$$

since

$$\varepsilon = \varepsilon_k + \varepsilon_p = \text{const} \tag{7-11}$$

Combining (7-7), (7-10), and (7-11) we have

$$\oint \varepsilon \, dt = \varepsilon T = \frac{\varepsilon}{\nu} = sh \tag{7-12}$$

From (7-12) we see that the radiation absorbed or emitted by the molecular oscillators of the blackbody must have an energy of

$$\varepsilon = nh\nu \tag{7-13a}$$

or

$$\varepsilon = \left(n + \frac{1}{2} \right) h\nu \tag{7-13b}$$

where ν is the frequency of the radiation. The energy of a molecule (oscillator) in the nth energy level of the system is given by (7-13). The system is non-degenerate so that all of the g_i in (3-16) are equal to unity, and (3-16) can then be written as

$$n_i = A e^{-\beta i h \nu} \tag{7.14}$$

where i is the index number and not $\sqrt{-1}$. The total number of particles in the system is obtained by summing over all energy levels so that

$$N = A \sum_{i=0}^{\infty} e^{-i\beta h\nu} \tag{7-15}$$

Planck called the sum appearing in (7-15) *the sum over states* (*Zustandsumme* in German). It is perhaps more commonly called the *partition function,* and is generally designated by the letter Z:

$$Z = \sum_{i=0}^{\infty} e^{-i\beta h\nu} \tag{7-16}$$

It is convenient to represent Z other than as an infinite sum, and to this end we note that if

$$S_n = 1 + t + t^2 + \cdots + t^{n-1} + t^n \tag{7-17}$$

then

$$tS_n = t + t^2 + \cdots + t^n + t^{n+1}$$

and

$$S_n(1 - t) = 1 - t^{n+1}$$

or

$$S_n = \frac{1}{1-t} - \frac{t^{n+1}}{1-t} \tag{7-18}$$

If in (7-16) we let

$$t = e^{-\beta h\nu} \tag{7-19}$$

we see that

$$\lim_{n \to \infty} t^{n+1} = 0$$

and consequently, the partition function can be written as

$$Z = \frac{1}{1 - e^{-\beta h\nu}} \tag{7-20}$$

From (7-16) we see that

$$\frac{\partial Z}{\partial \beta} = \sum_{i=0}^{\infty} -ih\nu e^{-i\beta h\nu}$$

$$= \frac{-1}{A} \sum_{i=0}^{\infty} w_i n_i$$

or

$$\frac{\partial Z}{\partial \beta} = -\frac{1}{A} U \tag{7-21}$$

But from (7-15) and (7-16),

$$\frac{1}{A} = \frac{Z}{N} \tag{7-22}$$

so that

$$\frac{\partial Z}{\partial \beta} = -Z\frac{U}{N}$$

or

$$-\frac{1}{Z}\frac{\partial Z}{\partial \beta} = \frac{U}{N} = u \tag{7-23}$$

where u is the mean energy per oscillator. We can express u as

$$u = -\frac{\partial(\ln Z)}{\partial \beta} = \frac{\partial}{\partial \beta}\ln(1 - e^{-\beta h\nu}) \tag{7-24}$$

or

$$u = \frac{h\nu}{e^{\beta h\nu} - 1} \tag{7-25}$$

If we consider the energy of the system levels to be given by (7-13b), we have

$$n_i = A_1 e^{-\beta(i + 1/2)h\nu} \tag{7-26}$$

so that

$$N = \sum_{i=0}^{\infty} n_i = A_1 Z_1 \tag{7-27}$$

Where

$$Z_1 = \sum_{i=0}^{\infty} e^{-\beta(i + 1/2)h\nu} = \frac{e^{-\beta h\nu/2}}{1 - e^{-\beta h\nu}} \tag{7-28}$$

or

$$Z_1 = e^{-\beta h\nu/2}Z \tag{7-29}$$

The mean energy per oscillator is given by

$$u_1 = \frac{1}{N}\sum_{i=0}^{\infty}\left(i + \frac{1}{2}\right)h\nu A_1 e^{-\beta(i + 1/2)h\nu}$$

$$= -\frac{1}{Z_1}\frac{\partial Z_1}{\partial \beta} = -\frac{\partial}{\partial \beta}\ln Z_1 \tag{7-30}$$

By combining (7-28) with (7-30) we have

$$u_1 = \frac{h\nu}{2} + \frac{h\nu}{e^{\beta h\nu} - 1}$$

or

$$u_1 = u + \frac{hv}{2} \tag{7-31}$$

where u is given by (7-25). Thus the two partition functions and the mean energy per oscillator differ by only a (multiplicitive and additive) constant (respectively), although the latter can be expressed in terms of the former by the same functional dependence, as seen by (7-24) and (7-30).

7-2 SPECIFIC HEAT CAPACITY OF A SYSTEM OF SHMO'S

From our discussion in the preceding chapter, we see that a term like (7-25) ought to occur in the expression for the internal energy of a diatomic molecule; and three such terms, with three principal frequencies (v_1, v_2, v_3), ought to appear in the description of the internal energy of a simple solid. In both cases the contribution by a simple harmonic oscillator to the system specific heat capacity should be the same (per d.o.f.).

Let us suppose for simplicity that in the case of a simple solid, all three principal frequencies are the same. The specific heat capacity of the system can then be written as

$$c_v = 3N_0 \frac{\partial u}{\partial T} \tag{7-32}$$

But

$$\frac{\partial u}{\partial T} = \frac{\partial u}{\partial \beta} \frac{d\beta}{dT} = \frac{-1}{kT^2} \frac{\partial u}{\partial \beta} \tag{7-33}$$

Since (7-25) and (7-31) differ only by a constant they will both make the same contribution to the specific heat capacity. From (7-25) we have

$$\frac{\partial u}{\partial \beta} = -u^2 e^{\beta hv} \tag{7-34}$$

and so

$$c_v = 3N_0 k \left[\frac{\Theta/T}{e^{\Theta/T} - 1} \right]^2 e^{\Theta/T} \tag{7-35}$$

where the "characteristic temperature"

$$\Theta \equiv \frac{hv}{k} \tag{7-36}$$

is different for different crystals, and varies with V/N within the same crystal. We note that (7-35) can be written as

$$c_v = 3Rf(\Theta/T) \tag{7-37}$$

which can be interpreted to mean that by suitably compressing or expanding the temperature scales, i.e., by measuring the temperature for different substances in terms of Θ for that substance, all experimental curves for c_v, for all monatomic crystals at least, should coincide. This is an illustration of the "law of corresponding states," with which the student may be familiar by means of the equation of state of a van der Waals gas, written in terms of the critical pressure, temperature, and volume, such that the constants describing the different gases do not appear.[3]

In the region of high temperatures where $T \gg \Theta$, $f(\Theta/T) \to 1$, and thus we recover the classical value of

$$c_v \to 3R \quad \text{as} \quad T \to \infty \tag{7-38}$$

On the other hand, when $T \ll \Theta$, the exponential terms in (7-35) dominate and this simple model predicts that

$$c_v \to 3R \left(\frac{\Theta}{T}\right)^2 e^{-\Theta/T} \quad \text{as} \quad T \to 0 \tag{7-39}$$

From (7-39) we see that this "Einstein crystal"[4] has a specific heat capacity which tends toward zero as the temperature approaches zero, as is required by experiment. Unfortunately, the specific heat capacity given by (7-39) tends to zero *much more rapidly* (exponentially) than is observed experimentally. Thus, although the behavior of the specific heat capacity is qualitatively correct, quantitatively there exists a discrepancy between the theory of a simple Einstein model of a crystal and experiment. The characteristic temperature given by (7-36) can be calculated by using the proper infrared frequency (i.e., the Reststrahl frequency[5]) v. Debye has given a theory which is better verified by experiment than the simple Einstein model, and which we shall develop in the following chapter, after a more thorough discussion of the blackbody.

[3]F. W. Sears, *Thermodynamics* (Reading, Mass.: Addison-Wesley Publishing Company, Inc., 1953), Chap. 6.

[4]A. Einstein, *Ann. Physik* **22,** 180, 800 (1906).

[5]C. Kittel, *Introduction to Solid State Physics*, 3rd ed. (New York: John Wiley & Sons, Inc., 1966), Chap. 5.

PROBLEMS

7-1. Verify Eq. 7-9. [*Hint*: take x to be given by (7-2b).]

7-2. Consider an ideal diatomic gas. The enthalpy and the internal energy can be separated into two parts, one for the oscillator portion and the other for the nonoscillator portion. Let the nonoscillator part be represented by $H_n = U_n + PV$. Show that $c_v = c_p$ for the oscillator contributions. (*Hint*: write H and U as the sum of the oscillator and nonoscillator terms.)

7-3. In a procedure analogous to Prob. 7-2 *supra*, show that for a mole of oscillators $A - U_0 = G - U_0 = RT \ln(1 - e^{-\beta h\nu})$ where A is the Helmholtz energy, G is the Gibbs free energy and U_0 is the ground state internal energy for a mole of one dimensional simple harmonic oscillators.

7-4. The specific heat capacity at constant volume of copper at $300°K$ is 2.06 cal/mole-$°K$. What is the Einstein temperature of copper?

7-5. If the Einstein temperature of diamond is $\Theta = 1380°K$ what is its specific heat capacity at $2000°K$?

7-6. Show that the entropy is the same for a one dimensional harmonic oscillator whether or not the term $h\nu/2$ is included in the energy.

8 | *Blackbody Theory of Solids*

8-I BLACKBODY RADIATION

It is known from experiment that those materials which are efficient absorbers of thermal (electromagnetic) radiation are also efficient emitters of radiation, and conversely, those materials which are poor absorbers of thermal radiation are also poor emitters. It thus follows that the best emitter is one which is the most efficient absorber; and that, of course, is an object which absorbs *all* of the radiation incident on it. Such a body is called a *blackbody*. If two objects, made (hypothetically) from two different materials, are both blackbodies, they are both equally efficient at absorbing or radiating electromagnetic radiation, and consequently any properties of the thermal radiation emitted by the blackbodies, such as the spectral distribution of the radiation, should be independent of the detailed nature (such as, composition, size, shape) of the blackbody. Further impetus to the study of blackbody radiation is provided by the fact that the properties of thermal radiation from any body may be calculated from that of a perfect blackbody with the knowledge of the absorption spectrum of the given body.

A practically perfect blackbody can be constructed (both experimentally and theoretically) by forming a hollow enclosure, from any suitable material, and drilling a small hole through the wall of the enclosure to connect the interior of the cavity with the outside. If the area of the inner surface of the cavity is much greater than the area of the hole, then radiation incident to the hole from the outside will be reflected back and forth by the walls of the cavity and eventually be completely absorbed by the walls, with only a negligible amount of the incident radiation being reflected back to the outside through the hole. Consequently, since all the radiation incident to the hole is absorbed by the cavity, the *hole* exhibits all the properties of the surface of a blackbody. Thus the radiation emitted by the hole will have a blackbody spectrum. But this radiation emitted by the hole is just a portion of and identical to the radiation inside the cavity, so the thermal radiation inside the cavity will also exhibit a blackbody spectrum, characteristic of the temperature of the walls of the cavity (since this is the only temperature defined for the system).

In the instant section we shall assume, for simplicity, that the radiation in the cavity is homogeneous and isotropic, and that the total energy of the radiation is distributed over the various wave lengths of the radiation such that the quantity $\varepsilon_\lambda\, d\lambda$ represents the energy associated with waves having wavelengths between λ and $\lambda + d\lambda$. Since the wavelength and frequency of any wave are related by

$$v\lambda = v \tag{8-1}$$

the problem could be (and frequently is) formulated in terms of frequency distributions. The total energy of the radiation in the cavity is found by summing (integrating) over all the wavelengths present in the cavity, weighted by the factor ε_λ:

$$\varepsilon = \int_0^\infty \varepsilon_\lambda\, d\lambda \tag{8-2}$$

The calculation of $\varepsilon_\lambda\, d\lambda$ may be carried out by counting the number of characteristic electromagnetic periods contained between λ and $\lambda + d\lambda$. We assume, for the purposes of this calculation, that under the conditions of thermodynamic equilibrium, each of these characteristic periods has associated with it an average energy w, which we identify as the mean energy of a harmonic oscillator of the solid (considered, as in Chap. 7, to be the source of the thermal radiation) at the wall temperature T.

The calculation of these characteristic periods is a simple matter when the enclosure has the shape of a rectangular parallelpiped or a cube; although the final results will be found to be independent of the particular shape of the cavity. Likewise the calculations of the characteristic periods is the same, *mutatis mutandis*, for acoustic vibrations as for optical vibrations. In either case, the various characteristic quantities of the wave propagate with a uniform velocity, v (the speed of sound in the case of acoustic waves in air and the speed of light when the medium is vacuum). Let ψ be one of these quantities; it will then satisfy the wave equation

$$\Box \psi = 0 \tag{8-3}$$

where

$$\Box \equiv \Delta - \frac{1}{v^2}\, \partial_t^2 \tag{8-4}$$

is the D'Alembertian operator and Δ is the usual three-dimensional Laplacian operator.[1] Letting a, b, c denote the sides of the parallelepiped, ψ will have a stationary solution to (8-3) of the form

$$\psi(x, y, z, t) = \sum_m \sum_n \sum_p \alpha_{mnp}(x, y, z) \cos(\omega_{mnp}t + \phi) \qquad (8\text{-}5)$$

In general, a complete solution for ψ requires a specification of initial and boundary conditions which ψ must satisfy. In particular if ψ is required to vanish on the boundaries of the cavity we have

$$\psi = \sum_m \sum_n \sum_p \eta_{mnp} \sin\frac{m\pi x}{a} \sin\frac{n\pi y}{b} \sin\frac{p\pi z}{c} \cos(\omega_{mnp}t + \phi) \qquad (8\text{-}6)$$

with

$$\left[\left(\frac{m\pi}{a}\right)^2 + \left(\frac{n\pi}{b}\right)^2 + \left(\frac{p\pi}{c}\right)^2\right] = \frac{\omega_{mnp}^2}{v^2} = \frac{4\pi^2}{\lambda_{mnp}^2} \qquad (8\text{-}7)$$

where we have used (8-1) and the relation

$$\omega = 2\pi v \qquad (8\text{-}8)$$

To each set of the three positive integers m, n, p there corresponds a characteristic frequency ω_{mnp}. To further simplify the calculation let us assume that the cavity has the shape of a cube, so that $a = b = c$. In this case (8-7) takes the form

$$\left[\frac{2a}{\lambda_{mnp}}\right]^2 = m^2 + n^2 + p^2 \qquad (8\text{-}9)$$

If we label the three axes of a rectangular cartesian coordinate system by m, n, p, each point represented by integer coordinates, situated in the positive octant of the reference frame ($m > 0$, $n > 0$, and $p > 0$) will correspond to a characteristic vibration whose wave length is given by (8-9). Since the size of the cavity is fixed, a given wavelength will correspond to a constant value of

$$m^2 + n^2 + p^2 = r^2 \qquad (8\text{-}10)$$

But in our coordinate frame r represents the radius of a sphere centered at the origin. The number of integer points contained between two such concentric spheres of radii r and $r + dr$, in the first octant is given by [cf. (5-8)]

$$dn = \frac{1}{8} 4\pi r^2 \, dr$$

$$= \frac{\pi}{6} d(r^3) \qquad (8\text{-}11)$$

[1]D. E. Johnson and J. R. Johnson, *Mathematical Methods in Engineering and Physics* (New York: The Ronald Press Company, 1965), Chap. 1.

From (8-9) and (8-10) we have

$$r = \frac{2a}{\lambda} \tag{8-12a}$$

and

$$d(r^3) = -24a^3 \frac{d\lambda}{\lambda^4} \tag{8-12b}$$

where the negative sign merely tells us that r decreases with increasing λ. Replacing a^3 by the volume of the (cubic) cavity and substituting (8-12b) into (8-11) we have [suppressing the minus sign in (8-12b)]

$$dn_l = \frac{4\pi V}{\lambda^4} d\lambda \tag{8-13a}$$

which gives the number of harmonics within the interval $d\lambda$ about λ for a longitudinal wave (such as a sound wave in air) within the cavity. On the other hand, for transverse vibrations, to each wavelength there corresponds an elliptical wave having a semimajor and a semiminor axis so the number of vibrations given by (8-13) for longitudinal waves must be doubled for transverse waves (reflecting the fact that longitudinal waves are unpolarized, whereas transverse waves sustain two orthogonal polarization directions)

$$dn_t = \frac{8\pi V}{\lambda^4} d\lambda \tag{8-13b}$$

For light waves we can write

$$\varepsilon_\lambda \, d\lambda = w \, dn = \frac{8\pi V w}{\lambda^4} d\lambda \tag{8-14}$$

and the radiation energy per unit volume (energy density) within the wavelength interval $d\lambda$ is

$$u_\lambda = \frac{8\pi w}{\lambda^4} \tag{8-15}$$

The total energy density is then given by

$$u = \int_0^\infty u_\lambda \, d\lambda \tag{8-16}$$

If we assign the value kT to the mean energy of each oscillator, as indicated by arguments based on the equipartition of energy, the spectral distribution function becomes

$$u_\lambda = \frac{8\pi k T}{\lambda^4} \tag{8-17}$$

and thus

$$u = 8\pi k T \int_0^\infty \frac{d\lambda}{\lambda^4}$$

$$= \frac{8\pi k T}{-3} \left[\frac{1}{\lambda^3} \right]_0^\infty \tag{8-18}$$

which becomes infinite for short wavelength or high frequencies. This is the classical result obtained by Lord Rayleigh in 1900 and further developed by J. H. Jeans; thus (8-17) is known as the *Rayleigh-Jeans radiation formula* for blackbody radiation. The failure of the Rayleigh-Jeans formula at small wavelengths is referred to as the *ultraviolet catastrophe*.

Planck solved the problem[2] after an attack from the point of view of seeking a description of the average energy of an oscillator, at a given temperature, which prevented the integral of (8-16) from diverging. The expression finally adopted by Planck for the mean energy of the oscillator was

$$w = \frac{h\nu}{e^{h\nu/kT} - 1} \tag{8-19}$$

which the student recognizes as the energy distribution for particles having energy $h\nu$ and obeying Bose-Einstein statistics [cf. Sec. 3-3 and (7-25)]. We can express the mean energy per oscillator in terms of the wavelength by means of (8-1) as

$$w = \frac{(hc/\lambda)}{e^{hc/\lambda kT} - 1} \tag{8-20}$$

where we have expressed the velocity of light by the letter c. Similarly, the spectral distribution function can be written as a function of either frequency or wavelength

$$u_\lambda \, d\lambda = \frac{8\pi hc}{e^{hc/\lambda kT} - 1} \frac{d\lambda}{\lambda^5} \tag{8-21}$$

$$u_\nu \, d\nu = \frac{8\pi h}{c^3} \frac{\nu^3 \, d\nu}{e^{h\nu/kT} - 1} \tag{8-22}$$

where we have made use of the relation

$$d\lambda = -c \frac{d\nu}{\nu^2} \tag{8-23}$$

obtainable from (8-1), and again ignored the minus sign, which merely tells us that as ν decreases, λ must increase, such that their product is constant.

[2]M. Planck, *Ann. Physik* **4**, 553 (1901).

The spectral distribution function of (8-21) is plotted in Fig. 8-1 as a function of wavelength. It can be seen that u_λ vanishes at the two extremes of $\lambda = 0$ and $\lambda = \infty$, with a maximum value occurring at $\lambda = \lambda_m$; which position is a function of the temperature.

The total energy density to be expected from the blackbody composed of Planck oscillators can be calculated by integrating (8-22) over all frequencies:

$$u = \frac{8\pi(kT)^4}{h^3c^3} \int_0^\infty \frac{x^3\,dx}{e^x - 1} \tag{8-24}$$

where we have made the substitution

$$x = \frac{h\nu}{kT} \tag{8-25}$$

To evaluate the integral in (8-24) we draw on some thaumaturgy which the student may have witnessed in one of his mathematical peregrinations,[3]

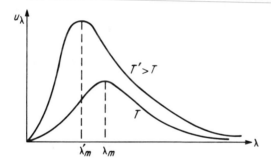

FIG. 8-1. Plot of (8-21) as a function of wavelength for two values of the absolute temperature.

and which was developed in the preceding chapter. Using the nomenclature developed therein, we can express (7-18) as

$$S_n(1 - t) = 1 - t^{n+1} \tag{8-26}$$

We now restrict our consideration to $t < 1$ and take the limit as n becomes infinite; in which case t^n becomes vanishingly small, and thus we have the interesting result that

$$(1 - t)^{-1} = \sum_{n=0}^\infty t^n \tag{8-27}$$

[3]L. Brand, *Advanced Calculus* (New York: John Wiley & Sons, Inc., 1955), Sec. 22.

To make use of (8-27) we rearrange the integral of (8-24) to form

$$\int_0^\infty x^3 e^{-x}(1 - e^{-x})^{-1}\, dx = \int_0^\infty x^3 e^{-x} \sum_{n=0}^\infty e^{-nx}\, dx$$

$$= \sum_{n=0}^\infty \int_0^\infty x^3 e^{-(n+1)x}\, dx$$

$$= \sum_{n=0}^\infty \frac{1}{(n+1)^4} \int_0^\infty [(n+1)x]^3\, e^{-[(n+1)x]}\, d[(n+1)x]$$

$$= \Gamma(4) \sum_{m=1}^\infty \frac{1}{m^4}$$

$$\int_0^\infty \frac{x^3\, dx}{e^x - 1} = \Gamma(4)\zeta(4) = \frac{\pi^4}{15} \tag{8-28}$$

where use has been made of (1-1), (1-4), (1-31), and (1-72). With the aid of (8-28) the total energy density becomes

$$u = \frac{8\pi^5 k^4}{15 h^3 c^3}\, T^4 \tag{8-29}$$

which is a form of the *Stefan-Boltzmann blackbody radiation law* (the latter will be discussed at greater length below).

We now turn our attention again to the spectral distribution function of (8-21), which we write in the form

$$u_\lambda = \frac{8\pi k^5 T^5}{h^4 c^4} \frac{x^5}{e^x - 1} \tag{8-30}$$

where

$$x = \frac{hc}{\lambda k T} \tag{8-31}$$

From Fig. 8-1 we see that u_λ has a maximum value, the location of which varies in some manner with the temperature. To find the location of the maximum value of u_λ; i.e., to find the value of $\lambda = \lambda_m$ (or $x = x_m$) corresponding to the largest value of u_λ, we follow the well-trodden path of differentiating (8-30) w.r.t. x, setting the result equal to zero, and solving the resulting equation for $x = x_m$.

$$\frac{du_\lambda}{dx} = \frac{(e^x - 1)5x^4 - x^5 e^x}{(e^x - 1)^2} = 0 \tag{8-32}$$

or

$$x^4[e^x(5 - x) - 5] = 0 \tag{8-33}$$

The student can easily convince himself that the solution $x = 0$ of (8-33) corresponds not to the maximum value of u_λ, but rather to the minimum value (see Prob. 8-2); consequently we seek the root of the transcendental equation

$$f(x) = e^x(5 - x) - 5 = 0 \tag{8-34}$$

as that value of x which maximizes u_λ. The root of (8-34) can be found graphically as the intersection of the two curves

$$y = e^{-x}$$
$$y = 1 - \frac{x}{5} \tag{8-35}$$

(see Prob. 8-4). Another common method of locating the roots of equations like (8-34) is by means of the *Newton-Raphson technique*,[4] in which the function $f(x)$ is approximated, in the neighborhood of the root, by the tangent to the function. Thus if x_n is the nth approximation to the desired root, then the next approximation will be given by

$$x_n + 1 = x_n - \frac{f(x_n)}{f'(x_n)} \tag{8-36}$$

and this result can then be substituted into the r.h.s. of (8-36) to yield the next approximation and the process repeated until the desired accuracy is achieved. Substituting (8-34) into (8-36) and rearranging yields

$$x_n + 1 = \frac{5[x_n - 1 + e^{-x_n}] - x_n^2}{4 - x_n} \tag{8-37}$$

For $x = 4$, $f(4) = e^4 - 5 \approx +50$ and for $x = 5$, $f(5) = -5$. Hence the root must lie near $x = 5$. Taking $x_0 = 5$ then, (8-37) yields $x_1 = 4.966$, and reinsertion of x_1 gives $x_2 = 4.9653$. Further application of this procedure leads to the more accurate value of

$$x_m = 4.9651 \ldots \tag{8-38}$$

which, when combined with (8-31) leads to the result

$$\lambda_m T = \frac{(hc/k)}{4.9651} \tag{8-39}$$

The quantity

$$\frac{hc}{k} = 1.4393 \text{ cm-deg} \tag{8-40}$$

---

[4]J. R. Britton, R. B. Kriegh, and L. W. Rutland, *University Mathematics* (San Francisco: W. H. Freeman and Company, 1965), Vol. I, p. 515.

is constant, and thus the product

$$\lambda_m T = 2899 \text{ micron-deg} \tag{8-41}$$

is also a constant. This result is known as the *Wien displacement law* for blackbody radiation, and indicates how the wavelength at which the maximum energy is radiated by the blackbody is displaced with the temperature of the blackbody. This law is well verified by experiment.

At this time it is apropos to describe some of the experimental aspects of blackbody radiation. A common practice is to drill a very small hole in the wall of the enclosure surrounding the cavity and then the radiation which leaves the cavity by means of this hole is measured to determine its properties. Equally effective as a blackbody radiator is a hollow right circular cylinder whose length is greater than about ten times the inside diameter of the hole.

Consider the radiations to emanate from a small source of surface area ds located a distance r from a detector whose aperture area is ds', with both ds and ds' being normal to r. The energy received by the detector per unit time will be proportional to ds, ds', and to $1/r^2$,

$$\delta^2\psi = B\frac{ds\,ds'}{r^2} \tag{8-42}$$

where the proportionality constant B is termed the brightness of the source, or the flux per unit solid angle. The total power received by the detector is denoted by $\delta^2\psi$. We now proceed to calculate the total energy flux (energy per unit time per unit area) which passes through a hemisphere perpendicular to the hole in the enclosure wall. In Fig. 8-2 we denote the surface area of the hole by δS and consider a small strip of width $r\,d\theta$ on the

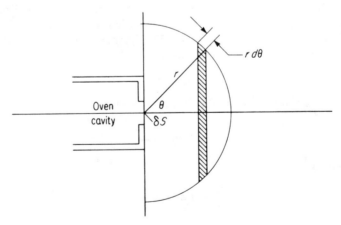

FIG. 8-2. Geometrical factors appearing in the interrelationships between brightness and flux from a blackbody.

surface of the hemisphere of radius r subtending an angle θ from the horizontal. The area of the detector is then the area of the zone on the hemisphere and can be written as

$$ds' = 2\pi r \sin \theta r \, d\theta$$

$$= -2\pi r^2 d(\cos \theta) \tag{8-43}$$

The surface area of the hole normal to the detecting surface is then

$$ds = \delta S \cos \theta \tag{8-44}$$

and (8-42) can now be integrated over the angle θ to give

$$\delta \psi = -2\pi B \, \delta S \int_0^{\pi/2} \cos \theta \, d(\cos \theta)$$

$$= \pi B \, \delta S \tag{8-45}$$

The energy flux through the hole is, by definition, the rate of energy flow across unit area of the hole, and can be written as

$$\Phi = \frac{\delta \psi}{\delta S} = \pi B \tag{8-46}$$

from which we see that the energy flux emanating from the blackbody is proportional to the brightness of the blackbody.

We now look for a relation between the total energy density u (energy per unit volume) and the energy flux. For this we consider a pencil of electromagnetic rays originating at some point at the interior of the blackbody cavity. These rays will travel with the velocity c and impinge on the detector whose surface area is ds', and so the pencil of rays will contribute an amount du to the total energy density and will represent the total power received by the detector, thus

$$\delta^2 \psi = (du)c \, ds \tag{8-47a}$$

$$= B \, ds \, d\Omega \tag{8-48b}$$

where (8-48b) was obtained from (8-42) by recognizing that

$$d\Omega = \frac{ds'}{r^2} \tag{8-49}$$

is the solid angle subtended by the detector at the point where the pencil of electromagnetic rays originate. Combining (8-47a) and (8-48b) we find that

$$c \, du = B \, d\Omega$$

or

$$cu = B4\pi \tag{8-50}$$

which follows trivially from integration over a complete closed surface surrounding the origin of the isotropic, homogeneous rays (B is independent of $d\Omega$). From (8-46) and (8-50) we see that the energy flux can be written as

$$\Phi = \frac{cu}{4} \tag{8-51}$$

and from (8-29) we have

$$\Phi = \frac{2\pi^5 k^4}{15 h^3 c^2} T^4 = \sigma T^4 \tag{8-52}$$

which is the customary statement of the Stefan-Boltzmann blackbody radiation law.[5] The quantity σ, known as *Stefan's constant* or as the *Stefan-Boltzmann constant*, depends on the nonclassical parameter h, and thus could not be deduced theoretically from classical physics, although it had been determined experimentally. The theoretical value of σ, as predicted by (8-52), is[6]

$$\sigma = 5.6687 \times 10^{-8} \frac{\text{watts}}{\text{m}^2\text{-deg}^4} \tag{8-53}$$

which is well verified by experiment.

One common method of measuring the brightness of a source is by means of a perfectly absorbing radiation detector (often a platinum ribbon covered with lampblack), functioning as a calorimeter, with a known surface area and placed a given distance r from the source. The power received by the ribbon is given by (8-42) with B given by

$$B = \frac{\sigma}{\pi} T^4 \tag{8-54}$$

by means of (8-46) and (8-52). The blackened platinum ribbon soon establishes equilibrium with the surroundings and reaches a stationary temperature. If the incident radiation is blacked out from the strip and an electric current i passed through the ribbon, by means of a potential V across the terminals, the resulting Joule heating can be adjusted to cause the ribbon to reach the same temperature as resulted from irradiation. Consequently the power received by the platinum ribbon must be the same in both instances

$$Vi = B \frac{SS'}{r^2} = \frac{\sigma}{\pi} T^4 \frac{SS'}{r^2} \tag{8-55}$$

[5] For a somewhat different derivation see J. Strong, *Concepts of Classical Optics* (San Francisco: W. H. Freeman and Company, 1958), Chap. 3 and 4.

[6] E. U. Condon and H. Odishaw (eds.), *Handbook of Physics* (New York: McGraw-Hill Book Company, 1958), 7,170.

The equality of the temperatures can be confirmed by ensuring that the resistance of the platinum ribbon (which is a function of the temperature) is the same under both conditions. In an experiment in which Vi, T, S, S', r, c, and the universal gas constant R, are all known quantities, (8-55) can be rearranged in the form [by making use of (5-25)].

$$N_0^4 h^3 = \frac{2(\pi T R)^4}{15 c^2 V i} \frac{S S'}{r^2} \tag{8-56}$$

where all the quantities on the r.h.s. are known.

Furthermore, the Wien displacement law, (8-39) can be written as [where again use has been made of (5-25)]

$$N_0 h = 4.9651 \frac{R}{c} \lambda_m T \tag{8-57}$$

The product $\lambda_m T$ had been measured experimentally near the turn of the century with the result that

$$\lambda_m T = 2885 \text{ micron-deg} \tag{8-58}$$

which compares quite favorably with the more recent theoretical prediction given by (8-41). Since all the quantities on the r.h.s. of (8-57) are known also, one can consider the experimental results flowing from the Stefan-Boltzmann blackbody radiation law and the Wien displacement law as furnishing two equations in the two unknowns of Planck's constant h and Avogadro's number N_0. From these experiments the value of N_0 was found to agree with the best experimental measurements of Avogadro's constant and this result led to a determination of the new constant

$$h = 6.57 \times 10^{-27} \text{ erg-sec} \tag{8-59}$$

which was in agreement to better than 1 percent with the more modern determination of that constant; the accepted value now being

$$\cdot\, h = 6.625 \times 10^{-27} \text{ erg-sec} \tag{8-60}$$

Eq. 8-55 can be employed to construct a total radiation pyrometer, since its development assumed that the resistance of the plantinum ribbon was the same both with and without radiation incident on the ribbon. We can express (8-55) in the form

$$\log V i = \alpha + 4 \log T \tag{8-61}$$

which is then a linear relation between $\log V i$ and $\log T$ (when each is expressed in proper units). Eq. 8-61 can be calibrated to prepare a table of the temperature, as a function of the power supplied to the ribbon, at two fixed temperatures such as the melting points of gold (1063°C) and palladium (1552°C); these temperatures being in the region where they can be established by a gas thermometer. The measurements of the total radiation (and this applies also to the determination of the Stefan-Boltzmann constant, σ) ought to be corrected to take into account the fact that the detector is not a perfect absorber. This correction will be relatively large in the infrared region. At temperatures between 1000 and 3000°C the optical pyrometer is to be preferred over the total radiation pyrometer.

The optical pyrometer utilizes the brightness of the object whose temperature is to be measured in the visible red wavelength region. This is achieved by interposing a monochromer (usually a red glass lens) which transmits only a single wavelength (actually a very narrow band) so that the instrument is operated at (say)

$$\lambda = 7000\text{Å} = \text{const} \qquad (8\text{-}62)$$

Replacing the total energy density in (8-50) by the spectral distribution function of (8-21) leads to the spectral brightness of the source in the form

$$B_\lambda = \frac{c}{4\pi} u_\lambda = \frac{2hc^2}{\lambda^5} \frac{1}{e^{hc/\lambda kT} - 1} \qquad (8\text{-}63)$$

If we assume that T is of the order of 1000°K, then we note from (8-39) and (8-41) that

$$\frac{hc}{\lambda kT} = 4.9651 \frac{\lambda_m}{\lambda}$$

$$= \frac{4.9651(2.899\mu)}{0.7000\mu}$$

$$\frac{hc}{\lambda kT} = 20.562 \qquad (8\text{-}64)$$

and consequently $e^{hc/\lambda kT} \gg 1$ so that (8-63) may be expressed as

$$\ln B_\lambda = \ln\left(\frac{2hc^2}{\lambda^5}\right) - \frac{hc/\lambda k}{T}$$

$$\ln B_\lambda = a - \frac{b}{T} \qquad (8\text{-}65)$$

where a and b are constants. The brightness of the aperture of the oven, whose temperature is to be measured, can be reduced by means of an absorbing wedge, and the brightness is adjusted until it is equal to that of an electric lamp filament supplied with constant current. When the two brightnesses are equal the filament will no longer be visible when superposed over the image of the aperture of the oven (or whatever the object is whose temperature is to be measured). Under this condition the attenuated spectral brightness B'_λ is equal to the spectral brightness of the filament, which is constant. Thus if κ is the attenuation coefficient of the wedge, and d the thickness of the wedge traversed by the radiation coming from the oven,

$$B'_\lambda = B_\lambda e^{-\kappa d} \qquad (8\text{-}66)$$

If y is measured from some reference line to the apex of the wedge, as shown in Fig. 8-3, with D being the distance from the axis of the ocular lens to the

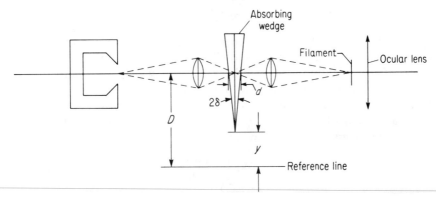

FIG. 8-3. Typical arrangement for disappearing filament type of optical pyrometer.

reference line, the thickness of the wedge needed to equalize the spectral brightness of the oven and the filament can be expressed as

$$d = 2(D - y) \tan \delta \qquad (8\text{-}67)$$

which, when substituted in (8-66), leads to

$$[\text{const} = \ln B'_\lambda = \ln B_\lambda - 2\kappa D \tan \delta + 2\kappa y \tan \delta]$$

which can be written, with the aid of (8-65),

$$y = \left[D + \frac{\ln B'_\lambda - a}{2\kappa \tan \delta} \right] + \frac{b/(2\kappa \tan \delta)}{T}$$

or

$$y = l + \frac{m}{T} \qquad (8\text{-}68)$$

where l and m are constants which can be evaluated by measuring y at two known temperatures. Since the displacement of the absorbing wedge is a linear function of $1/T$, it is generally calibrated directly in terms of the temperature. For further discussions of optical and total radiation pyrometers, the student should consult any of the various texts on experimental physics.[7]

[7]See, for example, H. G. Jerrard and D. B. McNeill, *Theoretical and Experimental Physics* (London: Chapman and Hall Ltd., 1960); T. B. Brown (ed.), *The Taylor Manual* (Reading, Mass.: Addison-Wesley Publishing Company, 1959).

We conclude this section with a few remarks concerning the results we have obtained. In our calculations we have adopted the energy of the nth harmonic oscillator as $w_n = nh\nu$, in accord with (7-13a), as furnished by the Bohr theory. As discussed in the preceding chapter the quantum mechanical theory gives the energy of (7-13b) and the average energy per oscillator of

$$w = \frac{h\nu}{2} + \frac{h\nu}{e^{\beta h\nu} - 1} \tag{7-31}$$

The first term in (7-31) does not depend on the temperature, and the second term is just the mean energy per oscillator predicted by the Bohr-Planck theory. Consequently the specific heat capacity, which is the derivative of the internal energy of the system with respect to the temperature at constant volume, is the same for either set of statistics, whether the substance is a physical solid or a blackbody. However, in the case of a blackbody there is an energy density given by (8-15) and (8-16):

$$u = 8\pi \int_0^\infty \frac{w(\lambda)}{\lambda^4} \, d\lambda \tag{8-69}$$

The second term of (7-31), when substituted into (8-69), leads to (8-29), but the first term of (7-31) yields an infinite result for the energy density. This energy is not observable and does not give rise to radiation (it exists outside of the blackbody as well as inside the cavity forming the blackbody) but the quantum theory does give rise to an infinite energy density existing in a vacuum, even at absolute zero of temperature. This vacuum energy is sometimes treated as the zero-point energy of an infinite assemblage of harmonic oscillators, and all energies are measured relative to it. The existence of this difficulty is recognized and treated under the headings of *photon self-energy, vacuum polarization, mass renormalization,* or *vacuum fluctuations,* but it cannot yet be said that the difficulty has been satisfactorily resolved.[8]

8-2 DEBYE THEORY OF SPECIFIC HEAT

A simplified representation of a solid (certainly a crystalline solid) might be obtained by considering each atom (or atomic ion, including electrons) as constrained to vibrate about its equilibrium position with simple harmonic motion. This type of problem is well known in classical

---

[8]See, for example, S. S. Schweber, *Relativistic Quantum Field Theory* (New York: Harper & Row, Publishers, Inc., 1961), p. 423; J. D. Bjorken and S. D. Drell, *Relativistic Quantum Mechanics* (New York: McGraw-Hill Book Company, 1964), Sec. 8.2, and *Relativistic Quantum Fields* (New York: McGraw-Hill Book Company, 1965), Sec. 12-4.

mechanics, and is frequently treated in terms of normal coordinates,[9] in which each normal coordinate corresponds to the situation in which the solid vibrates with only one frequency; there being as many vibrational frequencies (or normal modes of vibration) as there are degrees of freedom of the system. The Debye approximation consists, essentially, of considering these normal mode vibrations with long wavelengths as being elastic waves (consisting of both: the transverse, solenoidal, shear, S-waves, and the longitudinal, irrotational, compressional, P-waves) propagating throughout the (virtual continuum) solid.

The Debye approximation now evolves along the lines of the development of the theory of the blackbody (*mutatis mutandis*) as presented in Sec. 8-1. The harmonic vibration of frequency v has the same mean energy as a Planck vibrator, given either by (8-19) or (7-31) (we shall see that both expressions give the same contribution to the specific heat capacity, but differ in their contributions to the total internal energy of the solid).

For isotropic crystals or quasi-isotropic solid materials, the total number of acoustical (long wavelength) frequencies between v and $v + dv$ is given by the sum of (8-13a) and (8-13b) which can be written, with the aid of (8-23), as

$$dn = 4\pi V \left[\frac{1}{c_l^3} + \frac{2}{c_t^3} \right] v^2 \, dv \tag{8-70}$$

where c_l and c_t are the velocities of the longitudinal (P-) and transverse (S-) waves, respectively. In a manner analogous to the derivation of (8-22) we can write the spectral energy density distribution function for the solid as

$$u_v \, dv = 4\pi B h v^3 \, dv \left[\frac{1}{2} + \frac{1}{e^{\beta h v} - 1} \right] \tag{8-71}$$

where we have set

$$B = \frac{1}{c_l^3} + \frac{2}{c_t^3} \tag{8-72}$$

and the factor 1/2 in the square brackets of (8-71) does not appear in the Planck formulation of the mean energy per oscillator.

Up to this point there is essentially no difference with the development of the theory of blackbody radiation [if B in (8-72) is replaced by $2/c^3$ and the factor 1/2 in (8-71) deleted, (8-71) and (8-22) become identical]. Debye reasoned that a solid containing molecules ought to have $3N$ (why not $3N - 6$?) degrees of freedom, rather than an infinite number as in the case

[9]H. Goldstein, *Classical Mechanics* (Reading, Mass.: Addison-Wesley Publishing Company, Inc., 1950), Chap. 10.

of the blackbody. Furthermore, since the normal mode vibrations should approach elastic waves only for long wavelengths (low frequencies), it would be inconsistent to integrate over *all* frequencies from $v = 0$ to $v = \infty$, but rather the solid should not support waves with frequencies greater than a maximum value, v_0, (which is different for different materials and is a function of V/N for any given solid). These two requirements can be met mathematically in the form

$$\int_0^{v_0} dn = 4\pi BV \int_0^{v_0} v^2 \, dv = 3N$$

or

$$v_0^3 = \frac{9}{4\pi B}(N/V) \tag{8-73}$$

and

$$u = 4\pi Bh[I + D(x_0)] \tag{8-74}$$

where

$$I = \int_0^{v_0} \frac{1}{2} v^3 \, dv = \frac{v_0^4}{8} \tag{8-75}$$

$$x_0 = \beta h v_0 = \frac{h v_0}{kT} = \frac{\Theta_D}{T} \tag{8-76}$$

and

$$D(x_0) = \left(\frac{kT}{h}\right)^4 \int_0^{x_0} \frac{x^3 \, dx}{e^x - 1} \tag{8-77}$$

The molar internal energy of the solid can be written as

$$u^* = \frac{9}{8} N_0 h v_0 + 9RTf(x_0) \tag{8-78}$$

where

$$f(x_0) = \frac{1}{x_0^3} \int_0^{x_0} \frac{x^3 \, dx}{e^x - 1} \tag{8-79}$$

(see Prob. 8-7).

The first term on the r.h.s. of (8-78) arises from the factor of $1/2$ in (8-71) and is thus absent in the Planck formulation. However, since the temperature dependence is limited to the second term in (8-78), both the Planck and the quantum mechanical theories yield the same result for the molar specific heat capacity of the solid

$$c_v = 9Rf(x_0)\left[1 - x_0 \frac{d}{dx_0} \ln f(x_0)\right] \tag{8-80}$$

The molar specific heat capacity at constant volume predicted by the Debye theory, (8-80), is reminiscent of that given by the Einstein theory, (7-37), where of course the functions of $f(x_0)$ and $f(\Theta/T)$ are different. We note that $x_0 = \Theta_D/T$ is of the same form as Θ/T appearing in the Einstein formulation, but there is a marked difference in the interpretations. The *Debye temperature*, Θ_D, refers to the cutoff frequency ν_0 of the wave supported by the solid, whereas the Einstein characteristic temperature Θ, refers to the *only* frequency propagated by the solid. It is easily seen that the Debye theory, like Einstein's, leads to a law of corresponding states for the specific heat capacity [see discussion following (7-37)].

At low temperatures (relative to the Debye temperature), x_0 becomes very large and we can write (8-79) in the form

$$f(x_0) \approx \frac{1}{x_0^3} \int_0^\infty \frac{x^3\,dx}{e^x - 1}$$

which, from (8-28), becomes

$$f(x_0) \approx \frac{\pi^4}{15x_0^3} \qquad \frac{\Theta_D}{T} \gg 1 \tag{8-81}$$

By substituting (8-81) into (8-80), we see that the Debye approximation to the molar specific heat capacity of a solid is

$$c_v \approx \frac{12\pi^4}{5\Theta_D^3} RT^3 \qquad \frac{T}{\Theta_D} \ll 1 \tag{8-82}$$

At low temperatures the specific heat capacity of the solid approaches zero as T^3, rather than exponentially as does the Einstein model; this T^3 dependence is well verified by experiment.

At high temperatures, x_0 is very small and since the variable in (8-79) is never greater than x_0, we can expand the exponential term in the denominator and carry out the integration to obtain

$$f(x_0) \approx \frac{1}{3} - \frac{x_0}{8} + \frac{x_0^2}{60} - \cdots \tag{8-83}$$

from which the high temperature specific heat capacity can be written

$$c_v \approx 3R\left[1 - \frac{\Theta_D^2}{20T^2} + \cdots \right], \frac{\Theta_D}{T} \ll 1 \tag{8-84}$$

Thus at high temperatures the Debye approximation, like the Einstein approximation, also leads to the law of Dulong and Petit.

If we now label the specific heat capacities of (8-82) and (8-84) by c_0

and c_∞ respectively, and divide the former by the latter [where only the first term in (8-84) is retained], we find

$$\Theta_D = \left[\frac{4\pi^4}{5} \frac{c_\infty}{c_0} \right]^{1/3} T \tag{8-85}$$

This relation can be used to evaluate the characteristic Debye temperature of a given material, if c_0 is measured at some low temperature T. One can also use the elastic constants of the solid to calculate the transverse and longitudinal velocities of sound, which then yield the cutoff frequency, v_0, from (8-72) and (8-73). Having v_0, Θ_D can be evaluated from (8-76). The agreement between these two results is quite reasonable, as can be seen from Table 8-1.

Table 8-1.   Characteristic Debye Temperature for Four Metallic Elements Calculated from Elastic Constants and Measured from (8-85).

Solid	Debye Temperature (deg)	
	From Elastic Constants	Measured from (8-85)
Al	402	398
Cu	332	315
Ag	214	215
Pb	73	88

The development of the Debye approximation in this section has not been limited to crystalline solids, but is equally applicable to a substance having an amorphous state and propagating transverse vibrations. Similarly, the theory can be extended to include compounds such as FeS, where both the Fe and S atoms occupy sublattice points and there are $2 \times 3N$ degrees of freedom for the system, since the Fe and S atoms can be considered independent. The Debye theory allows the atomic heat capacities of Fe and S to combine additively (according to the law of Woestyne) at high temperatures, and at low temperatures the T^3 dependence of c_v subsists. The specific heat capacity at constant pressure, c_p, can be related to c_v by means of (6-79), as discussed in Sec. 6-3.

Experiments show that the cutoff frequency v_0, is very nearly the *Reststrahl* frequency, discussed briefly at the end of the preceding chapter. If we consider the absolute zero of temperature to correspond to the smallest energy realizable by the system, this temperature will be attained when all the oscillators of the system are located in the cell of minimum energy ($w = 0$ in the Planck representation or $w = hv/2$ from the quantum analysis).

There is only one way that all the particles can be distributed such that they all are in the lowest energy configuration, and so by (4-18),

$$S(T = 0) = k \ln 1 = 0 \tag{8-86}$$

and the absolute entropy is thus null at the absolute zero of temperature. This is in accord with the (somewhat imprecise statement of the) Nernst theorem[10] that at the absolute zero of temperature all perfect crystalline substances have a null absolute entropy.

[10]W. Nernst, *Nachr. kgl. Ges. Wiss. Gottingen Math-physik*, K1 (1906), p. 1.

PROBLEMS

8-1. Verify that (8-5) and (8-6) are proper solutions to (8-3). (*Hint*: See Chap. 8 of Ref. 1.)

8-2. Demonstrate that the root $x = 0$ of (8-33) corresponds to an extreme value of u_λ, but that this extreme value is a minimum. (*Query*: How do you reconcile this result with the fact that

$$\left. \frac{d^2 u_\lambda}{dx^2} \right|_{x=0} = 0 \tag{H1}$$

A condition which most students interpret as meaning u_λ has an inflection point at $x = 0$?

8-3. Beginning with (8-32) show that

$$\left. \frac{d^2 u_\lambda}{dx^2} \right|_{x = x_m} < 0 \tag{H2}$$

thus demonstrating that u_λ takes its maximum value at $x = x_m$. From your work obtain (H1).

8-4. Show that the roots of (8-34) are given by the intersection of the two curves of (8-35). (*Query*: How many intersection points are there, and how can they be interpreted?) Carefully plot the two curves of (8-35) and determine the value of x_m from your graph.

8-5. Beginning with an initial guess of $x_0 = 5$, find the next three approximations to x_m from (8-37).

8-6. Show that (8-70) follows as a special case of the relation

$$\frac{dn}{dV} = 4\pi v^2 \, dv \left[\frac{1}{c_x^3} + \frac{1}{c_y^3} + \frac{1}{c_z^3} \right] \tag{H3}$$

where c_x, c_y, c_z, are the coordinate components of the velocity of sound in the medium.

8-7. Show that (8-77) is compatible with (8-74), and that the latter leads to (8-78). [*Hint*: remember that the specific energy, u, is the total energy divided by the volume of the system, whereas the molar energy is the total energy per mole of substance. Avogadro's number is the ratio of the number of particles to the number of moles. See (5-25). Also, make use of the relation (8-73).]

8-8.   Verify (8-82) and (8-84).

8-9.   Find the ratio of the energy flux of blackbody radiation at 100°K to that at 1000°K.

8-10. What is the temperature of a blackbody if its maximum wavelength is in the red region? In the violet region?

8-11. The sun has a temperature T_s, a radius r_s, and the earth has a radius r_e. The distance between the sun and the earth is R. Considering the bodies to be in equilibrium between themselves and to be blackbodies, what is the temperature of the earth? (*Hint*: Assume both the sun and earth are perfect blackbodies).

8-12. For the frequency of radiation which has the maximum energy density at a given temperature, show that the energy density is proportional to T^3.

8-13. Find the temperature dependence of the specific heat capacity at constant volume of a one-dimensional Debye solid when $T \ll \Theta_D$.

9 | *The Photon Gas*

The theory of the blackbody developed in the preceding chapter depended on the fact that light is considered (classically at least) as a wave. In order to explain the photoelectric effect, Einstein found it necessary to attribute particlelike features to light. These "particles of light" are termed *photons*. In this short chapter it is proposed to obtain the results of the blackbody theory from the corpuscular theory of light. This will be done by assuming that the radiation can be represented by a system of noninteracting photons; i.e., a photon gas. In order to decide what kind of statistics these photons obey, we must resort to results obtained in the laboratory (the table in Sec. 2-5 was not available to physicists when the present calculation was first performed). It is now well established that photons obey Bose-Einstein statistics, and the results thus obtained are in excellent agreement with experiment. The rest mass of the photon is taken to be null (because photons are *light particles*) and its (relativistic) momentum is related to its energy by

$$p = \frac{\varepsilon}{c} \tag{9-1}$$

But the Planck hypothesis requires the energy of the photon (again considered as an oscillator) to be proportional to the frequency of the radiation

$$\varepsilon = hv = \frac{hc}{\lambda} \tag{9-2}$$

so that

$$p = \frac{hv}{c} = \frac{h}{\lambda} \tag{9-3}$$

The density of states is given by (twice) Eq. 5-9 (to account for the two polarization states of the photon) or 8-13b [which can be easily obtained from (5-9) with the aid of (9-3); see Prob. 9-1] and thus the total internal energy of the photon gas system is given by

$$U = \int_0^\infty \frac{8\pi\alpha V v^2 \, dv}{c^3} \, h\nu \, \frac{1}{e^{\beta h\nu} - \alpha} \tag{9-4}$$

where the last term in (9-4) represents the Bose-Einstein distribution function found in (3-23a). Eq. 9-4 contains the first Lagrange undetermined multiplier, α, which we recall (from Sec. 3-3) was introduced as the coefficient of Eq. 3-11; which equation is certainly valid for a closed system of material particles. However, photons are not conserved – they may be absorbed by any convenient atom (whose energy level separations are properly related to the photon energy), which is then raised to an excited state; or an arbitrary number of photons may be emitted by an atom, in returning to its ground state (consistent, of course, with the conservation of energy and angular momentum). Thus, instead of the two conditions given by (3-11) and (3-13), only (3-13) remains to be satisfied. Since (3-11) is not valid for our photon gas, we can most easily adjust the results of Chap. 3 by setting the coefficient of (3-11) identically equal to zero. Thus

$$\ln \alpha = 0$$

or

$$\alpha = 1 \tag{9-5}$$

Upon substitution of (9-5) into (9-4), the latter takes the form

$$U = \frac{8\pi V k^4}{c^3 h^3} T^4 \int_0^\infty \frac{x^3 \, dx}{e^x - 1} \tag{9-6}$$

which is manifestly equivalent to the Stefan-Boltzmann law, expressed by (8-24). It is easily seen that the theory of the photon gas proceeds in direct analogy with the blackbody theory developed in the preceding chapter.

We now conclude this chapter with an evaluation of the absolute entropy for the system. With the aid of (9-5) we can write (4-43) in the form

$$S = \frac{U}{T} - k \int_0^\infty \frac{8\pi V}{c^3} v^2 \, dv \ln (1 - e^{-\beta h\nu}) \tag{9-7}$$

$$= \frac{U}{T} - \frac{8\pi V k^4 T^3}{3c^3 h^3} J \tag{9-8}$$

where

$$J = \int_0^\infty \ln (1 - e^{-x}) \, d(x^3) \tag{9-9}$$

The integral (9-9) can be evaluated by a partial integration [see the discussion re (5-28) in Sec. 5-2B] and with the help of (8-28) (see Prob. 9-2):

$$J = - \int_0^\infty \frac{x^3 \, dx}{e^x - 1} \tag{9-10}$$

By means of (9-6) and (9-10) we can write

$$S = \frac{U}{T} + \frac{U}{3T} = \frac{4}{3} \frac{U}{T} \tag{9-11}$$

and from (8-51) and (8-52) this can be expressed as

$$S = \frac{16V\sigma}{3c} T^3 \tag{9-12}$$

where σ is the Stefan-Boltzmann constant, given by (8-52). The student should note that (9-11), developed for a massless photon, does not agree with (5-54) [when ln $\alpha = 0$], which was derived for a nonrelativistic boson having a nonzero rest mass. We can now show that (2-94), which was developed for a system of noninteracting particles with nonzero rest mass on the basis of the (nonrelativistic) virial theorem. is also not obeyed by our photon gas. To show this, we make use of the Maxwell equations [discussed in Sec. 2-2]

$$P = - \left(\frac{\partial U}{\partial V} \right)_S \tag{9-13}$$

From (9-11), we have

$$U = \frac{3}{4} TS \tag{9-14}$$

and so

$$P = - \frac{3}{4} S \left(\frac{\partial T}{\partial V} \right)_S$$

$$P = - \frac{3S}{4 \left(\dfrac{\partial V}{\partial T} \right)_S}$$

or

$$P = \frac{4\sigma T^4}{3c} \tag{9-15}$$

where the derivative has been evaluated by means of (9-12). With the use of (9-12) we can express (9-14) in the form

$$U = \frac{4\sigma V T^4}{c} \tag{9-16}$$

and comparing (9-16) with (9-15) leads us to conclude that, in lieu of (2-94), the photon gas obeys an equation of state of the form

$$PV = \frac{1}{3} U \tag{9-17}$$

We see from (9-12), (9-15), and (9-16), that the entropy, pressure, and internal energy of the photon gas all tend to zero as the temperature approaches zero.

PROBLEMS

9-1. Obtain (8-13b) from (5-9) and verify that the former correctly describes the density of states for a photon gas system.

9-2. Obtain (9-10) from (9-9).

9-3. Verify (9-15).

9-4. Obtain an expression for the mean number of photons in the system as a function of P, V, and T. [*Hint*: recall equation (1-31) and the technique used to evaluate (8-28).]

10 | Rotation Terms and Quantum Degeneracy in Diatomic Molecules

10-1 RIGID ROTATOR IN A PLANE

The rigid-rotator model of a diatomic molecule, introduced in Sec. 6-3, is not actually realized in practice, but it is relatively simple to analyze and is conceptually useful as a graphic picture of the motion of a diatomic molecule. As mentioned in Chap. 6, the total energy of a diatomic molecule will consist of (essentially) separable contributions from the translational motion of the molecule as a whole (usually treated in terms of the x, y, z coordinates of the center of mass), the rotational energy of the molecule (as it rotates about the center of mass, described in terms of the polar angles θ and ϕ), the vibrational energy (due to the two atoms vibrating along the axis separating them, usually considered as a simple harmonic oscillator in terms of the distance r separating the atoms), and the energy associated with the electronic states of the molecule.

The translational contribution is just that of a system of noninteracting point particles and has already been discussed in Chaps. 2 and 5. At ordinary temperatures (below about 2000°K) the electronic and vibrational states of most diatomic molecules are not excited. In all cases the rotational energy states of the molecule are excited long before (i.e., at much lower temperatures than) the vibrational states. Thus in the instant chapter we shall confine our attention to the rotational contribution to the internal energy (and other thermodynamic potentials) of diatomic molecules. In the present section we consider the motion of a rigid rotator in a plane and evaluate the rotational contribution to the specific heat capacity. In the following section we treat the general three-dimensional rotational motion about the center of mass. We conclude this chapter with a discussion of the symmetry complications which arise in the case of a symmetrical diatomic molecule at low temperatures (cf. Chap. 11).

For rotational motion in a plane, we can choose our coordinate system such that

$$\theta = \frac{\pi}{2} = \text{const} \tag{10-1}$$

in which case the rotational kinetic energy in (6-71) reduces to

$$\varepsilon_k = \frac{1}{2}I\dot{\phi}^2 \tag{10-2}$$

where I is the moment of inertia of the molecule about the center of mass. Since the rotational potential energy is constant, the (angular) momentum conjugate to ϕ is, from (1-100),

$$p_\phi = I\dot{\phi} \tag{10-3}$$

and the Hamiltonian of the system (taking the constant potential energy to be zero) given by (1-102), is

$$H(p_\phi, \phi) = \frac{p_\phi^2}{2I} \tag{10-4}$$

The phase space for the rotator is two-dimensional and the extension in ϕ is 2π. Since the plane rotator has only one degree of freedom, the phase volume given by (5-3) becomes

$$h = \oint dp_\phi d\phi = 2\pi\!\int dp_\phi$$
$$h = 2\pi\Delta p_\phi$$

or

$$\Delta p_\phi = \frac{h}{2\pi} \equiv \hbar \tag{10-5}$$

We can interpret (10-5) as meaning that the angular momentum of the plane rotator changes by an amount $\hbar$ (which just happens to be the angular momentum associated with an emitted or absorbed photon) when the state of the rotator is changed as indicated in Fig. 10-1.

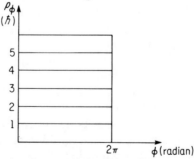

FIG. 10-1. Phase space for a plane rigid rotator depicting continuous range of ϕ and the discrete increments in p_ϕ.

From (10-5) we see that the angular momentum of the rotator in its mth state can be written as

$$p_\phi = m\hbar + \text{const} \tag{10-6}$$

Eq. 10-6 has been developed from a semi-classical approach (no equation containing Planck's constant can truly be said to be a result of classical mechanics), but the same equation follows rigorously from quantum mechanics if the constant is taken to be null.[1] Thus the Hamiltonian of the system which, for this conservative system, represents the total (kinetic) energy is

$$H = \varepsilon_k = m^2 \frac{\hbar^2}{2I} \tag{10-7}$$

when the plane rotator is in the mth excited state. But this is just the energy of the (plane rotator model of the) atom in its mth energy state, which we have been designating as

$$w_i = i^2 \frac{\hbar^2}{2I} \tag{10-8}$$

As mentioned in Sec. 5-3, perfect gases are generally not degenerate (except when the temperature is very low or when the density of the system is extremely large) and so we may use the canonical distribution to describe the system. Since the different energy states of the plane rotator are all labeled by the (quantum) index i, there is only one energy state of the rotator per energy level (the energy levels are then also said to be nondegenerate) and so the density of states

$$g_i = 1, \text{ all } i \tag{10-9}$$

Hence the canonical distribution function takes the form [cf. (3-16)].

$$n_i = \alpha \exp\left(-i^2 \frac{\beta \hbar^2}{2I}\right) \tag{10-10}$$

In analogy with (7-16) we can define the canonical partition function as

$$Z = \sum_{i=0}^{\infty} e^{-\beta w_i} \tag{10-11a}$$

$$= \sum_{i=0}^{\infty} e^{-i^2(\beta \hbar^2/2I)} \tag{10-11b}$$

so that

$$N = \alpha Z \tag{10-12}$$

[1] H. Eyring, J. Walter, and G. E. Kimball, *Quantum Chemistry* (New York: John Wiley & Sons, Inc., 1944), Chap. 5.

and the mean energy per atom becomes

$$u \equiv \frac{U}{N} = -\frac{\partial}{\partial \beta}(\ln Z) \qquad (10\text{-}13)$$

The molar specific heat capacity at constant volume is then given by

$$c_v = N_0 \frac{\partial u}{\partial T} \qquad (10\text{-}14)$$

Unfortunately, the sum appearing in (10-11b) can not be evaluated in closed form for all values of T. It is convenient to define a characteristic temperature for rotation

$$\theta_r = \frac{\hbar^2}{2Ik} \qquad (10\text{-}15)$$

so that the sum over states in (10-11) can be written

$$Z = \sum_{i=0}^{\infty} e^{-i^2(\theta_r/T)} \qquad (10\text{-}11c)$$

If we consider, as an example, the nonsymmetric molecule of carbon monoxide we can obtain an idea of the magnitude of the characteristic rotation temperature of (10-15). The moment of inertia of CO can be written as

$$I_{\text{c.m.}} = \mu r_e^2 \qquad (10\text{-}16)$$

where the reduced mass of the CO molecule is

$$\mu = \frac{12 \cdot 16}{12 + 16}\, \text{amu}$$

$$= 11.38 \times 10^{-24}\, \text{gm} \qquad (10\text{-}17)$$

and the equilibrium separation distance of the carbon and oxygen atoms is known experimentally to be

$$r_e = 1.128\text{Å} \qquad (10\text{-}18)$$

With these parameter values the student can easily verify (see Prob. 3) that

$$\theta_r = 2.78\, \text{deg} \qquad (10\text{-}19)$$

The value of θ_r given by (10-19) is fairly typical for most diatomic gases. Even for the lightest diatomic gas, H_2, θ_r is about 85°K whereas for the halogens the characteristic rotation temperature is less than 0.5°K. The meaning of this result is that for common diatomic gases at ordinary temperatures (indeed, even at fairly low temperatures) T is much larger than θ_r. Consequently the successive terms in the partition function sum do not differ appreciably in magnitude and we can evaluate (10-11c) by means of the Euler-Maclaurin summation formula, discussed in Chapter 1. Letting

$$f_i = e^{-i^2(\theta_r/T)} \tag{10-20}$$

we see that

$$f_\infty = 0$$

and so

$$Z = \sum_{i=0}^\infty f_i = \int_0^\infty e^{-(\theta_r/T)x^2}\,dx + \frac{1}{2} + \cdots$$

$$= \frac{1}{2}\sqrt{\frac{\pi T}{\theta_r}}\left[1 + \sqrt{\frac{\theta_r}{\pi T}} + \cdots\right]$$

$$= \sqrt{\frac{\pi/k\theta_r}{2}}\,\beta^{-1/2}\left[1 + \beta^{1/2}\sqrt{\frac{k\theta_r}{\pi}} + \cdots\right], \frac{\theta_r}{T} \ll 1 \tag{10-21}$$

If we ignore the terms in β within the square brackets, (10-21) reduces to

$$\ln Z = \ln[\text{const}] - \frac{1}{2}\ln\beta \tag{10-22}$$

which, when substituted into (10-13), leads to

$$u = \frac{1}{2\beta} = \frac{kT}{2} \tag{10-23}$$

Thus our plane rotator, with one degree of freedom, exhibits the classical equipartition of energy discussed in Sec. 6-2. The high temperature molar specific heat capacity of the plane rotator, from (10-14) and (10-23), is

$$c_v = \frac{R}{2} \tag{10-24}$$

which we expect to be quite accurate at ordinary temperatures.

At (very) low temperatures such that

$$\frac{\theta_r}{T} \gg 1 \tag{10-25}$$

the partition function can be expanded as

$$Z = 1 + e^{-\theta_r/T} + e^{-4(\theta_r/T)} + \cdots, \quad \frac{\theta_r}{T} \gg 1 \tag{10-26}$$

and, retaining the first two terms only, we have, from (1-16),

$$\ln Z \simeq e^{-\theta_r/T}$$

$$\simeq e^{-\beta k \theta_r} \tag{10-27}$$

Thus the internal energy per particle and the constant volume molar specific heat capacity at low temperatures approach zero exponentially as

$$u \approx k\theta_r e^{-\theta_r/T} \tag{10-28}$$

and

$$c_v \simeq R \left(\frac{\theta_r}{T}\right)^2 e^{-\theta_r/T} \qquad \frac{\theta_r}{T} \gg 1 \tag{10-29}$$

Comparison between (10-29) and (7-39) shows that the diatomic gas behaves similarly to a one-dimensional Einstein crystal at low temperatures, both obeying the law of corresponding states.

10-2 RIGID ROTATOR IN SPACE

The rigid rotator in three dimensions has two degrees of freedom (corresponding to rotation in the θ- and ϕ-directions) and the kinetic energy is given by the second term in (6-71). As in the case of the plane rotator, one can set up the Lagrangian function and obtain the generalized momenta of the system and substitute them into the Hamiltonian function, which still represents the total energy of the system. When this is done, the energy again takes the form of (10-4) with the azimuthal angular momentum, p_ϕ, replaced by the total angular momentum L,

$$E = \frac{L^2}{2I} \tag{10-30}$$

Since the azimuthal angular momentum, which can be regarded as the z-component of the total angular momentum (and in fact was the total angular momentum, being in the z-direction, for the plane rotator), could only assume discrete values, given by (10-6), we should expect an analogous situation to exist for the rigid rotator in three dimensions. This indeed is the case but now we must resort to a quantum-mechanical solution of the rigid rotator problem to determine the allowed values of L^2 in (10-30). This problem is rather standard in courses in quantum mechanics and atomic physics, and so we shall just quote the result[1]

$$L^2 = l(l + 1)\hbar^2 \tag{10-31}$$

where l is called the *azimuthal quantum number* and takes on integer values.*
The spectroscopic term classification, used in molecular and atomic spectroscopy as well as in nuclear physics, is determined by the orbital angular
momentum of the system, which is labeled by the azimuthal quantum
number[2] l.

The energy levels of the three-dimensional rigid rotator, in contrast to
the plane rotator, are highly degenerate. There are n different allowed values
of l for the principal (or total) quantum number n:

$$l = 0, 1, 2, ..., n - 1 \qquad (10\text{-}32)$$

and $2l + 1$ allowed values of m for a given azimuthal quantum number:

$$m = 0, \pm 1, \pm 2, ..., \pm l \qquad (10\text{-}33)$$

Since the energy of the rigid rotator (model of the diatomic molecule) does
not depend on n we can ignore the l-degeneracy and consider only the
m-degeneracy which we account for by setting the density of states:

$$g_l = (2l + 1) \qquad (10\text{-}34)$$

From (10-30) and (10-31) we have

$$w_l = \frac{l(l + 1)\hbar^2}{2I} \qquad (10\text{-}35)$$

and thus the canonical distribution function becomes

$$n_l = \alpha(2l + 1)e^{-l(l + 1)\beta\hbar^2/2I} \qquad (10\text{-}36)$$

The canonical partition function can then be written as

$$Z = \sum_{l = 0}^{\infty} (2l + 1)e^{-l(l + 1)\beta\hbar^2/2I} \qquad (10\text{-}37)$$

Eq. 10-37, like (10-11), cannot be evaluated in closed form, but the
characteristic rotational temperature, given by (10-15) and denoted in this
section as Θ_r, appears in the sum-over states for the rigid rotator in space
as it did for the plane rotator, and we can evaluate the high-temperature
results by means of the Euler-Maclaurin summation formula as

$$Z \simeq \frac{T}{\Theta_r}\left[1 + \frac{\Theta_r}{3T} + O\left(\frac{\Theta_r}{T}\right)^2\right], \frac{\Theta_r}{T} \ll 1 \qquad (10\text{-}38)$$

*The three quantum numbers n, l, and m representing the total quantum number,
the azimuthal quantum number, and the magnetic quantum number, respectively
of the Bohr-Sommerfeld prequantum mechanical treatment of the single-electron
atom, arise naturally from the postulates of quantum mechanics and have retained
the older names (cf. Ref. 2 below).

[2] See, for example, R. B. Leighton, *Principles of Modern Physics* (New York:
McGraw-Hill Book Company, 1959), Chap. 5.

Retaining only the first two terms in (10-38) we find

$$\ln Z = \frac{\beta k \Theta_r}{3} - \ln \beta - \ln k \Theta_r \tag{10-39}$$

where the approximate relation

$$\ln (1 + \varepsilon) \simeq \varepsilon \qquad \varepsilon \ll 1 \tag{10-40}$$

has been again used [cf. (1-16)]. From (10-13) and (10-39) we find the mean energy per atom to be

$$u = k \left(T - \frac{\Theta_r}{3} \right), \qquad \frac{\Theta_r}{T} \ll 1 \tag{10-41}$$

and the molar specific heat capacity is

$$c_v = R \qquad \frac{\Theta_r}{T} \ll 1 \tag{10-42}$$

Again, at sufficiently high temperatures where $\Theta_r/3$ can be ignored compared to T, the three-dimensional rigid rotator exhibits the familiar equipartition of energy between the two d.o.f.

At very low temperatures, where (10-25) is valid, the partition function, (10-37), can be expanded as

$$Z = 1 + 3e^{-2\Theta_r/T} + 5e^{-6\Theta_r/T} + \cdots, \qquad \frac{\Theta_r}{T} \gg 1 \tag{10-43}$$

in analogy with the plane rotator result of (10-26). Retaining only the first two terms in (10-43) and using (10-40), we can write

$$\ln Z \simeq 3e^{-2\Theta_r/T} = 3e^{-2\beta k \Theta_r} \tag{10-44}$$

and hence

$$u \simeq 6k\Theta_r e^{-2\beta k \Theta_r} \qquad \frac{\Theta_r}{T} \gg 1 \tag{10-45}$$

and

$$c_v \simeq 3R \left(\frac{2\Theta_r}{T} \right)^2 e^{-2\Theta_r/T} \qquad \frac{\Theta_r}{T} \gg 1 \tag{10-46}$$

Again, we see that the molar specific heat capacity at constant volume obeys the law of corresponding states.

Also, as in the case of the plane rotator, the ratio of the characteristic rotational temperatures of two different diatomic gases is inversely proportional to the ratio of their moments of inertia:

$$\frac{\Theta_r}{\Theta_r'} = \frac{I'}{I} \tag{10-47}$$

Thus the characteristic rotational temperature will be higher the smaller the moment of inertia of the gas. The equilibrium separation distance of the symmetric diatomic molecules H_2 and N_2 is $0.740\,\text{Å}$ and $1.095\,\text{Å}$, respectively. For H_2, Θ_r is about $85.4°K$. For nitrogen then, we see that

$$\Theta_r = \frac{(0.740)^2}{14(1.095)^2}\,85.4$$

$$= 2.78°K \tag{10-48}$$

which compares favorably with the value of $2.86°K$ determined experimentally from the spectroscopic rotational spectrum of N_2. We also note that Θ_r for nitrogen is near that found for carbon monoxide in (10-19). It is clear that, due to the experimental difficulties inherent in reaching the temperatures of (10-48), the conditions under which (10-25) is valid are not presently attainable except for the isotopically substituted forms of hydrogen ($\Theta_r = 64°K$ for HD and $42.7°K$ for deuterium, D_2). Because of the experimental interest in hydrogen, we shall devote the following section to this interesting diatomic molecule.

10-3   MOLECULAR HYDROGEN AT LOW TEMPERATURES

Thus far in the present chapter we have confined our attention to nonsymmetrical diatomic molecules. To be sure, the moment of inertia term, appearing in (10-8) and (10-35), can be evaluated as well for symmetric as for nonsymmetric molecules; however, the configuration shown in Fig. 6-2 is clearly distinct from that in which m_1 and m_2 are interchanged if m_1 and m_2 refer to different species of atoms. This distinction disappears if m_1 and m_2 are identical atoms, yet the two indistinguishable configurations will both be (erroniously) counted in the partition function (sum-over states). Thus the partition function of (10-11) or (10-37), although (classically) correct for heteronuclear (unsymmetric) molecules, is twice as large as it should be for homonuclear (symmetric) molecules, due to the fact that it represents an overcounting of the distinguishable states of the molecule. To correct this condition, and yet retain the generality of the form of the partition function, it is customary to divide the r.h.s. of (10-11) or (10-37) by a temperature independent constant σ, called the *symmetry factor*, which has the value 1 if the molecule is heteronuclear, and the value 2 if the molecule is homonuclear. This symmetry factor, which is inserted in an *ad hoc* manner for the classical partition function, arises naturally from the quantum-mechanical symmetry restrictions on the wave function describing the diatomic molecule.

The notion of symmetry or antisymmetry is applied to the wave function of the system and arises through the intrinsic spin angular momentum associated with the particles comprising the system under consideration. The symmetry concept only comes into play when there are two (or more) identical (indistinguishable) particles present at the same time. The fact that, quantum-mechanically, it is impossible to distinguish between identical particles can lead to (quantum) effects which have no classical analogue. Consequently, the student often remembers his first encounter with the concept of symmetry as being enveloped in an abstract aura of mystery and intrigue. Averments to the contrary may be ineffectual to those students not having yet studied the intricacies of quantum mechanics; but we hasten to assure the students falling in this class that there is a logical (?) relation between quantum mechanics, with its symmetry restrictions, on the one hand, and statistical mechanics on the other.[3] The wave function describing the system of identical particles is said to be symmetric if the interchange of any pair of particles (actually, the coordinates of the particles, including both positional and spin coordinates) leaves the wave function unchanged. The wave function is said to be antisymmetric if the interchange of (the coordinates of) any pair of identical particles changes the sign of the wave function. Particles obeying Fermi-Dirac statistics are described by antisymmetric wave functions, and particles obeying Bose-Einstein statistics are described by a symmetric wave function.

Let us now see how these ideas apply to our diatomic hydrogen molecule, when we retain the three-dimensional rigid-rotator description. When the Schrödinger equation is solved for the rigid rotator composed of two identical atoms, the wave function describing the spatial coordinates θ and ϕ, (there are only two d.o.f. for the rigid rotator in space) is easily shown to be[1]

$$\psi(\theta,\phi) = Y_l^{\pm m}(\theta,\phi)$$

$$= N_{lm}\, e^{\pm im\phi}\, P_l^m(\cos\theta) \tag{10-49}$$

where $Y_l^{\pm m}$ is known as a *spherical harmonic*, N_{lm} is a normalization constant, and P_l^m is an *associated Legendre function*, which can be expressed as

$$P_l^m(\cos\theta) = \frac{(-)^l (\sin\theta)^m}{2^l l!} \frac{d^{l+m}}{d(\cos\theta)^{l+m}} [\sin\theta]^{2l} \tag{10-50}$$

The effect of interchanging the two atoms of the rigid rotator can be seen more clearly with the aid of Fig. 10-2. When the (identical) atoms A and B are interchanged, the coordinates θ and ϕ, describing particle A are

---

[3]L. I. Schiff, *Quantum Mechanics*, 3rd ed. (New York: McGraw-Hill Book Company, 1968), Chaps. 7, and 10.

replaced by $\pi - \theta$, $\phi + \pi$, which is equivalent to reflecting atom A through the origin. In other words, the coordinates of atoms A and B are interchanged; the coordinates describing A before interchange, describe B after the exchange.

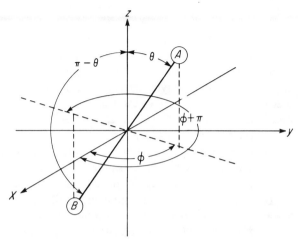

FIG. 10-2. Angular coordinates describing the two identical atoms A and B of a homonuclear rigid rotator.

Consequently, after exchange of the two atoms, the wave function is represented by

$$\psi[(\pi - \theta), (\phi + \pi)] = Y_l^{\pm m}[(\pi - \theta), (\phi + \pi)] \tag{10-51}$$

which takes the form

$$Y_l^{\pm m}[(\pi - \theta), (\phi + \pi)] = N_{lm} e^{\pm im\phi}[e^{\pm im\pi}] \frac{(-)^l[\sin(\pi - \theta)]^m}{2^l l!}$$

$$\times \frac{d^{l+m}}{d[\cos(\pi - \theta)]^{l+m}}[\sin(\pi - \theta)]^{2l} \tag{10-52}$$

Since $\sin(\pi - \theta) = + \sin\theta$ and $\cos(\pi - \theta) = -\cos\theta$, we can write (10-52) as

$$Y_l^{\pm m}[(\pi - \theta), (\phi + \pi)] = (-)^l N_{lm} e^{\pm im\phi} \frac{(-)^l(\sin\theta)^m}{2^l l!} \times \frac{d^{l+m}}{d(\cos\theta)^{l+m}}[\sin\theta]^{2l}$$

$$= (-)^l Y_l^{\pm m}(\theta, \phi) \tag{10-53}$$

Consequently the wave function describing the rigid rotator has the property

$$\psi_{[(\pi - \theta), (\phi + \pi)]} = (-)^l \psi_{(\theta, \phi)} \tag{10-54a}$$

and is said to have the *parity* of l. Parity is a nonclassical description of the state of a system and arises through the change in sign of the space coordinates in the (wave) function. By referring to Fig. 10-2, the student can easily verify that the exchange of the two identical particles is equivalent to the reflection through the origin of each particle and consequently is the same as replacing x, y, z by $-x$, $-y$, $-z$, respectively (see Prob. 10-9). Thus (10-54a) can be written equivalently (although not as conveniently) as

$$\psi_{(-x, -y, -z)} = (-)^l \psi_{(x, y, z)} \tag{10-54b}$$

In texts on quantum mechanics it is shown that the dichotomy of wave functions into even and odd types is a direct result of the fact that the potential energy of the system is symmetric about the origin* (remember we assumed that the potential energy of the rigid rotator was constant, and thus symmetric about the origin). In the preceding section we showed that the energy levels for the rigid rotator are degenerate with respect to the quantum number m (for $l > 0$), as given by (10-34); however, the degenerate wave functions all have the same parity, l, as given by (10-54). By the energy degeneracy described by (10-34) we mean that there exist $2l + 1$ states of the system, labeled by l and m, all having the same energy. There exists another degeneracy of the system, called exchange degeneracy, which arises from inter- (or ex-) change of the two indistinguishable, identical particles, but this will not be pursued further here.

From (10-54) we see that if l is even, the permutation of the two atoms does not change the wave function, which is then said to be symmetric in the space coordinates. On the other hand, if l is odd, the wave function changes sign and is said to be antisymmetric in the space coordinates.

The hydrogen atom consists of a proton and an electron, both having a spin angular momentum of $\frac{1}{2}\hbar$ (see the table in Sec. 2-5), and consequently both the proton and the electron obey Fermi-Dirac statistics, which means that the hydrogen molecule must be described by a *total* wave function which is antisymmetric in the interchange of either the two electrons or the two protons. Since the electron and proton are separate entities, we can write the total molecular wave function as the product of an electronic and nuclear contribution

$$\psi = \psi_e \psi_N \tag{10-55}$$

The electronic wave function can be expressed as a product of a spatial wave function, $\phi_{(r)}$, and a spin wave function, χ_e,

$$\psi_e = \phi_{(r)} \chi_e \tag{10-56}$$

The spin function of the electron is antisymmetric due to the fact that the covalent bond couples the two electronic spins to a resultant spin of zero.

*See Chap. 2 of Ref. 3.

This is accomplished by having the electronic spins of the two electrons oriented antiparallel to each other, i.e.,

$$s_1 = +\frac{1}{2}\hbar$$
$$s = s_1 + s_2 = 0 \qquad (10\text{-}57)$$
$$s_2 = -\frac{1}{2}\hbar$$

Since the total spin $s = 0$, there is only one spin state available to the system, and this is termed a *singlet* state. If the two electrons are interchanged, their spin is reversed, and this is then described by an antisymmetric spin function. Now ψ_e in (10-56) must be antisymmetric, so $\phi_{(r)}$ must be a symmetric function of the spatial coordinates. Generally the Schrödinger equation must be solved by numerical methods for $\phi_{(r)}$, but this need not concern us here, as the electrons will generally be in their ground state, or lowest, energy configuration at ordinary temperatures.

Of much more interest is the nuclear wave function ψ_N. We have mentioned that the diatomic molecule can be described in terms of the translation of the center of mass (c.m.), the rotation about the c.m., and the vibration of the two atoms along an axis connecting them. This, of course, is only an approximation as the c.m. is usually computed using only the nuclear masses (however; it is, in general, a quite valid approximation). Thus we may write the nuclear wave function (approximately) as the product of translational, vibrational, rotational, and spin wave functions:

$$\psi_N = \psi_t\psi_v\psi_r\chi_N \qquad (10\text{-}58)$$

Neither the translational wave function (which depends only on the coordinates of the c.m.) nor the vibrational wave function (which depends only on the internuclear separation) is affected by exchanging nuclei; hence both of these functions (and their product) are symmetrical in the interchange of nuclei. Since ψ_N must be antisymmetrical in the interchange of nuclei, this means that the product $\psi_r\chi_N$ must be antisymmetric. We know from (10-54), that ψ_r has the parity of l, and so if l is even, χ_n must be antisymmetrical, and if l is odd, χ_N must be symmetrical. From (10-57) we know that if the nuclear spins are antiparallel to each other, the molecule will be in an antisymmetric, singlet, nuclear spin state [since electrons and protons both have spin of $\frac{1}{2}\hbar$, (10-57), originally obtained for electrons, is equally valid for protons (or any other spin $\frac{1}{2}\hbar$ particle)]. This means that the singlet nuclear spin state must be combined (only) with the even rotational states, $l = 0, 2, 4, \ldots$. Hydrogen molecules are indeed found in this configuration (as may be verified from spectroscopic data) and in this state the gas is termed parahydrogen, or p-H_2. What if the nuclear spins are parallel to each other? Well, if $s_1 = s_2 = \frac{1}{2}\hbar$, the interchange of nuclei leaves the spin state unchanged and so χ_N must be symmetric. In this case ψ_r must be antisymmetric, which means that $l = 1, 3, 5, \ldots$. Again, hydrogen is found to exist in these odd rotational states, and is called orthohydrogen or o-H_2, when it does. Furthermore, when the nuclear spins are aligned

$$s_1 = s_2 = \frac{1}{2}\hbar \quad s = 1\hbar \tag{10-59}$$

and the allowed spin angular momentum states of the system are given, in analogy with (10-33), by

$$\sigma = 0, \pm s = \hbar \tag{10-60}$$

Thus, there are three spin substates of the nucleus in which the total spin angular momentum is $1\hbar$, consequently this is called a *triplet* state, corresponding to a spin degeneracy of 3 (i.e., there are three substates, all with the same total spin of $1\hbar$). The total degeneracy of the states must now be the product of the energy degeneracy given by (10-34) and the spin degeneracy, g_s,

$$g = g_l g_s \tag{10-61}$$

with

$$g_s = 1 \text{ if } l = 2p$$
$$3 \text{ if } l = 2p + 1 \tag{10-62}$$

The partition function for a gas of parahydrogen molecules is

$$Z_p = \sum_{l \text{ even}} (2l + 1)e^{-l(l + 1)y}$$

$$= \sum_{p = 0}^{\infty} (4p + 1)e^{-2p(2p + 1)y} \tag{10-63}$$

where, in an effort to save printer's ink, we have set

$$y = \frac{\beta\hbar^2}{2I} \tag{10-64}$$

Similarly, the partition function for a system composed of orthohydrogen molecules is

$$Z_o = \sum_{l \text{ odd}} 3(2l + 1)e^{-l(l + 1)y}$$

$$= 3 \sum_{p = 0}^{\infty} (4p + 3)e^{-2(p + 1)(2p + 1)y} \tag{10-65}$$

Since molecular hydrogen exists in both the p-H_2 and the o-H_2 configurations, it is logical to assume that the total partition function for normal hydrogen should be given by the sum of (10-63) and (10-65). Under the terms of this assumption the rotational contribution to the molar specific heat capacity at constant volume is given by (see Prob. 10-10)

$$c_v(\text{rot}) = -\frac{R}{(kT)^2}\frac{\partial^2}{\partial\beta^2}\ln(Z_p + Z_o) \qquad (10\text{-}66)$$

whereas that for a gas of p-H_2 and o-H_2, separately, would be

$$c_v(\text{para}) = -\frac{R}{(kT)^2}\frac{\partial^2}{\partial\beta^2}\ln Z_p \qquad (10\text{-}67a)$$

and

$$c_v(\text{ortho}) = -\frac{R}{(kT)^2}\frac{\partial^2}{\partial\beta^2}\ln Z_o \qquad (10\text{-}67b)$$

respectively.

Unfortunately, the "logical" prediction for $c_v(\text{rot})$ given by (10-66) bears no resemblance whatever to the experimentally observed values of $c_v(\text{rot})$. As a guess, we might try the sum of (10-67a) and (10-67b) for the specific heat capacity

$$c_v = -\frac{R}{(kT)^2}\frac{\partial^2}{\partial\beta^2}\ln(Z_p Z_o) \qquad (10\text{-}68)$$

But, as the student has no doubt encountered in guessing on examinations, this guess is also incorrect as (10-68) does not agree with experiment either. Consequently we are forced to contemplate the meaning of equations (10-66) and (10-68). Experimental observations leave no doubt whatever that the states appearing in (10-66) are correctly enumerated.[4] However; these same observations also indicate that there are no transitions between the symmetric and the antisymmetric states of H_2 which occur in time periods characteristic of times needed to obtain the experimental data.*

But (10-66) impliedly assumes that there is free conversion between the ortho- and para- states at all time. Thus we now understand why (10-66) does not agree with experiment. The behavior of hydrogen as a metastable mixture of two gases should mean that we are justified in adding their contributions to the specific heat capacity as we did in (10-68). However,

---

[4]T. Hori, *Z. Physik* **44**, 834 (1927).

*Later experiments have demonstrated that there are transitions between the states of o-H_2 and p-H_2, even at low temperature, which characteristically take several days.[5] This is interpreted to mean that diatomic hydrogen behaves, not like a gas in true thermodynamic equilibrium, the condition under which (10-66) is valid, but rather like a metastable mixture of two gases, o-H_2 and p-H_2. The metastable lifetime can be shortened, and the transitions hastened, by keeping the gas at high pressure over a charcoal catalyst.

[5]K. F. Bonhöffer and P. Harteck, *Z. Physikal Chem.* **4**, 113 (1929). A. Eucken and K. Hiller, *ibid.* **4**, 131 (1929); A. Farkas, *Light and Heavy Hydrogen* (London: Cambridge University Press, 1935).

(10-68) was obtained from the assumption that there exists equal amounts of the two species in the experimental sample. From (10-12), (10-63), and (10-65) we see that

$$\frac{N_o}{N_p} = \frac{Z_o}{Z_p} = 3\frac{\sum\limits_{p=0}^{\infty}(4p+3)e^{-2(p+1)(2p+1)y}}{\sum\limits_{p=0}^{\infty}(4p+1)e^{-2p(2p+1)y}} \tag{10-69}$$

At very low temperatures y becomes very large and we can expand the sums in (10-69), retaining only the first few terms; this leads us to conclude that

$$\frac{N_o}{N_p} \to 0 \qquad \text{as } T \to 0 \tag{10-70}$$

or, in other words, at very low temperatures the equilibrium mixture of diatomic hydrogen approaches pure p-H_2 (in the $l = 0$ rotational state). At high temperatures y becomes small and we may evaluate the sums in (10-69) via the Euler-Maclaurin summation formula (see Prob. 10-16).

$$\frac{N_o}{N_p} = 3\frac{[1+3y-\cdots]}{[1+y+\cdots]} \to 3 \text{ as } T \to \infty \tag{10-71}$$

Thus at elevated temperatures [at room temperature (10-71) is valid to within 0.1 per cent] there are three times as many orthohydrogen molecules as parahydrogen molecules in the equilibrium mixture of molecular hydrogen. Since the total number of molecules is the sum of N_o and N_p,

$$N = N_o + N_p \tag{10-72}$$

$$N_p = \frac{N}{4} \qquad \text{and} \qquad N_o = \frac{3}{4}N \tag{10-73}$$

at ordinary temperatures. But, as we saw earlier, the conversion from ortho-to-parahydrogen has a lifetime of several days and so (10-73) holds even at low temperatures, instead of the equilibrium composition at that temperature, for the period of time usually needed to obtain the experimental data. So, instead of adding (10-67a) and (10-67b) to obtain (10-68), we find that we should incorporate (10-73) into (10-67a) and (10-67b) to obtain

$$c_v(\text{rot}) = \frac{3}{4}c_v(\text{ortho}) + \frac{1}{4}c_v(\text{para}) \tag{10-74}$$

which is in excellent agreement with experimental results. This approach to the problem was first taken by Dennison,[6] who cogently reasoned that (10-74) must be the correct form for the molar specific heat capacity of hydrogen.

[6]D. M. Dennison, *Proc. Roy. Soc.* **A115**, 483 (1927).

PROBLEMS

10-1.   Verify (10-13) by evaluating U from (3-2) and dividing the result by (10-12).

10-2.   From the definitions of center of mass and moment of inertia, verify that (10-16) is valid for any diatomic molecule.

10-3.   Verify (10-19).

10-4.   Verify (10-21) and obtain the next term in the square brackets.

10-5.   Calculate the frequency at which the Einstein temperature, given by (7-39), is equal to the rotational temperature, given by (10-15).

10-6.   Approximate (10-37) by means of the Euler-Maclaurin summation formula with

$$f(x) = (2x + 1)\exp\left[-x(x + 1)\frac{\Theta_r}{T}\right]$$

Note that $(2x + 1)\, dx = d[x(x + 1)]$. Show, and use the result that $f'(\infty) = 0$; $f'(0) = (2 - \Theta_r/T)$ to verify (10-38).

10-7.   Evaluate $f'''_{(\infty)}$ and $f'''_{(0)}$ and determine the coefficient of $(\Theta_r/T)^2$ in (10-38).

10-8.   Use (10-40) to evaluate the next order terms in β appearing in (10-22) when both terms in the square brackets of (10-21) are retained. Use your result to obtain the next approximation to u and c_v in (10-23) and (10-24). Compare your results to (10-41) and (10-42) and make any appropriate comments.

10-9.   Write the transformation equations from spherical polar to rectangular cartesian coordinates and show explicitly that replacing r, θ, ϕ by r, $\pi - \theta$, $\phi + \pi$ is equivalent to replacing x, y, z by $-x$, $-y$, $-z$.

10-10. Using equations (10-13), (10-14), and (5-25), obtain (10-66).

10-11. The energy of a diatomic molecule can be expressed as

$$\varepsilon = \varepsilon_{\text{Translation}} + \varepsilon_{\text{Rotation}} + \varepsilon_{\text{Vibration}} + \varepsilon_{\text{Electronic}}$$

For a nondegenerate gas of N diatomic heteronuclear molecules the total partition function of the gas is

$$Z = \frac{1}{N!}(z)^N$$

where z is the partition function of a single molecule.
(a) Show that
$$\ln Z = N(\ln z_{\text{Tran}} + \ln z_{\text{Rot}} + \ln z_{\text{Vib}} + \ln z_{\text{Elec}})$$

where $z_{\text{Tran}} = \Sigma\, e^{-\beta \varepsilon_{\text{Trans}}}$, etc.
(b) Show that the internal energy is

$$u = u_{\text{Tran}} + u_{\text{Rot}} + u_{\text{Vib}} + u_{\text{Elec}}.$$

10-12. (a) What is the classical Hamiltonian for the vibrator portion of the diatomic molecule?
(b) What is the frequency of the vibrator?
(c) If the quantum mechanical energy of the vibrator is

$$\varepsilon_{\text{Vib}} = (n + \tfrac{1}{2})\hbar\omega \qquad\qquad n = 0, 1, 2, \dots$$

What is the partition function for the vibrator?

10-13. The HCl molecule has a moment of inertia $I = 2.6 \times 10^{-40}$ gm-cm^2 and a vibrator frequency $\omega = 5.4 \times 10^{14}$ rad/sec. Calculate the energy required to excite the rotor and the vibrator to their first excited state and compare these energies.

10-14. Consider a neutron which is scattered by a diatomic molecule which is in the ground state. Compare what happens if the molecule is considered to be classical (classical rotor and/or classical vibrator) to a molecule which is quantum mechanical. Particularly explain what happens in the quantum molecule if the neutron energy imparted to it is less than the first excited state of the vibrator. If the diatomic molecule is hydrogen viewed as a quantum molecule, do you expect the neutron scattering to be different for para-hydrogen and ortho-hydrogen? Why?

10-15. Apply the equipartition theorem to a gas of diatomic molecules. What is the expected heat capacity at constant volume? How does the heat capacity vary with temperature?

10-16. Verify (10-70) and (10-71).

11 | Quantum Symmetry Restrictions

11-1 SPIN ANGULAR MOMENTUM

The Schrödinger equation, which represents the quantum mechanical description of the motion of a particle, in analogy with the Hamiltonian (classical) description of a particle, assigns to the particle a wave function, in terms of both spatial and temporal coordinates, which can be written in the form[1]

$$\Psi(x, y, z, t) = \psi_{l, m, n}(x, y, z)e^{-i\omega t} \tag{11-1}$$

where l, m, n are called the *quantum numbers*, which take on only a characteristic limited range of values (some of which, however, may be infinite). To a given value of the energy of the system

$$\varepsilon = \hbar\omega \tag{11-2}$$

there will often correspond several, say g_e, wave functions of the system. One then says that there exists a space (or energy) degeneracy of the system of degree g_e. We have seen in Chap. 2 [from Table 2-1 in Sec. 2-5] that particles found in nature possess an intrinsic spin angular momentum of magnitude $s\hbar$, where s is either a nonnegative integer $(0, 1, 2, ...)$ or an odd half-integer $(\frac{1}{2}, \frac{3}{2}, \frac{5}{2}, ...)$. The projection of this angular momentum along an arbitrary direction (usually taken to be the z-axis) gives, when it is measured, a series of possible values (at constant energy):

$$m_s = -s, -(s-1), ..., +(s-1), +s \tag{11-3}$$

The intrinsic spin angular momentum obeys all the rules associated with

[1] See, for example, L. I. Schiff, *Quantum Mechanics*, 3rd ed. (New York: McGraw-Hill Book Company, 1968), Chap. 2.

the (more classical) orbital angular momentum, and we see from (11-3) that there are

$$g_s = 2s + 1 \qquad (11\text{-}4)$$

different spin states associated with a given energy of the system, where $2s$ is a nonnegative integer. It is customary to term g_s the spin degeneracy of the system. As we saw in Sec. 10-3, the total degeneracy of the system is then given by [see the discussion re (10-61)]

$$g = g_e g_s$$
$$g = (2s + 1)g_e \qquad (11\text{-}5)$$

The student should enumerate m_s and g_s for several values of s (encouragement toward this end is given by Prob. 11-1).

There thus corresponds $(2s + 1)$ distinguishable spin orientation states to each spatial wave function $\psi(x, y, z)$. It is convenient to take the spin wave function to be a generalized function of the type discussed in Sec. 1-5, which we shall denote here by $\chi(\xi - \sigma)$, where ξ is the spin variable and σ is any of the values appearing in the series of (11-3). Actually the spin of the system, denoted here by ξ, can take on a finite number of integer or half-integer values only, not a continuous range of values, as is required to completely specify the spatial wave function. The complete wave function, containing the spatial, temporal, and spin dependence can then be written in the form

$$u = \Psi(x, y, z, t)\chi(\xi - \sigma) \qquad (11\text{-}6a)$$
$$= \psi_{l, m, n}(x, y, z)e^{-i\omega t}\chi_\sigma(\xi - \sigma) \qquad (11\text{-}6b)$$

where the spin wave function has been labeled by the quantum number σ, which tells us in what spin state the system is to be found.

The total wave function given by (11-6) is normalized and any two such wave functions, corresponding to different (space *or* spin) states are orthogonal to each other. These conditions can be expressed by

$$\int u^* u \, d\tau = \iiint_{-\infty}^{\infty} \psi^*_{l, m, n}\psi_{l', m', n'} \, dx \, dy \, dz \int_{-\infty}^{\infty} \chi^*_\sigma \chi_{\sigma'} \, d\xi$$
$$= \delta_{ll'}\delta_{mm'}\delta_{nn'}\delta_{\sigma\sigma'} \qquad (11\text{-}7)$$

Thus if any one of the four quantum numbers (l, m, n, σ) differs between two states the corresponding wave functions are orthogonal. If, for example, the three spatial quantum numbers are the same and the spin quantum numbers are different, the second integral in (11-7) vanishes [see (1-137)]. Similarly if $\sigma = \sigma'$ but $(l, m, n) \neq (l', m', n')$, the first integral in (11-7) will be null.

The total wave function of (11-6) does not exhibit any obvious *a priori* symmetry properties. However, we recall our encounter in Sec. 10-3 with the symmetry restrictions placed on homonuclear diatomic molecules, and thus we will not be surprised by any symmetry restrictions which are placed on the wave function of (11-6). The requirements imposed on the complete wave function can be expressed in terms of the generalized Pauli principle: *the complete wave function describing a collection of identical particles is symmetric under the interchange of all the coordinates* (space and spin) *of any two particles, whenever the spin quantum number, s, of the particles takes on integer values, antisymmetric for those particles whose spin quantum number assumes odd half-integer values, and in no case is it ever asymmetric.* The postulate that the state function describing a system of fermions is totally antisymmetric under the exchange of any two fermions is just a precise and general statement of the well-known *Pauli exclusion principle,*[2] which forbids two fermions from occupying a single quantum state.[3]

Let us now see if we can gain some insight into the meaning to be attached to the generalized Pauli principle. First of all we see that the symmetry character of the wave function is applicable only when one has an ensemble of several identical particles (at least two). Before we jump in and try to obtain the wave function describing two or more identical, independent particles, let us recall first how one obtains the wave function describing a single (free) particle, unfettered by an external potential. The nonrelativistic Hamiltonian for a conservative system can be written as (cf. App. III)

$$H = \varepsilon_k + \varepsilon_p \qquad (11\text{-}8)$$

where the kinetic energy can be written in terms of the particle momentum as

$$\varepsilon_k = \frac{p^2}{2m} = \frac{p_x^2 + p_y^2 + p_z^2}{2m} \qquad (11\text{-}9)$$

Now one of the fundamental postulates of quantum mechanics is that the Hamiltonian function and the total energy of the particle (which are equal to each other for conservative systems) are to be considered as operators, which operate on the wave function $\Psi(x, y, z, t)$. Since the Hamiltonian and the total energy are equal, the result of the operation, independent of the form of the operators, must be

$$H\Psi = E\Psi \qquad (11\text{-}10)$$

In texts on quantum mechanics it is shown[1] that the energy and momen-

---

[2] W. Pauli, *Z. Physik* **31**, 765 (1925).

[3] F. A. Kaempffer, *Concepts in Quantum Mechanics* (New York: Academic Press, Inc., 1965) Secs. 16, 17.

tum of the particle can be represented by differential operators which act on the wave function as

$$E = i\hbar\partial_t \tag{11-11}$$

and

$$\mathbf{p} = -i\hbar\nabla \tag{11-12}$$

$$p_x\hat{i} + p_y\hat{j} + p_z\hat{k} = -i\hbar[\partial_x\hat{i} + \partial_y\hat{j} + \partial_z\hat{k}]$$

By combining Eqs. 11-8 through 11-12 we can write the Schrödinger equation, describing the nonrelativistic motion of a single particle of mass μ as

$$\frac{-\hbar^2}{2\mu}\Delta\Psi + \varepsilon_p\Psi = i\hbar\partial_t\Psi \tag{11-13}$$

where the scalar Laplacian operator is defined by

$$\Delta = \nabla\cdot\nabla = \partial_y^2 + \partial_x^2 + \partial_z^2 \tag{11-14}$$

We now limit our attention to the case of a free particle, which is characterized by the absence of an external potential. For this case we attempt to solve (11-13) for the state function by means of the standard technique[4] of separating the spatial and temporal dependence of the wave function in the form

$$\Psi(x, y, z, t) = \psi(x, y, z)T(t) \tag{11-15}$$

Substitution of (11-15) into (11-13), with ε_p set equal to zero, leads to

$$T(t)\left[-\frac{\hbar^2}{2\mu}\Delta\psi(x, y, z)\right] = \psi(x, y, z)\left[i\hbar\partial_t T(t)\right] \tag{11-16}$$

which, when both sides are divided by (11-15), can be written as

$$\frac{-\hbar^2}{2\mu}\frac{\Delta\psi}{\psi} = \frac{i\hbar d(\ln T)}{dt} \tag{11-17}$$

Now the left-hand side of (11-17) is a function of the spatial coordinates alone and the right-hand side is a function only of time. Since the spatial and temporal coordinates are independent, we conclude that (11-17) can be satisfied for all t only if each side is a constant, say ε, in which case

$$T(t) = e^{\varepsilon t/i\hbar} \tag{11-18a}$$

and

$$\frac{-\hbar^2}{2\mu}\Delta\psi = \varepsilon\psi \tag{11-18b}$$

[4]J. Irving and N. Mullineux, *Mathematics in Physics and Engineering* (New York: Academic Press, Inc., 1959), Chap. 1.

Eq. 11-18b is known[1] as an *eigenvalue equation* in which the constant ε

is the *eigenvalue* and ψ is the *eigenfunction* of the operator $\left(\dfrac{-\hbar^2}{2\mu\Delta}\right)$.

The object of the game of quantum mechanics is to determine the eigen-functions of the system and to evaluate the eigenvalues allowed for the system. In the present example the student may have noticed that (11-15) can be brought into accord with (11-1) if the constant ε, in (11-18a), is given by (11-2).

Let us proceed with our example by assuming that the particle under discussion is to be confined to a cubical domain of side length L. The student should be able to show (see Prob. 11-4) that the eigenfunctions for such a system are given by

$$\psi(x, y, z) = Ne^{i(2\pi/L)(lx + my + nz)} \tag{11-19}$$

and the energy eigenvalues are given by[5]

$$\varepsilon = \frac{2\pi^2\hbar^2}{\mu L^2}[l^2 + m^2 + n^2] \tag{11-20}$$

where the quantum numbers l,m,n are integers (positive, negative, or zero). Thus the energy spectrum is found by giving to l,m,n all the integer values consistent with (11-20). In general there will be an energy degeneracy when-ever there exist three numbers l',m',n' such that

$$l'^2 + m'^2 + n'^2 = l^2 + m^2 + n^2 \tag{11-21}$$

The degree of degeneracy is found by investigating the number of positive integer values of l,m,n, such that the particle energy lies between ε and $\varepsilon + d\varepsilon$, analogous to our analysis in Sec. 5-1, and is given by (5-9), where we now call the density of states $g(p)$ the energy degeneracy, g_e:

$$g_e = \frac{4\pi V p^2\, dp}{h^3} \tag{11-22}$$

and where the relation between the kinetic energy [given here by (11-20)] and the momentum, p, of the particle is still given by (5-6) [or (11-9)].

We can express the energy degeneracy in terms of the de Broglie wave-length, λ, which is related to the particle momentum by

$$p = \frac{h}{\lambda} = \hbar k \tag{11-23}$$

and

$$k = \frac{2\pi}{\lambda} \tag{11-24}$$

[5]E. Merzbacher, *Quantum Mechanics, 2nd ed.* (New York: John Wiley & Sons, Inc., 1970) Chap. 10.

is called the *wave number* or the magnitude of the propagation vector:

$$\mathbf{k} = \frac{2\pi}{L}(l\hat{i} + m\hat{j} + n\hat{k}) \tag{11-25}$$

written here in terms of the orthogonal cartesian unit vectors (note that $\hat{k}$ is the unit vector in the $+z$-direction, and has no other relation to the propagation vector). Substitution of (11-23) into (11-22) leads to

$$g_e = 4\pi V \frac{d\lambda}{\lambda^4} \tag{11-26}$$

where we have suppressed the negative sign arising from differentiating (11-23) [see the discussion re (8-12b)].

We also see that (11-25) can be used to express the spatial wave function of (11-19) as

$$\psi(x, y, z) - N e^{i\mathbf{k} \cdot \mathbf{r}} \tag{11-27}$$

(see Prob. 11-5) where the normalization factor N is such that

$$\int \psi^* \psi \, d\tau = N^* N V = 1 \tag{11-28}$$

We can safely evaluate, from (11-28),

$$N = N^* = V^{-1/2} = L^{-3/2} \tag{11-29}$$

We have seen that the particle spin does not arise in a natural way in the nonrelativistic Schrödinger description of the behavior of the particle, and so it must be introduced in an *ad hoc* fashion as given by (11-6b). Thus, for our single free particle, constrained to a cubical region with periodic boundary conditions,

$$u = L^{-3/2} e^{i\mathbf{k} \cdot \mathbf{r}} e^{-i\omega t} \chi(\xi - \sigma) \tag{11-30}$$

where the propagation vector and the energy are related [from (11-20) and (11-25)] by

$$\varepsilon = \frac{\hbar^2 k^2}{2\mu} \tag{11-31}$$

and the energy and angular frequency are related by (11-2). The total degeneracy is given [from (11-5) and (11-22)] by

$$g = (2s + 1) \frac{4\pi V p^2 \, dp}{h^3}$$

Having considered this simple example of a single particle, to which the generalized Pauli principle does not apply, we are now ready to focus our attention to the case where there are two, three, or more independent identical particles in the system. These cases will be taken up in the following sections.

11-2   WAVE FUNCTIONS DESCRIBING TWO IDENTICAL PARTICLES

We now assume that the system consists of two identical particles, which are confined to a cubic region of space with side length L, having periodic boundary conditions and where the potential energy (due to both interaction between the particles and external forces) is null. In analogy to (11-13) we can write the Schrödinger equation as

$$\frac{-\hbar^2}{2\mu}(\Delta_1 + \Delta_2)\Psi = i\hbar\partial_t\Psi \tag{11-33}$$

where, in analogy with (11-14),

$$\Delta_i = \partial_{x_i}^2 + \partial_{y_i}^2 + \partial_{z_i}^2, \quad i = 1, 2 \tag{11-34}$$

is the Laplacian operator which acts only on particle i (although the particles are identical, we assume for the moment that they have been numbered to render them distinguishable). We can progress with (11-33) by separating the variables of the first and second particle in the form

$$\Psi = \Psi_1(x_1,y_1,z_1,t) \cdot \Psi_2(x_2,y_2,z_2,t) \tag{11-35}$$

in which case

$$\Delta_i\Psi_i\Psi_j = \Psi_j\Delta_i\Psi_i \quad i,j = 1, 2 \tag{11-36}$$

Thus (11-33) takes the form

$$\frac{-\hbar^2}{2\mu}\left[\Psi_2\Delta_1\Psi_1 + \Psi_1\Delta_2\Psi_2\right] = i\hbar\left[\Psi_2\partial_t\Psi_1 + \Psi_1\partial_t\Psi_2\right]$$

and, dividing through both sides by (11-35), we have

$$\frac{-1}{\Psi_1}\left[\frac{\hbar^2}{2\mu}\Delta_1\Psi_1 + i\hbar\partial_t\Psi_1\right] = \frac{1}{\Psi_2}\left[\frac{\hbar^2}{2\mu}\Delta_2\Psi_2 + i\hbar\partial_t\Psi_2\right] \tag{11-37}$$

We note that the left-hand side of (11-37) is a function only of the coordinates of particle one, while the right-hand side is a function only of the coordinates of particle two; moreover they are both the same function. From the argument following (11-17) we conclude that each side is a constant, say δ. Denoting the operator within the square brackets of (11-37) by M, we express our conclusion via

$$-\frac{1}{\Psi_1}M\Psi_1 = \delta = +\frac{1}{\Psi_2}M\Psi_2 \tag{11-38a}$$

But, since the particles are identical, the subscripts "one" and "two" are artificial and we can just as validly write

$$-\frac{1}{\Psi_2}M\Psi_2 = \delta = +\frac{1}{\Psi_1}M\Psi_1 \tag{11-38b}$$

from which we are forced to conclude that

$$\delta = 0 \qquad (11\text{-}39)$$

and hence

$$\frac{-\hbar^2}{2\mu} \Delta_1 \Psi_1 = i\hbar \partial_t \Psi_1 \qquad (11\text{-}40a)$$

$$\frac{-\hbar^2}{2\mu} \Delta_2 \Psi_2 = i\hbar \partial_t \Psi_2 \qquad (11\text{-}40b)$$

Since both of (11-40) are of the same form as (11-13) [with $\varepsilon_p = 0$], the solutions will also be the same form

$$\Psi_1 = N_1 e^{i\mathbf{k}_1 \cdot \mathbf{r}_1} e^{-i\omega_1 t}$$
$$\Psi_2 = N_2 e^{i\mathbf{k}_2 \cdot \mathbf{r}_2} e^{-i\omega_2 t} \qquad (11\text{-}41)$$

and the complete wave function for the system, including the spin coordinates, is

$$u = N\chi(\xi_1 - \sigma_1)\chi(\xi_2 - \sigma_2)e^{i\mathbf{k}_1 \cdot \mathbf{r}_1}e^{i\mathbf{k}_2 \cdot \mathbf{r}_2}e^{-i\omega t} \qquad (11\text{-}42)$$

where N is a normalization factor which is only defined up to a complex factor of magnitude unity, and the energy of the system is given by

$$\varepsilon = \hbar\omega = \hbar(\omega_1 + \omega_2) = \varepsilon_1 + \varepsilon_2 \qquad (11\text{-}43)$$

The energy of our system appears in the state function only through the last term in (11-42). From (11-43) we see that the system energy is just the sum of the energies of the particles comprising the system. Although this situation is not surprising, and in fact, from a classical point of view, is so to be expected that it is not worthy of note, it does mean that the system has an energy degeneracy. Thus if the two identical particles are inter-changed so that, in effect, particle 1 is placed in the state previously occupied by particle 2, and conversely, the energy of the system will be unchanged and still given by (11-43); although the transposed wave function will now be of the form

$$u' = N\chi(\xi_1 - \sigma_2)\chi(\xi_2 - \sigma_1)e^{i\mathbf{k}_1 \cdot \mathbf{r}_2}e^{i\mathbf{k}_2 \cdot \mathbf{r}_1}e^{-i\omega t} \qquad (11\text{-}44)$$

The fact that the two states, represented by u and u', have the same energy is termed *exchange degeneracy*, which can be shown [6] to be a property of the solutions of the Schrödinger equation for any system composed of (any number of) identical particles, independent of the nature of any forces acting upon the particles (the student wishing more information on this

[6] D. S. Saxon, *Elementary Quantum Mechanics* (San Francisco: Holden-Day, Inc., 1968), p. 241.

interesting sidelight is urged to consult Ref. 6; this chapter is already sufficiently intractable, mathematically, to justify omission of this topic in a
treatment at the level of this text). It is well known (to physics professors
and better graduate students) that a linear combination of wave functions
is also a wave function. Thus if α and β are any two arbitrary constants
(it is alleged that)

$$U = \alpha u + \beta u' \tag{11-45}$$

will also be a wave function describing the system of two identical particles.
This means that U must be a solution of the Schrödinger equation (11-33)
[with Ψ of (11-35) replaced by U of (11-45)]. Since the differential operators
in (11-33) do not act on the spin functions appearing in u and u', we may
conserve ink by omitting the spin functions in our demonstration that U
is a valid system wave function (the incredulous student with a large sheet
of paper may wish to follow our discussion by retaining the spin terms).

The left-hand side of (11-33) takes the form

$$\frac{-\hbar^2}{2\mu}(\Delta_1 + \Delta_2) U = \frac{-\hbar^2}{2\mu} Ne^{-i\omega t}(\Delta_1 + \Delta_2)\left[\alpha e^{i\mathbf{k}_1 \cdot \mathbf{r}_1}e^{i\mathbf{k}_2 \cdot \mathbf{r}_2} + \beta e^{i\mathbf{k}_1 \cdot \mathbf{r}_2}e^{i\mathbf{k}_2 \cdot \mathbf{r}_1}\right]$$

$$= \frac{-\hbar^2}{2\mu} Ne^{-i\omega t}\{[-k_1^2\alpha e^{i\mathbf{k}_1 \cdot \mathbf{r}_1}e^{i\mathbf{k}_2 \cdot \mathbf{r}_2} - k_2^2\beta e^{i\mathbf{k}_1 \cdot \mathbf{r}_2}e^{i\mathbf{k}_2 \cdot \mathbf{r}_1}]$$

$$+ [-k_2^2\alpha e^{i\mathbf{k}_1 \cdot \mathbf{r}_1}e^{i\mathbf{k}_2 \cdot \mathbf{r}_2} - k_1^2\beta e^{i\mathbf{k}_1 \cdot \mathbf{r}_2}e^{i\mathbf{k}_2 \cdot \mathbf{r}_1}]\}$$

$$= \frac{-\hbar^2}{2\mu}(-k_1^2 - k_2^2)Ne^{-i\omega t}[\alpha e^{i\mathbf{k}_1 \cdot \mathbf{r}_1}e^{i\mathbf{k}_2 \cdot \mathbf{r}_2} + \beta e^{i\mathbf{k}_1 \cdot \mathbf{r}_2}e^{i\mathbf{k}_2 \cdot \mathbf{r}_1}]$$

$$= \left[\frac{\hbar^2 k_1^2}{2\mu} + \frac{\hbar^2 k_2^2}{2\mu}\right] U \tag{11-46}$$

as the student can verify by simple differentiation. With the aid of (11-31)
and (11-43), we can express (11-46) as

$$\frac{-\hbar^2}{2\mu}(\Delta_1 + \Delta_2)U = (\varepsilon_1 + \varepsilon_2)U = \varepsilon U \tag{11-47}$$

The student can easily show (see Prob. 11-7) that

$$\varepsilon U = i\hbar \partial_t U \tag{11-48}$$

since both u and u' have the same temporal dependence, with the energy
and angular frequency being related by means of (11-43). From (11-48)
and (11-47) we see that indeed the linear combination of wave functions,
U given by (11-45), is itself a state function of the system for arbitrary
coefficients α and β. In general then (i.e., for arbitrary values of α and β)
the solutions of the form given by (11-45) will be *asymmetric*; that is, if one

interchanges the particles the resulting wave function will exhibit no symmetry properties with regard to the original wave function. However, one
can force the symmetry properties, required by the generalized Pauli principle,
on the wave function U by a judicious choice of α and β. In particular, if we
let

$$\alpha = -\beta \qquad\qquad (11\text{-}49)$$

we find that U is antisymmetric on the interchange of particles, whereas if

$$\alpha = +\beta \qquad\qquad (11\text{-}50)$$

the wave function is symmetric. To see this we note that the system energy,
given by (11-43), is constant under exchange of the (coordinates of the)
two particles (indeed this fact is the source of our present logorrhea) and so
the time dependence occurs as a symmetric term in the wave function. In an
effort to reduce writer's cramp, let us set

$$\psi_l(m) = \chi(\xi_l - \sigma_m)e^{i\mathbf{k}_l \cdot \mathbf{r}_m} \qquad l, m = 1, 2 \qquad (11\text{-}51)$$

so that, in our abbreviated symbolism, we have

$$u = N\psi_1(1)\,\psi_2(2)e^{-i\omega t} \qquad\qquad (11\text{-}42a)$$

and

$$u' = N\psi_1(2)\,\psi_2(1)e^{-i\omega t} \qquad\qquad (11\text{-}44a)$$

Now, for the special case when $\alpha = -\beta$, we can write

$$U_-(1, 2) = \alpha N[\psi_1(1)\,\psi_2(2) - \psi_1(2)\,\psi_2(1)]e^{-i\omega t} \qquad (11\text{-}52)$$

as the antisymmetric wave function describing the system of two identical
particles. To verify that $U_-(1, 2)$ is an antisymmetric function, we merely
interchange the rôles of the two particles to obtain (trivially)

$$U_-(2, 1) = \alpha N[\psi_1(2)\,\psi_2(1) - \psi_1(1)\,\psi_2(2)]e^{-i\omega t}$$
$$U_-(2, 1) = -U_-(1, 2) \qquad\qquad (11\text{-}53)$$

The quantity αN, which is just another constant coefficient, can be
determined by requiring that $U_-(1, 2)$ be normalized:

$$\int U_-^*(1, 2)\,U_-(1, 2)d\tau_1\,d\tau_2 = 1 \qquad\qquad (11\text{-}54)$$

In order to ascertain the meaning of (11-54) we recall that $\psi_i(j)$ contains
both the spatial and spin coordinates of particle j wrapped up in the wave
function having the quantum numbers of particle i. In the (dis) guise of
this nomenclature, the orthogonality conditions of (11-7) can be written as

$$\int \psi_i^*(j)\psi_{i'}(j)\,d\tau_j = \delta_{ii'} \qquad\qquad (11\text{-}55)$$

The student should note that less ink is required to display (11-55) than (11-7); although both equations convey the same information. [At this point the student may find himself well advised to equip himself with pencil and paper and perhaps an eraser and convince himself that he understands the meaning of both (11-7) and (11-55), and that they both have the same meaning.]

We are now prepared to evaluate the normalization constants of U_- by substituting (11-52) into (11-54):

$$
\begin{aligned}
1 = |\alpha N|^2 \{ &\int \psi_1^*(1)\psi_2^*(2)\psi_1(1)\psi_2(2)\,d\tau_1\,d\tau_2 \\
&- \int \psi_1^*(1)\psi_2^*(2)\psi_1(2)\psi_2(1)\,d\tau_1\,d\tau_2 \\
&- \int \psi_1^*(2)\psi_2^*(1)\psi_1(1)\psi_2(2)\,d\tau_1\,d\tau_2 \\
&+ \int \psi_1^*(2)\psi_2^*(1)\psi_1(2)\psi_2(1)\,d\tau_1\,d\tau_2 \}
\end{aligned}
\tag{11-56}
$$

Since particles 1 and 2 are independent, the integration over the (spatial and spin) coordinates of both particles, which is required in the integrals appearing on the r.h.s. of (11-56), can be separated, and the four integrals can be written, respectively, as

$$\int \psi_1^*(1)\psi_1(1)\,d\tau_1 \int \psi_2^*(2)\psi_2(2)\,d\tau_2 = 1 \cdot 1 = 1 \tag{11-57a}$$

$$\int \psi_1^*(1)\psi_2(1)\,d\tau_1 \int \psi_2^*(2)\psi_1(2)\,d\tau_2 = 0 \cdot 0 = 0 \tag{11-57b}$$

$$\int \psi_2^*(1)\psi_1(1)\,d\tau_1 \int \psi_1^*(2)\psi_2(2)\,d\tau_2 = 0 \cdot 0 = 0 \tag{11-57c}$$

$$\int \psi_2^*(1)\psi_2(1)\,d\tau_1 \int \psi_1^*(2)\psi_1(2)\,d\tau_2 = 1 \cdot 1 = 1 \tag{11-57d}$$

where the separate integrals have been evaluated by means of (11-55). Substitution of (11-57) into (11-56) leads to the condition that

$$\alpha^2 N^2 = \frac{1}{2} \tag{11-58}$$

Now if u and u' were chosen to be normalized such that $N^2 = 1$, then the antisymmetric wave function should be synthesized by choosing

$$\alpha = -\beta = \pm \frac{1}{\sqrt{2}} \tag{11-59}$$

The antisymmetric wave function can be expressed in a more elegant fashion by making use of the properties associated with determinants. Thus, if we assume that u and u' have been normalized, we may write

$$
U_-(1,2) = \alpha \begin{vmatrix} \psi_1(1) & \psi_1(2) \\ \psi_2(1) & \psi_2(2) \end{vmatrix} e^{-i\omega t}
\tag{11-60}
$$

which the student can easily expand to verify the equivalence of (11-60) with (11-52). The interchange of particles·is mathematically equivalent to the interchange of columns in the determinant, which changes the sign of the determinant and thus leads to the antisymmetrical character of the wave function. This determinant, whose elements are single particle wave functions, is known as the *Slater determinant*[7] and is frequently used to construct anti-symmetric wave functions for a system of identical particles. If the two identical particles are in the same quantum state, the wave function of (11-60) obviously [see Prob. 11-8] vanishes, as is required by the Pauli exclusion principle for fermions.

The student can now readily see that if the linear combination of u and u' is chosen so that (11-50) is satisfied, the resulting wave function will be symmetric on the interchange of the two particles

$$U_+(1, 2) = \alpha N[\psi_1(1)\,\psi_2(2) + \psi_1(2)\,\psi_2(1)]e^{-i\omega t} \qquad (11\text{-}61a)$$

$$U_+(1, 2) = U_+(2, 1) \qquad (11\text{-}61b)$$

We can again determine the magnitude of αN by requiring that U_+ be normalized to unity

$$\int U_+^*(1, 2)\,U_+(1, 2)\,d\tau_1\,d\tau_2 = 1 \qquad (11\text{-}62)$$

from which we deduce that the symmetric wave function should be obtained by choosing

$$\alpha = \beta = \pm\frac{1}{\sqrt{2}} \qquad (11\text{-}63)$$

when u and u' are normalized such that $N^2 = 1$. The symmetric wave function can be expressed in an analogous manner to the antisymmetric state function by taking the sign of every term in the determinant to be positive,

$$U_+(1, 2) = \alpha \begin{Vmatrix} \psi_1(1) & \psi_1(2) \\ \psi_2(1) & \psi_2(2) \end{Vmatrix} e^{-i\omega t} \qquad (11\text{-}64)$$

When this is done (11-64) can then be seen to be equivalent to (11-61a). The symmetric solution is thus not zero when the two particles are in the same quantum state, and in fact undergoes no modification when the two particles exchange their roles.

We now can interpret the generalized Pauli principle as having the following significance: A collection of two identical particles is never found in an asymmetric state. If the two identical particles possess half-integer spin, the only possible states accessible to the system are those which correspond to an antisymmetric wave function, and the particles, which are called fermions, can never be found in the same quantum state at the same time. If the two identical particles possess integer spin, only those states

[7]J. C. Slater, *Phys. Rev.* **34**, 1293 (1929).

which correspond to a symmetric wave function are accessible to the system, and the particles, which are known as bosons, are capable of occupying the same quantum state simultaneously.

The one particle time-independent wave function of (11-51) contains the spatial- and spin-dependence, when there is no interaction potential acting on the particles, in the form of a product of spin and spatial wave functions. The wave-function solution to Schrödinger's equation, given by (11-42a) and (11-44a), was expressed as a product of the two one-particle wave functions, and the principle of superposition allowed us (and the generalized Pauli principle forced us) to take a linear combination of u and u' as the system state function. In the linear combination of u and u' that we chose to formulate U_+ and U_- [which we can generically write as $U_\pm$, where the $+$ $(-)$ sign indicates the symmetric (antisymmetric) total wave function], the spin and spatial coordinates of either particle are inseparable. It turns out, however, that it is frequently convenient to consider system wave functions in which the spin and spatial wave functions each, separately, obey certain symmetry conditions (the student may recall the discussion concerning the rotation spectrum of homonuclear diatomic molecules in Sec. 10-3).

To pursue this topic a little further it is convenient to rewrite (11-51) in the form

$$\psi_l(m) = \chi_l(m)\,\phi_l(m) \tag{11-51a}$$

where the spin wave function has been abbreviated as

$$\chi_l(m) = \chi(\xi_l - \sigma_m) \tag{11-65a}$$

and the free-particle momentum eigenfunction for the spatial dependence has been designated as

$$\phi_l(m) = e^{i\mathbf{k}_l \cdot \mathbf{r}_m} \tag{11-65b}$$

although it is clear that if there were an external potential acting on the particle one could still (in principle) write the time-independent spatial wave function, and call it $\phi_l(m)$. Furthermore, we can now introduce symmetric and antisymmetric linear combinations of the spin and space wave functions, as

$$\chi_\pm(1,2) = \frac{1}{\sqrt{2}}\left[\chi_1(1)\,\chi_2(2) \pm \chi_1(2)\,\chi_2(1)\right] \tag{11-66a}$$

and

$$\phi_\pm(1,2) = \frac{1}{\sqrt{2}}\left[\phi_1(1)\,\phi_2(2) \pm \phi_1(2)\,\phi_2(1)\right] \tag{11-66b}$$

It is now intuitively obvious (every textbook writer feels compelled to to use this phrase) that

(a) A symmetric total system wave function will result from the product of either an antisymmetric space function and an antisymmetric spin function, $\phi_- \chi_-$, or a symmetric space function and a symmetric spin function, $\phi_+ \chi_+$.

(b) An antisymmetric total system wave function will arise from the product of either an antisymmetric space function and a symmetric spin function, $\phi_- \chi_+$, or a symmetric space function and an antisymmetric spin function, $\phi_+ \chi_-$.

Note that, although $U_-(1, 2)$, $[\phi_+(1, 2)\,\chi_-(1, 2)]$, and $[\phi_-(1, 2)\,\chi_+(1, 2)]$ are all antisymmetric in the exchange of particles, they are not necessarily equal to each other (however, they will be linearly dependent) as we now demonstrate. Let us form the product $\chi_+ \phi_-$ from (11-66):

$$\chi_+(1, 2)\phi_-(1, 2) = \tfrac{1}{2}[\chi_1(1)\phi_1(1)\chi_2(2)\phi_2(2) - \chi_1(1)\phi_1(2)\chi_2(2)\phi_2(1)$$
$$+ \chi_1(2)\phi_1(1)\,\chi_2(1)\phi_2(2) - \chi_1(2)\phi_1(2)\,\chi_2(1)\phi_2(1)]$$

We can use (11-51a) to rewrite the first and last terms in the square brackets and we have

$$\chi_+(1, 2)\phi_-(1, 2) = \tfrac{1}{2}[\psi_1(1)\,\psi_2(2) - \psi_1(2)\psi_2(1)]$$
$$+ \tfrac{1}{2}[\chi_1(2)\phi_1(1)\chi_2(1)\phi_2(2) - \chi_1(1)\phi_1(2)\chi_2(2)\phi_2(1)] \qquad (11\text{-}67)$$

Similarly, we can now form the product

$$\chi_-(1, 2)\phi_+(1, 2) = \tfrac{1}{2}[\chi_1(1)\phi_1(1)\chi_2(2)\phi_2(2) + \chi_1(1)\phi_1(2)\chi_2(2)\phi_2(1)$$
$$- \chi_1(2)\phi_1(1)\chi_2(1)\phi_2(2) - \chi_1(2)\phi_1(2)\chi_2(1)\phi_2(1)]$$
$$= \tfrac{1}{2}[\psi_1(1)\psi_2(2) - \psi_1(2)\psi_2(1)]$$
$$- \tfrac{1}{2}[\chi_1(2)\phi_1(1)\chi_2(1)\phi_2(2) - \chi_1(1)\phi_1(2)\chi_2(2)\phi_2(1)]$$
$$\qquad (11\text{-}68)$$

We now add (11-67) and (11-68) (forming a linear combination of the two antisymmetric product functions)

$$\chi_+\phi_- + \chi_-\phi_+ = \psi_1(1)\psi_2(2) - \psi_1(2)\psi_2(1) \qquad (11\text{-}69)$$

where we have suppressed the arguments of the function on the l.h.s. of (11-69). Substituting (11-69) into (11-52), we find that

$$U_-(1, 2) = \frac{1}{\sqrt{2}}\,[\chi_+\phi_- + \chi_-\phi_+]e^{-i\omega t} \qquad (11\text{-}70)$$

when $\alpha N = 1/\sqrt{2}$. In a similar manner $U_+(1,2)$ can be expressed as a linear combination of $\chi_+\phi_+$ and $\chi_-\phi_-$ (see Prob. 11-10).

In Sec. 10-3 we expressed the total system wave function for the homonuclear hydrogen diatomic molecule as a product of space and spin wave functions. Since the molecular wave function was required to be antisymmetric on the interchange of two protons or two electrons, we noted that for a symmetric spatial wave function there corresponded a series of states of equal energy which was equal to the number of antisymmetric spin wave functions, and for an antisymmetric spatial wave function there corresponded a series of states equal to the number of symmetric spin wave functions. Similarly, a system composed of two particles with integer spin must have a symmetric total wave function. To a symmetric spatial wave function there will correspond a number of states equal to the number of symmetric spin wave functions, and to an antisymmetric spatial wave function there will correspond a series of states equal in number to the number of antisymmetric spin wave functions.

In either case it is useful to know the number of symmetric and antisymmetric spin functions. Let the two particles have spin quantum numbers σ_1 and σ_2, then from (11-4) σ_1 and σ_2 can each, independently, take on $(2s + 1)$ values. The number of possible pairs of values for σ_1 and σ_2 is thus $(2s + 1)^2$. Among these $(2s + 1)^2$ possible pairs of values for σ_1 and σ_2 will be the situation in which $\sigma_1 = \sigma_2$, which will occur $(2s + 1)$ times. When $\sigma_1 = \sigma_2$ the spin function will be symmetric. Removing these combinations, leaves

$$(2s + 1)^2 - (2s + 1) = (2s + 1)2s \qquad (11\text{-}71)$$

combinations of pairs of values where $\sigma_1 \neq \sigma_2$. These $2s(2s + 1)$ pairs of values for $\sigma_1 \neq \sigma_2$ may correspond to either a symmetric or an antisymmetric spin function. But in either event the identification of σ_1 and σ_2 is irrelevant and the combination $(\sigma_1 \sigma_2)$ is identical to the combination $(\sigma_2 \sigma_1)$ and thus the number of distinct combinations of pairs of values with $\sigma_1 \neq \sigma_2$ (or equivalently $\sigma_2 \neq \sigma_1$) is given by one half of (11-71) or $s(2s + 1)$. Hence there will be $s(2s + 1)$ symmetric and $s(2s + 1)$ antisymmetric spin functions for which $\sigma_1 \neq \sigma_2$. But since the antisymmetric spin functions can occur only when $\sigma_1 \neq \sigma_2$, the total number of antisymmetric spin functions is given by

$$N_{\text{anti spin}} = s(2s + 1) \qquad (11\text{-}72)$$

The number of symmetric spin functions is given by the sum of the number found when $\sigma_1 \neq \sigma_2$ and the number to be found when $\sigma_1 = \sigma_2$ is

$$N_{\text{sym spin}} = s(2s + 1) + (2s + 1)$$
$$= (s + 1)(2s + 1) \qquad (11\text{-}73)$$

The ratio of the number of antisymmetric spin functions to the number of symmetric spin functions is then given from (11-72) and (11-73) as

$$\frac{N_{\text{anti spin}}}{N_{\text{sym spin}}} = \frac{s}{s + 1} \qquad (11\text{-}74)$$

Eq. 11-74 appears frequently in the theory of rotation spectra and specific heat capacities for homonuclear diatomic molecules. In fact we have implicitly made use of (11-74) in Sec. 10-3 [cf. (10-69)].

EXAMPLE

Relative Intensities of the Rotation Spectra of Homonuclear Diatomic Molecules.

The energy levels associated with the rigid rotator model of a homonuclear diatomic molecule in space were developed in Sec. 10-2 as

$$\varepsilon_l = l(l+1)\frac{\hbar^2}{2I} \tag{10-35}$$

The electric dipole selection rules for emission or absorption of radiation by the atomic system (independent of the particular model used to represent the system) requires that the total angular momentum quantum number decrease or increase, respectively, by unity[8]

$$l' = l - 1 \qquad \text{emission by molecule} \tag{11-75a}$$

or

$$l' = l + 1 \qquad \text{absorption by molecule} \tag{11-75b}$$

We shall limit our consideration to the absorption spectra for a rigid rotator, although the analysis would be the same *mutatis mutandis* for the emission spectrum (see Prob. 11-11). The energy difference between two adjacent levels with angular momentum quantum numbers $l + 1$ and l is given by

$$\varepsilon = \frac{\hbar^2}{2I}[(l+2)(l+1) - l(l+1)]$$

$$= \frac{\hbar^2}{I}(l+1) \tag{11-76}$$

and, with the aid of (11-2), the frequency of the absorbed light quantum is given by

$$\nu_l = (l+1)\nu_0 \tag{11-77}$$

where the fundamental frequency is given by

$$\nu_0 = \frac{\hbar}{2\pi I} \tag{11-78}$$

From (11-77) we see that all harmonics of the spectrum are absorbed since

[8]D. Bohm, *Quantum Theory* (Englewood Cliffs, N.J.: Prentice-Hall, Inc., 1951), Chap. 18.

l takes on all integer values [consistent, of course, with (10-32)], the intensities of all the allowed harmonics, however, are not the same.

It is experimentally observed that the intensities of successive rotational lines in the spectra of all homonuclear diatomic molecules alternates in some constant ratio which is dependent on the nuclear spins of the molecule.[9] From (11-72) and (11-73) we see that the number of states corresponding to the different l values varies with l, and thus the intensity of a given absorption (or emission) line ought to be proportional to the number of states corresponding to a given value of l. The selection rules of (11-75) $\Delta l = \pm 1$, along with the selection rule $\Delta s = 0$ are actually only approximations, which are quite good when the coupling between the resultant orbital and spin angular momentums is weak.

We are now interested in the nuclear spin, which we shall designate (in accordance with custom) as I, rather than s. Let us first concentrate our attention on symmetric nuclei which, of course, are bosons. The total wave function for the two nuclei (which is the product of the spatial and spin wave functions) must be symmetric on the interchange of the two nuclei. Thus if the spatial wave function is symmetric so is the spin function, and if the spatial wave function is antisymmetric the spin function is also antisymmetric on interchange of the two nuclei. In Sec. 10-3 we found that the symmetric wave functions for the rigid rotator are those wave functions corresponding to even l [cf. (10-54a)] and thus, for boson nuclei, the symmetric spin wave functions will also correspond to even values of l. It then follows that when l is an odd integer both the spatial and the spin wave functions will be antisymmetric.

From Table 2-1 we see that O_2^{16} has a nuclear spin of zero, as does C_2^{12} and S_2^{32}. Thus from (11-74) we find that

$$\frac{N_{\text{anti spin}}}{N_{\text{sym spin}}} = \frac{I}{I+1} = 0 \qquad (11\text{-}79)$$

and thus the number of states with antisymmetric spin wave functions, which correspond to odd values of l, is null compared to those with symmetric spin functions, which correspond to even values of l. Hence the terms $v_0, v_2, v_4, \ldots$ in (11-77) will be found with equal intensities, whereas the terms $v_1, v_3, v_5, \ldots$ will be totally absent (in the approximation we are considering, viz., electric dipole transitions with weak coupling between spin and orbital angular momentum), although they are allowed by other spectroscopic selection rules.

[9]More detailed discussions of the alternation in the intensity of spectral lines for homonuclear molecules are given in texts on molecular spectroscopy. See, for example, G. W. King, *Spectroscopy and Molecular Structure* (New York: Holt, Rinehart and Winston, Inc., 1964), and G. Herzberg, *Spectra of Diatomic Molecules* (New York: D. Van Nostrand Co., Inc., 1950).

Again from Table 2-1 we note that N_2^{14} has nuclear spin $I = 1$, as does D_2 (diatomic deuterium) and hence we find that the ratio of the number of states with odd l values to those with even l values is

$$\frac{N_{\text{anti spin}}}{N_{\text{sym spin}}} = \frac{I}{I + 1} = \frac{1}{2} \tag{11-80}$$

and consequently the intensities of the terms v_0, v_2, v_4, ... will be twice the intensity of the terms v_1, v_3, v_5, ...

If the nucleus of the homonuclear diatomic molecule is a fermion, rather than a boson, the total nuclear wave function must be antisymmetric on the interchange of nuclei and consequently the symmetric spatial wave function, corresponding to even l values, will be associated with antisymmetric spin wave functions. Conversely, the symmetric spin functions will correspond to odd values of l. Thus for H_2, and N_2^{15}, which, from Table 2-1, have $I = 1/2$, we see that

$$\frac{N_{\text{anti spin}}}{N_{\text{sym spin}}} = \frac{I}{I + 1} = \frac{1}{3} \tag{11-81}$$

and the intensities of v_0, v_2, v_4, ... and v_1, v_3, v_5, ... alternate in the ratio of one to three. The student can easily show that for Li_2^7, B_2^{11}, and Na_2^{23} which have $I = 3/2$, the intensities alternate as three to five (see Prob. 11-12).

This intensity alternation has been investigated for a large number of homonuclear molecules and in fact provides a rather convenient method of experimentally determining the nuclear spin of these nuclei. The technique is quite unambiguous when $I = 0$, for then every other line is completely absent; whereas for larger I values the intensity alteration is slight and it is rather difficult to achieve an experimental accuracy sufficient to yield a unique value for I.

11-3 SYSTEMS WITH THREE OR MORE PARTICLES

A system of three or more identical particles, each having an intrinsic spin angular momentum s, will be capable of manifesting $(2s + 1)$ spin states per particle for a given energy state. The total wave function for the system will be given, in analogy with (11-45) for two particles, as a linear combination of products of one-particle wave functions. But here again, we are constrained by the generalized Pauli principle to require the total system wave function to be either symmetric or antisymmetric on the interchange of *any two* of the identical particles.

Thus for a system composed of fermions it is easy to see that antisymmetric

combinations of one-particle wave functions will arise from a generalization
of (11-60), which we can express as

$$U_{-(1, 2, \ldots, n)} = Ne^{-i\omega t} \begin{vmatrix} \psi_1(1) & \psi_1(2) \ldots \psi_1(n) \\ \psi_2(1) & \psi_2(2) \ldots \psi_2(n) \\ \cdot & \cdot & \cdot \\ \cdot & \cdot & \cdot \\ \cdot & \cdot & \cdot \\ \psi_n(1) & \psi_n(2) \ldots \psi_n(n) \end{vmatrix} \tag{11-82}$$

where $\psi_l(m)$ is given by (11-51) or (11-51a). The Slater determinant of (11-82)
is easily verified to be antisymmetric on the interchange of any two of the
identical particles since, as was noted in Sec. 11-2, this is mathematically
equivalent to the interchange of the two columns in which the coordinates
of the two particles appear, which operation thus changes the sign of the
determinant. Of course, if two fermions should have the same set of quantum
numbers (i.e., occupy the same state), then two columns of the determinant
will be identical, and the total wave function vanishes. This situation is then
interpreted in terms of the Pauli exclusion principle as meaning that *two
identical fermions are not capable of occupying the same quantum state.*

   This aspect of the Pauli exclusion principle, when applied to atoms,
leads to an explanation of the form of the periodic table as formulated by
D. I. Mendeleev in 1869. We consider the atom as being composed of a
positively charged nucleus, with charge Ze provided by the Z protons, which
determines the chemical element identity of the atom, and Z identical electrons to ensure the electrical neutrality of the atom. The electrons are
responsible for most of the chemical and physical properties of the atom.
From the Pauli exclusion principle two electrons associated with a given
atom cannot occupy the same quantum state; thus if the first electron occupies the lowest energy state of the atom, the second electron must occupy a
more energetic state. If we consider the four quantum numbers n, l, m, and s
introduced in Sec. 10-2, the lowest energy state will correspond to the
smallest allowed values of these quantum numbers. This would be the state
$n = 1, l = 0, m = 0$, which will accommodate the two electron spin quantum
numbers $m_s = +\frac{1}{2}$ and $m_s = -\frac{1}{2}$. We note from (10-32) and (10-33) that
there are n allowed values of l for a given n value and there are $(2l + 1)$
values of m for a given l value. To our approximation that the energy of the
atom is dependent only on the principal quantum number n, we see that
there exist

$$g_e = \sum_{l=0}^{n-1} (2l + 1) = n^2 \tag{11-83}$$

spatial quantum states per energy level (see Prob. 11-13). In other words, for
a given principal quantum number n, corresponding to a given energy of the

atom, there exists a spatial degeneracy of n^2. This degeneracy can, of course, be removed by the presence of a magnetic or electric field (which fields may be provided by the other electrons in a many-electron atom). From (11-5) we see that the total degeneracy of the electron states of the atom is

$$g = 2n^2 \qquad (11\text{-}84)$$

since $s = \frac{1}{2}$ for electrons. Thus for a given value of the principal quantum number, n, there will be a maximum of $2n^2$ electrons. The spectroscopists have customarily denoted the different n values by letters and we now speak of the electrons associated with a given n as being grouped in a *shell*. Thus the K shell, corresponding to $n = 1$, has, by (11-84), a maximum of 2 electrons; the L shell, corresponding to $n = 2$, will hold a maximum of 8 electrons; the M shell ($n = 3$) may contain a maximum of 18 electrons; and the N shell (corresponding to $n = ?$) requires 32 electrons to be filled. The spectroscopists also assign letters to indicate the various values of the azimuthal quantum numbers according to the scheme $s, p, d, f, g, \ldots$ which correspond to $l = 0, 1, 2, 3, 4, \ldots$ [subject of course, to the restriction that l may be no greater than $(n - 1)$]. The two electrons in the K shell of the atom will have quantum numbers of $n = 0$, $l = 0$, $m = 0$, and $m_s = +\frac{1}{2}$ and $-\frac{1}{2}$, respectively. The *ground-state electron configuration* for hydrogen is then represented as $1s^1$ and that for helium as $1s^2$. The first number specifies the value of n (for both hydrogen and helium, $n = 1$), the lowercase letter specifies the orbital quantum number of the individual electrons in the atom in accordance with the scheme outlined above (s represents the value $l = 0$), and the postsuperscript indicates the number of electrons in the atom having the prespecified values of n and l (in hydrogen there is only one electron and in helium two). We have already seen that there can be at most two electrons with a principal quantum number value of $n = 1$ (the K shell). Lithium has the next ascending atomic number $Z = 3$ and so the third electron will have to take the value $n = 2$ in the ground state. The lowest energy of this third electron will occur for $l = 0$, and the ground-state electron configuration of lithium will be represented by $1s^2\,2s^1$, which indicates that two electrons are in the closed K shell and one electron (the valence electron) is in the incomplete [it takes two electrons to fill the $l = 0$ subshell] $l = 0$ subshell of the L shell. The next element is beryllium with $Z = 4$, and the fourth electron then fills the $l = 0$ subshell of the L shell, yielding a ground-state electron configuration of $1s^2\,2s^2$. The student should be able to proceed in this manner to develop the ground-state electron configurations of other atoms (see Prob. 11-14).

As the atomic number increases we should expect that the one-electron approximation will become progressively worse and electron energy may very well depend on the values of n and l in a nontrivial manner. Thus we will not be surprised to find that the state with $n = 4$ and $l = 0$ (the $4s$ state) may have a lower energy than the state with $n = 3$ and $l = 2$ (the $3d$ state), and that the $6s$ state has less energy than the $4f$ state (see Prob. 11-15). The determination of the energies of electron states as a function of the various quantum numbers specifying the states is today a very active field of endeavor by physicists and chemists, and to proceed further in this discussion would take us beyond the scope of this text. If the students' appetite for more information in this area has been whetted, he may find refreshment from other sources.[10]

For a system composed of particles obeying Bose-Einstein statistics the total wave function, as we have seen, must be symmetric on the interchange of any two particles. The symmetric linear combination of products of n one-particle wave functions can be expressed as a generalization of (11-64)

$$U_+(1, 2, \ldots, n) = Ne^{-i\omega t} \begin{Vmatrix} \psi_1(1) & \psi_1(2) \ldots \psi_1(n) \\ \psi_2(1) & \psi_2(2) \ldots \psi_2(n) \\ . & . & . \\ . & . & . \\ . & . & . \\ \psi_n(1) & \psi_n(2) \ldots \psi_n(n) \end{Vmatrix} \tag{11-85}$$

in which every term in the expansion of the determinant is taken to be positive, and the one-particle wave functions are given by (11-51) or (11-51a). Since all the terms are taken to be positive on expansion of the determinant, the interchange of two columns, which corresponds mathematically to the exchange of two particles, does not change the sign of the total wave function. Similarly, the total wave function does not vanish when two or more bosons have the same set of quantum numbers. Hence there is no restriction on the number of identical bosons which may occupy the same quantum state, and there is no exclusion principle applicable to bosons.

11-4   EFFECTS OF NONZERO INTERACTION POTENTIALS

In our discussions thus far in the instant chapter we have confined our analysis to the situation in which the total potential energy of the system,

---

[10]See, for example, T. A. Ashford, *The Physical Sciences*, 2nd ed. (New York: Holt, Rinehart, and Winston, Inc., 1967), Chap. 10; R. T. Weidner and R. L. Sells, *Elementary Modern Physics*, 2nd ed. (Boston: Allyn and Bacon, Inc., 1968), p. 296; G. Herzberg, *Atomic Spectra and Atomic Structure*, 2nd ed. (New York: Dover Publications, 1944), Chap. 3; G. P. Harnwell and W. E. Stephens, *Atomic Physics* (New York: McGraw-Hill Book Company, 1955), p. 197; and *Periodic Table of the Elements*, available from E. H. Sargent & Co., Chicago, Ill.

arising from both external forces and interactions between the particles comprising the system, has been null. In the absence of any potential energy the system was found to be represented by either a symmetric or an antisymmetric wave function, and in no event by an asymmetric wave function.

The authors now propose to demonstrate that, by means of reasonable assumptions, the symmetric character of a potential field is not changed from that which results in the absence of a potential term.

The student may pause to reflect on the fact that most (if not all) of the potential energy terms he has encountered in his reading and problem assignments have been fairly simple functions of the distance between two particles (e.g., Coulomb, gravitational, van der Waals, Hooke's law forces) or of the displacement of one particle from its equilibrium position. This leads us to assume that in a system composed of many particles the interaction potential energy between the particles can be analyzed on the basis of the so-called *two-body interaction*, which plays an important role in the theories of nuclear physics.[11] In the two-body interaction, each particle is assumed to interact with each of the other particles independently of the remaining particles, and the total effect on the motion of a given particle is found by summing the two-body interactions over the other particles. This procedure is generally followed in elementary physics courses as for example when the student is asked to find the total gravitational or electric force on a point particle which is in some neighborhood about other point particles.

Thus we assume that the total system interaction potential energy can be written in the form

$$V_{\text{inter}} = \sum_{i, j}' f^I(r_{ij}) \tag{11-86}$$

where the prime on the double sum in (11-86) indicates that the terms with $i = j$ are to be omitted, and

$$r_{ij} = |\mathbf{r}_{ij}| = \sqrt{(x_i - x_j)^2 + (y_i - y_j)^2 + (z_i - z_j)^2} = r_{ji} \tag{11-87}$$

is the separation distance between the ith and jth molecules. We see that the separation distance between any two molecules of a substance does not change if the coordinates of the two molecules are interchanged, and hence the potential energy of interaction of the system is a symmetric function of the coordinates of the particles.

In addition to the interaction potential between the particles of the system, there may also be an external potential, as for example, an impressed electric field which is exterior to the system. This external field will affect

[11]See, for example, the discussions, references, and applications in R. R. Roy and B. P. Nigam, *Nuclear Physics* (New York: John Wiley & Sons, Inc., 1967), p. 321; and R. R. Roy and R. D. Reed, *Interactions of Photons and Leptons with Matter* (New York: Academic Press, Inc., 1968), p. 56.

all of the identical particles of the system in exactly the same manner, which will depend only on the displacement of the molecule from some specified coordinate axes. Consequently, the potential energy of a system of identical particles due to an external field may be written, quite generally as

$$V_{\text{ext}} = \sum_{i=1}^{n} f^{II}(r_i) \tag{11-88}$$

where the location of the ith molecule is intimated by

$$r_i = |\mathbf{r}_i| = \sqrt{x_i^2 + y_i^2 + z_i^2} \tag{11-89}$$

Since the sum on the r.h.s. of (11-88) is to be taken over all of the particles in the system, its value is the same irrespective of the order of summation. Ergo, the external potential energy is also symmetric on the exchange of any two of the identical molecules making up the system. Hence the total potential energy of the system, comprising both the internal and external contribution, is a symmetric function of the coordinates of the particles in the system, and can be expressed simply as

$$E_p = V_{\text{inter}} + V_{\text{ext}} \tag{11-90}$$

The Hamiltonian operator is then also completely symmetric on exchange of particles, and the Schrödinger equation

$$\left[\frac{-\hbar^2}{2m} \sum_{j=1}^{n} \Delta_j + E_p \right] U = - i\hbar \partial_t U \tag{11-91}$$

must still have solutions which are either symmetric or antisymmetric as before, when E_p was taken to be null. It may also be that the potential energy is a function of time (i.e., one may think of the interaction or external force as being "turned on", or "off", at a particular time); this will, of course, not affect the spatial symmetry properties of the potential energy term.

From our discussion above, we have convinced ourselves that the Hamiltonian function is symmetric, no matter what the value of E_p. Consequently the l.h.s. of (11-91) has the same symmetry as the system wave function U. But the r.h.s. of (11-91) must have the same symmetry as the l.h.s., if (11-91) is truly the equation of motion for the system. This means that if U is symmetric (antisymmetric) then $\partial_t U$ is also symmetric (antisymmetric). Since the wave function is differentiable, we can expand it in a Maclaurin expansion in which we ignore terms higher than first order:

$$U(0 + dt) = U_0 + \partial_t U \bigg|_{t=0} dt + \cdots \tag{11-92}$$

We can imagine that at some time $t = 0^-$, just prior to time zero, the particles in the system are in a force free environment and hence the total wave function has some definite symmetry property, say U is symmetric (the student may wish to follow this argument for an antisymmetric wave function). The potential E_p is then turned on at time $t = 0^+$, and we desire to investigate the symmetry property of U at time dt later. Inasmuch as U is (assumed to be) symmetric at $t = 0$, the constant term U_0 in (11-92) must be symmetric, and from (11-92) $\partial_t U$ is symmetric at all time, it is *a fortiori* symmetric at $t = 0$. Consequently we are forced to the conclusion that the system wave function at time dt after the potential has been "turned on" is the same as it was when no potential acted on the system. Since the symmetry of the wave function has not changed in time dt after the application of a potential field to the system, we could proceed in increments from time dt to $2dt$ and from $2dt$ to $3dt$, etc. until we arrive at any time t, when the symmetric character of the wave function is still the same as it was at any previous time.

In other words, the symmetric or antisymmetric character of a particle or collection of particles is intrinsic, and it is not changed when the particles are exposed to a potential field.

11-5 SYMMETRY CHARACTERISTICS OF NUCLEI

The symmetry characteristics of the elementary building blocks from which nuclei and atoms and molecules are established (e.g., neutrons, protons, and electrons) are rather abstract and not readily susceptible to simple, intuitive, interpretation or representation on a classical basis (a statement with which the student will undoubtedly readily agree). In reminiscing through Chap. 2, the student may recall from Table 2-1 that the electron, neutron, and proton are all fermions with spin $\frac{1}{2}$. The nucleus is composed of N neutrons and Z protons, which may be thought of as being two possible (isobaric spin) states of one and the same particle, the so-called *nucleon*, which is discussed at greater length elsewhere.[12] The mass number of the nucleus is given by

$$A = Z + N \tag{11-93}$$

where the atomic number Z, is the number of protons in the nuclide, and N the number of neutrons.

If we consider a system formed by two identical nuclei, which for the time being we may call 1 and 2, e.g., the homonuclear diatomic molecules discussed in Secs. 10-3 and 11-2, the system will be composed of $2N$ neutrons

[12]P. Roman, *Theory of Elementary Particles* (Amsterdam: North-Holland Publishing Company, 1960), p. 415; J. Bernstein, *Elementary Particles and Their Currents* (San Francisco: W. H. Freeman & Company, 1968), Chap. 3.

and $2Z$ protons. One can permute the roles of nuclides 1 and 2 by permuting successively the Z protons of nuclide 1 with those of nuclide 2 and then by permuting the roles of the neutrons in the two nuclides. As a consequence of permuting the proton roles, the wave function of the system is multiplied by $(-)^Z$, and it is multiplied by $(-)^N$ after permutation of the neutrons. The final result of exchanging the two nuclides in the system is that the system wave function is multiplied by $(-)^{Z+N}$. We thus conclude that the wave function describing the nucleus is symmetric or antisymmetric accordingly as the mass number of the nuclide is even or odd. In other words, *nuclei with odd A values are fermions and nuclei with even A values are bosons.* This statement has been presented in the form of a theorem, and a rigorous proof thereof has been provided by Ehrenfest and Oppenheimer.[13]

The wave function of a nucleus, being either symmetric or antisymmetric on the exchange of two identical particles, can be expressed in the form

$$U(Z, N, t) = \sum_{j=1}^{Z} \alpha_j e^{-i(\omega_j t + \delta_j)} + \sum_{j=1}^{N} \beta_j e^{-i(\omega_j t + \delta_j)} \qquad (11\text{-}94)$$

where the α_j and β_j are some (how properly chosen) eigenfunctions which are symmetric (if the nuclide mass number is even) or antisymmetric (if A is odd) in the space and spin coordinates of all the protons and neutrons, respectively. In permuting the role of any two of the nucleons, the total nuclide wave function either remains unchanged, in which case all the phases in (11-94) remain unchanged, or U in (11-94) changes sign, in which case the effect is the same as if the phases of all the terms in (11-94) had been changed by π.

Now, in general, the nuclear wave function is not written in the form of (11-94), but it is convenient to write (11-94) since it reminds us (perhaps, after considerable coaxing) of an analogous ordinary mechanical problem, which can be analyzed to advantage in gaining insight on the problem of understanding symmetry characteristics of identical particles. Consider a pair of identical simple pendulums; each having a bob of mass m, and length l, coupled together by means of a massless spring with spring constant, k, as shown in Fig. 11-1. A rigorous analysis of this mechanical problem shows[14] that there are two so-called *normal modes of oscillation*, which are analogous to the eigenfunction description of U in (11-94), in which no energy is exchanged between the two pendulums by means of the coupling spring, as shown in Figs. 11-2 and 11-3.

In Fig. 11-2 we see the normal mode of oscillation in which the two pendulums move in phase with each other. The displacements of the two pendulums are equal and the coupling spring remains in its equilibrium

[13]P. Ehrenfest and J. R. Oppenheimer, *Phys. Rev.* **37**, 333 (1931).

[14]R. A. Becker, *Introduction to Theoretical Mechanics* (New York: McGraw-Hill Book Company, 1954) Chap. 14; A. Sommerfeld, *Mechanics* (New York: Academic Press, Inc., 1964), Sec. 20.

position at all times. The angular frequency of vibration of each pendulum is $\omega_0 = \sqrt{g/l}$ which is just that of a simple pendulum of length l. When the system is in this normal mode of vibration, the result would not be changed if the two pendulums were interchanged. Thus by permuting the roles of the two identical pendulums, the state of the motion of the system is not altered. The student can readily see that this state of motion of an ordinary mechanical system behaves in a manner very analogous to a system of two bosons.

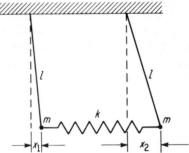

FIG. 11-1. Two identical pendulums of mass m and length l coupled by means of a massless spring of force constant k.

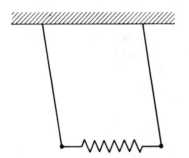

FIG. 11-2. One normal mode of oscillation in which $x_1 = x_2$ and the spring remains in equilibrium for all times. The two pendulums are perpetually in phase.

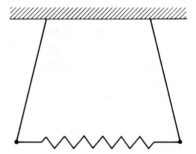

FIG. 11-3. The other normal mode of oscillation, in which $x_1 = -x_2$ and the two pendulums are always in opposite phase.

The normal mode vibration in which $x_1 = -x_2$ and the two pendulums are out of phase with each other by π radians, is shown in Fig. 11-3. Both pendulums have the same angular frequency of vibration $\omega_1 = \sqrt{g/l + 2k/m} > \omega_0$. When the system is in this normal mode of vibration state, the interchange of the two pendulums places the system in the state it would occupy half a period later; i.e., the phase of the system is changed by π. When the system is in this normal mode state it behaves quite similarly to a system of two fermions.

This illustration lends some insight into the nature of the symmetry requirements on the wave function describing a system of identical particles. But the student must not place too much reliance on the classical interpretation, for the analogy eventually breaks down (e.g., the general description of the motion of the coupled pendulums can be written in terms of a linear combination of the two normal mode vibrations, which in terms of our analogy is a linear combination of symmetric and antisymmetric states of the system. Such a combination of symmetric and antisymmetric wave functions is not found from a quantum description).

Returning now to the theorem of Ehrenfest and Oppenheimer that nuclei with even A are bosons and those with odd A values are fermions, we find that this theorem is confirmed by experimental investigations. It is found that the symmetry characteristic of the nuclide is predictable but the exact value of the nuclear spin is not amenable to a priori calculation.

As an example, consider the following:

The ordinary hydrogen atom, whose nucleus is the proton $_1H^1$. In this case $A = 1$ and $(-)^A = -1$. The nuclide obeys Fermi-Dirac statistics, and from Table 2-1 we see that the spin is $\frac{1}{2}$.

Deuterium, whose nucleus is the deuteron, consisting of a closely bound proton and neutron. Here $Z = N = 1$ and $A = 2$, so $(-)^A = +1$ and the deuteron is a boson. The nuclear spin could be zero (in which case the spins of the proton and neutron would be antiparallel) or one (in which event the constituent spins must be parallel), but experimental investigations of the band spectra of deuterium reveal that $I = 1$.

Helium, $_2He^4$, whose nucleus is the alpha particle composed of two protons and two neutrons. $Z = N = 2$ and $A = 4$. The alpha particle is also a boson, and the nuclear spin could be 0, 1, or 2. These values are easily seen by schematic representation of the nucleon spin by arrows pointing up or down, to represent the two spin states. The four spin states can be shown as ↑↓↑↓, ↑↑↑↓, or ↑↑↑↑. The order of the arrows is irrelevant, so that the first diagram is equivalent to ↓↑↑↓ or ↑↓↓↑, say, and the spins cancel in pairs, leading to a resultant nuclear spin of zero. The arbitrary directions "up" and "down" are indistinguishable, so that third diagram is the same as ↓↓↓↓, the important feature being that all four nucleon spins are aligned parallel to each other. Since the value of each nucleon spin quantum number is $\frac{1}{2}$, this last diagram represents a resultant nuclear spin of 2. The student should be able to show that the middle diagram represents a resultant nuclear spin of 1. From Table 2-1 we note that the observed value of the nuclear spin for ordinary helium is $I = 0$.

The nuclear spin quantum number has been tabulated elsewhere[15] for both stable and radioactive nuclear species. The experimental techniques

[15]R. B. Leighton, *Principles of Modern Physics* (New York: McGraw-Hill Book Company, 1959) App. G.

for evaluating I include analysis of the alternating intensities of the rotation terms in the band spectra of homonuclear diatomic molecules (cf. the example in Sec. 11-2 *supra*), the measurements of the specific heat capacities of the gas (cf. the discussion of molecular hydrogen in Sec. 10-3 *supra*), and the hyperfine structure found in atomic spectra.

PROBLEMS

11-1. Enumerate the various values of m_s and g_s, given by (11-3) and (11-4), respectively, and complete the following table:

Particle	s	g_s	m_s
He^4 nucleus	0		
electron, proton	$\frac{1}{2}$		
photon, phonon	1		
C^{13} nucleus	$\frac{3}{2}$		

11-2. Verify that (11-18a) and (11-18b) follow from (11-17). Discuss the effects to be expected if ε is complex; real, and positive, zero, or negative; or imaginary.

11-3. Show that ε appearing in (11-18a) has the same units or dimensions as the ε in (11-2), and consequently the two might be identified with each other.

11-4. Obtain (11-19) and (11-20) from (11-18b) by setting

$$\psi(x, y, z) = X(x)Y(y)Z(z)$$

and by using (11-14). Call the (three) separation constants k_x, k_y, and k_z, and obtain three equations of the form

$$\frac{d^2 X}{dx^2} + k_x^2 X = 0$$

show that the periodic boundary conditions $X(0) = X(L)$ dictate that $k_x = (2\pi/L)n$. For a thorough discussion of this exercise see Ref. 5.

11-5. By writing $\mathbf{r} = x\hat{\imath} + y\hat{\jmath} + z\hat{k}$ and using (11-25) show that (11-27) is equivalent to (11-19).

11-6. Make use of (11-6), (11-35), (11-41), and (11-43) to show that the complete state function, describing a system of two identical, independent, free, non-interacting particles, is given by (11-42). Evaluate N in terms of N_1 and N_2, and explain why N is thus indeterminate to within a complex factor of unit magnitude; i.e., if a new normalization constant is defined by

$$N' = Ne^{i\delta}$$

then N' is as satisfactory as N for a normalization factor (remember that $|e^{i\delta}| = 1$).

11-7. Retain the spin functions in the definition of U, given by (11-45), (11-44), and (11-42) and verify (11-48) where ε and ω are related by (11-43). What would be the effect of neglecting the spin terms in your demonstration?

11-8. If particle 1 and 2 are in the same quantum state, meaning that both particles are described by the same set of quantum numbers (i.e., the same single particle wave functions), show that the two rows in the Slater determinant, (11-60), are identical, and consequently the system wave function vanishes.

11-9. (a) Given that the system wave function is defined by (11-61a). verify that (11-61b) follows directly. (b) Starting with the wave function of (11-61a) and the normalization condition of (11-62), verify (11-63).

11-10. Express $U_t(1,2)$ as a suitable linear combination of $\phi_+\chi_+$ and $\phi_-\chi_-$ in a form analogous to (11-70).

11-11. Calculate the relative intensities of the *emission* spectra for a homonuclear diatomic molecule and compare your results with the example in Sec. 11-2.

11-12. Show that for homonuclear diatomic molecules with nuclear spin $I = \frac{3}{2}$, the absorption spectra consists of lines with intensities alternating in the ratio of $3:5$. What is ratio for O_2^{17}?

11-13. Verify that the spatial degeneracy given by the l.h.s. of (11-83) is indeed equal to n^2. (*Hint:* Expand the sum and combine the first and last terms, the second and penultimate terms, etc., all of which combinations add to $2n$, and then count the number of such combinations.)

11-14. Write the ground-state electron configuration for the first eighteen elements; starting with $1s^1$ for hydrogen and ending with $1s^2\, 2s^2\, 2p^6\, 3s^2\, 3p^6$ for argon. Note that the inert gases He and Ne represent the filled K and L shells, respectively, but Ar does not have a filled M shell. Why then does Ar properly belong in the inert-gas column of the periodic table?

11-15. The electron ground-state configuration of potassium is found, experimentally, to be $1s^2\, 2s^2\, 2p^6\, 3s^2\, 3p^6\, 4s^1$; this is interpreted to mean that, in many-electron atoms, the $4s$ energy state is lower than the $3d$ energy state. Experimental evidence indicates that the electron subshells are filled with increasing atomic number in the following general order:

$$1s,\ 2s,\ 2p,\ 3s,\ 3p,\ 4s,\ 3d,\ 4p,\ 5s,\ 4d,\ 5p,\ 6s,\ 4f,\ 5d,\ 6p,\ 7s,\ 6d,\ 5f$$

(a) What would be the expected electron configuration of the ground-state of K if the electron energy increased strictly with increasing n and l? (b) Write the ground-state electron configuration for the atoms from potassium through radon in the periodic chart, based on the filling order given above, and compare your results with accepted values given in Ref. 10. You will notice that there are several exceptions to the order listed above, primarily in the transition metals and the rare earths.

11-16. At one time it was thought that a neutron could be considered as a closely bound composite system made up of only a proton and an electron. (a) Show that the considerations of the Ehrenfest and Oppenheimer theorem would require such a neutron to be a boson. (b) Show that if the neutron is assumed to consist of three particles; the proton, the electron, *and* a chargeless, massless, spin $-\frac{1}{2}$ particle (called a neutrino, v_e), the Ehrenfest-Oppenheimer theorem would predict that the neutron should be a fermion, in consonance with Table 2-1.

11-17. Given a system of two identical particles with three nondegenerate energy levels; what are the possible arrangements of the particles if they are (a) bosons? (b) fermions?

11-18. What are the total wave functions of a system of three and a system of four particles if the particles are bosons? If the particles are fermions? In general, how many terms will the total wave function have (in terms of the single particle wave functions)?

11-19. If a system of two identical particles, under interchange

$$\psi(r_1, r_2) = e^{i\alpha}\psi(r_2, r_1)$$

use indistinguishability to show that $e^{i\alpha} = \pm 1$.

11-20. Consider a system of two particles which do not interact and which each have two quantum states ϕ and ψ. Find the possible forms of the total wave function for the system if the particles are (a) distinguishable, (b) identical and bosons, (c) identical and fermions.

11-21. A helium atom is made up of a nucleus of charge 2 and two electrons. What is the form of the total wave function, including spin, for the two electrons if the single particle wave function s are considered hydrogenic? [*Hint*: let $\chi_{1,2}(\uparrow)$ and $\chi_{1,2}(\downarrow)$ represent the spin wave function for electron one or two in the "spin up" and "spin down" states, respectively; and let $\phi_{1,2}(1)$ and $\phi_{1,2}(2)$ be the coordinate wave functions for hydrogenic atoms of charge 2, and construct symmetric and antisymmetric linear combinations thereof.]

12 | *The Bose-Einstein Gas*

12-1 INTRODUCTION

In the preceding chapter we considered the energy degeneracy for a gas composed of particles undergoing pure translation, with the result that the energy degeneracy for such a system is the same as the density of states for the system and is given by

$$g_e = \frac{4\pi V p^2 \, dp}{h^3} \tag{11-22}$$

Coupled with the energy degeneracy is the fact that there exist several angular momentum states associated with a given energy state. Of course, there may also be electronic states of the atoms or molecules, as well as vibrational and rotational states; but in the present chapter we shall assume that these states, if they exist, are not excited. In Secs. 10-3 and 11-1 we were introduced to the concept of the spin angular momentum, which we found was a parameter of the system which acted in conjunction with the orbital angular momentum of the system. The two angular momenta of the ith particle combine to yield the resultant total angular momentum of that particle (in units of $\hbar$) as

$$j_i = l_i + s_i \tag{12-1}$$

and the total angular momentum of the system is

$$J = \sum_{i=1}^{N} j_i \tag{12-2}$$

If there is just one particle under consideration, or if all the particles are prepared in the identical state, we may repress the subscript in (12-1) and merely speak of the resultant angular momentum, which may take on any of the values

$$j = l + s, l + s - 1, \ldots |l - s| \tag{12-3}$$

For a given energy state there corresponds $2j + 1$ possible angular momentum orientations of the system, and consequently the angular momentum degeneracy for the system is given by

$$g_j = 2j + 1 \tag{12-4}$$

in analogy with (10-34) for the orbital angular momentum of the particle. We then find the total degeneracy for a system of particles undergoing translation to be

$$g = (2j + 1)\frac{4\pi V}{h^3} p^2 \, dp \tag{12-5}$$

The relation (12-5) gives the proper description of the density of states for systems of fermions as well as for systems of bosons. Inasmuch as the heading of the present chapter is *The Bose-Einstein Gas*, we should ask ourselves "To what kinds of gases do the Bose-Einstein statistics apply?" The desired response is of course: "These statistics apply to systems of particles which are described by wave functions that are symmetric upon the interchange of any two identical particles which make up the system." The symmetry of the system occurs whenever the resultant angular momentum quantum number, j, is an integer, including zero. This is easily seen from the definition of j in (12-1). Since l is necessarily an integer by (10-32), the only way in which j can be an integer, from (12-3) is for s to also be an integer. And from the discussion in Sec. 2-5, particles possessing integer spin angular momentum are by definition bosons. To see whether an atom or molecule obeys Bose statistics, then, we might look to the value of j for the atom in the internal state of least energy (i.e., the ground state). We recall from the discussion of the periodic table in Sec. 11-3 that a complete electron shell will have a null j value (since m_l and m_s will antialign in pairs). Thus for atoms having closed electron shells, such as the rare gases and alkaline ions, the Bose-Einstein statistics will be applicable, and the angular momentum quantum degeneracy of (12-4) will be unity. We have seen from Table 2-1 and Sec. 11-3 that the helium atom is a boson with $j = 0$. We also found in Chap. 10 that diatomic hydrogen at very low temperatures has $j = 0$ and ought to be described by the quantum statistics of indistinguishable particles not bound by the exclusion principle. And of course in Chap. 9 we used the Bose-Einstein statistics to represent the photon, having an intrinsic spin angular momentum of one $\hbar$.

Thus we see that it is more than an academic exercise to investigate the properties of the Bose-Einstein gas; there are actually particles found in nature which can be expected to exhibit the properties determined for such a gas. Before we find such properties as the internal energy, specific heat capacity, and entropy, pertaining to the gas of bosons, in Sec. 12-3, we first must evaluate the second Lagrange undetermined multiplier α appearing in the boson distribution function of (3-23).

12-2 EVALUATION OF α

In the ensuing discussion of the present chapter we shall assume that $j = 0$ so that the factor $2j + 1 = 1$ and won't have to be explicitly carried throughout our calculations. (For other values of j the student can easily supply the omitted factor.)

From (5-11) we can express the number of particles in the system as

$$\frac{N}{V} = N_c \frac{2}{\sqrt{\pi}} \int_0^\infty \frac{\alpha x^{1/2}\, dx}{e^x - \alpha} \tag{12-6}$$

where N_c is given by (5-41) and we have set

$$x = \frac{\beta p^2}{2m} \tag{12-7}$$

The integral on the r.h.s. of (12-6) is of course a function of the second Lagrange undetermined multiplier α, and we may indicate this in an explicit manner by setting

$$F(\alpha) \equiv \frac{2}{\sqrt{\pi}} \int_0^\infty \frac{\alpha x^{1/2}\, dx}{e^x - \alpha} \tag{12-8}$$

so that the density of bosons becomes

$$\frac{N}{V} = N_c F(\alpha) \tag{12-9}$$

From (12-7) and the integral itself, we see that the domain of x in (12-8) is

$$0 \leq x \leq \infty \tag{12-10}$$

We can get some idea of the range of α from our discussion in Sec. 5-3, where we evaluated α for the corrected boltzon gas. In any system of particles, irrespective of the type of statistics they might obey, the effective density of states must never be less than the density of particles; in other words there must be at least one energy state available for every particle in the system. Now (12-9) would be identical to (5-40) if $F(\alpha) = \alpha$ (a result we shall find to be valid when the system is very weakly degenerate). So it certainly appears plausible that the maximum value of α is unity (in which case the system is strongly degenerate). On the other hand the least number of particles the system could contain is zero (N can never be negative) and this then represents the lower bound for α which we reason must be constrained to the domain given by

$$0 \leq \alpha \leq 1 \tag{12-11}$$

We can convince ourselves that (12-11) represents the gamut of α from other physical grounds as well. The integral in (12-8) diverges if α is greater than unity, and since the density of particles must be finite, we again conclude that $\alpha \leq 1$. Also, a negative value of α implies a negative particle density, which as before we discard as being not physically meaningful (see Prob. 12-2).

The restriction of (12-11) enables us to replace the integral in (12-8) by an infinite sum. Toward this end we multiply numerator and denominator of the integral by e^{-x} with the realization that (12-10) and (12-11) imply that αe^{-x} is never greater than unity, so that the binomial expansion

$$(1 - \varepsilon)^{-1} = \sum_{n=0}^{\infty} \varepsilon^n \tag{12-12}$$

always converges when we set

$$\varepsilon = \alpha e^{-x} < 1 \tag{12-13}$$

Following this recipe leads to

$$F(\alpha) = \frac{2}{\sqrt{\pi}} \int_0^{\infty} \frac{x^{1/2} \, dx \, \alpha e^{-x}}{1 - \alpha e^{-x}}$$

$$= \frac{2}{\sqrt{\pi}} \int_0^{\infty} x^{1/2} \, dx \sum_{n=0}^{\infty} \alpha^{n+1} e^{-(n+1)x} \tag{12-14}$$

We next assume that the order of summation and integration can be reversed [an assumption which is valid, since the ε of (12-13) is a continuous function of x and the series of (12-12) converges uniformly[1]] so that

$$F(\alpha) = \sum_{n=1}^{\infty} \frac{2\alpha^n}{\sqrt{\pi}} \int_0^{\infty} x^{1/2} e^{-nx} \, dx \tag{12-15}$$

If the substitution

$$y = nx \tag{12-16}$$

is made, we can write

$$F(\alpha) = \frac{2}{\sqrt{\pi}} \int_0^{\infty} y^{1/2} e^{-y} \, dy \sum_{n=1}^{\infty} \frac{\alpha^n}{n^{3/2}} \tag{12-17}$$

---

[1]W. Kaplan, *Advanced Calculus* (Reading, Mass.: Addison-Wesley Publishing Company, Inc., 1952), Sec. 6–14.

where the student may recognize that the numerical factor preceding the sum is just a fancy way of writing 1 [if you don't recognize this fact, go back to Chap. 1 and reinvestigate the merits of equations (1-1), (1-2), (1-27), and (1-28)]. We thus conclude that

$$F(\alpha) = \sum_{n=1}^{\infty} \frac{\alpha^n}{n^{3/2}} \qquad (12\text{-}18)$$

and α can be obtained (in principle at least) by inverting the equation

$$\frac{N/V}{N_c} = \sum_{n=1}^{\infty} \frac{\alpha^n}{n^{3/2}} \qquad (12\text{-}19)$$

We have performed a similar inversion in the development in Chap. 1 from (1-17) to (1-22) where the expression for t^2 in terms of powers of θ was inverted to yield θ as a power series in t (see Prob. 12-3).

Actually (12-19) is only valid at high temperatures when all molecules have substantial kinetic energy. The use of the differential form of the degeneracy factor in (12-5) is justified only for larger values of p when the number of states for a given energy is rather large; its use at low temperatures when the kinetic energy of the particles is nearly zero (and of course p will be nearly zero at that time) is not legitimate, as the number of particles with energies near zero are not accounted for. If we denote the number of particles having nearly zero kinetic energy by N_0, the total number of particles in the system will be given by

$$N = N_0 + N_c V F(\alpha) \qquad (12\text{-}20)$$

From the definition of the effective density of states in (5-41) we see that N_c approaches zero as the temperature approaches zero, and the number of particles in the system tends toward N_0 independently of α.

We can identify the number of mobile particles in the system (that is, the number of particles having nonzero kinetic energy) as

$$N_m = N - N_0 = N_c V F(\alpha) \qquad (12\text{-}21)$$

We shall be interested in learning more about the properties of N and N_m in the following section.

12-3   INTERNAL ENERGY AND ENTROPY

The internal energy for a boson gas without cohesion and covolume derived from particles whose kinetic energy arises solely from translation, may be written as

$$U = \frac{4\pi V}{h^3} \int_0^\infty \frac{p^2}{2m} \frac{\alpha p^2 \, dp}{e^{\beta p^2/2m} - \alpha}$$

$$= \frac{2}{\sqrt{\pi}} V N_c kT \int_0^\infty \frac{\alpha x^{3/2} \, dx}{e^x - \alpha} \tag{12-22}$$

where the change of variable in (12-7) has been made. In analogy with (12-8) we can define a new function of α as

$$G(\alpha) = \frac{4}{3\sqrt{\pi}} \int_0^\infty \frac{\alpha x^{3/2} \, dx}{e^x - \alpha} \tag{12-23}$$

so that the system internal energy becomes

$$U = \frac{3}{2} kT N_c V G(\alpha) \tag{12-24}$$

We can express the integral in (12-23) as an infinite sum by a procedure similar to the development of (12-18) for $F(\alpha)$. The details of the calculation will be left as an exercise for the student (see Prob. 12-4).

$$G(\alpha) = \frac{4}{3\sqrt{\pi}} \int_0^\infty x^{3/2} \, dx \, \alpha e^{-x} \sum_{n=0}^\infty \alpha^n e^{-nx} \tag{12-25}$$

$$= \sum_{n=1}^\infty \frac{4\alpha^n}{3\sqrt{\pi}} \int_0^\infty x^{3/2} e^{-nx} \, dx \tag{12-26}$$

$$= \frac{4}{3\sqrt{\pi}} \Gamma(5/2) \sum_{n=1}^\infty \frac{\alpha^n}{n^{5/2}} \tag{12-27}$$

or finally

$$G(\alpha) = \sum_{n=1}^\infty \frac{\alpha^n}{n^{5/2}} \tag{12-28}$$

At this point let us pause to regroup and take stock of the information content of the above equations. First of all we notice that the second Lagrange undetermined multiplier, which is related to the chemical potential of the system [see Sec. 5-3], can be expressed as a function of

$$\xi = \frac{N/V}{N_c} \tag{12-29}$$

or, more accurately, from (12-21) as a function of $\xi - \dfrac{N_0}{N_c V}$. In most instances we shall be concerned with closed systems in which N and N_0 are taken as constant, so the difference will be immaterial and

$$\xi = \frac{N}{V} \frac{h^3}{(2\pi m k T)^{3/2}} = \frac{const}{V T^{3/2}} \tag{12-30}$$

From (12-18), (12-19), and (12-29) we can formally write

$$\alpha = F^{-1}(\xi) = f(\xi) \tag{12-31}$$

where, as we have mentioned previously, if $f(\xi) = \xi$, α is identical to the form obtained in Sec. 5-3 for corrected boltzons.

From (12-24) we find the specific internal energy

$$u = \frac{U}{N} = \frac{3}{2}kT\frac{1}{\xi}G[f(\xi)]$$

or

$$u = \frac{3}{2}kTg(\xi) \tag{12-32}$$

The specific heat capacity at constant volume is given by

$$c_v = \frac{3}{2}k\,g(\xi) + \frac{3}{2}kTg'(\xi)\left(\frac{\partial\xi}{\partial T}\right)_V$$

and from (12-30)

$$\left(\frac{\partial\xi}{\partial T}\right)_V = -\frac{3}{2}\frac{\xi}{T} \tag{12-33}$$

so that

$$c_v = \frac{3}{2}k\left[g(\xi) - \frac{3}{2}\xi g'(\xi)\right]$$

$$= \frac{3}{2}k\phi(\xi) \tag{12-34}$$

One can define a "characteristic temperature" by

$$\Theta = \frac{h^2}{2\pi mk}\left(\frac{N}{V}\right)^{2/3} \tag{12-35}$$

so that

$$\xi = \left(\frac{\Theta}{T}\right)^{3/2} \tag{12-36}$$

and the chemical potential, through α, and the specific heat capacity both obey a law of corresponding states which was discussed in Sec. 7-2. For two boson gases having the same particle density the characteristic temperature, defined by (12-35), varies inversely with the molecular mass. This result is in consonance with the ratio of the rotational characteristic temperatures of two different diatomic gases having the same interatomic distances, given by (10-47) (see Prob. 12-5).

From (5-54) we can express the specific entropy for our boson gas without cohesion and covolume as

$$s = \frac{S}{N} = \frac{5}{3}\frac{u}{T} - k \ln \alpha \tag{12-37}$$

$$= k\left[\frac{5}{2}g(\xi) - \ln f(\xi)\right]$$

or

$$s = k\Phi(\xi) \tag{12-38}$$

where we have incorporated (12-31) and (12-32) into (12-37).

Hence from (12-31), (12-32), (12-34), and (12-38) we see that the quantities α, u/T, c_v, and s all depend solely on ξ and all obey a law of corresponding states, so that these properties will take the same form for all boson gases at the same value of ξ. The value of ξ will be determined by the value of α consistent with (12-21). Since α is a measure of the degeneracy of the gas, we shall be particularly interested in the two limiting values of α; viz., when the gas is very nondegenerate or nearly classical in its behavior, corresponding to $\alpha \simeq 0$, and the case when the gas is strongly degenerate or very quantal in the behavior, corresponding to $\alpha \simeq 1$.

Case I: $\alpha \ll 1$

When α is very small the gas is nondegenerate and all the molecules will be mobile. In other words, at high temperatures, required for small α, the number of molecules with nearly zero kinetic energy will be a negligible fraction of the total number of molecules in the gas. Thus from (12-21) and (12-19) we have

$$\frac{N_m}{N} = 1 = \frac{\alpha}{\xi}\left[1 + \frac{\alpha}{2^{3/2}} + \cdots\right] \quad \begin{array}{c} \alpha \ll 1 \\ N \gg N_0 \end{array} \tag{12-39}$$

which, in the limit of small α, implies that

$$\xi \simeq \alpha \ll 1 \tag{12-40}$$

From the definition of ξ in (12-30) we find that ξ [and therefore α, by virtue of (12-40)] approaches zero as $VT^{3/2}$ becomes indefinitely large, or in the

$$\lim_{\alpha \to 0} VT^{3/2} = \infty \quad \Rightarrow \quad \alpha = \xi \tag{12-41}$$

The relation of (12-41) is consistent with our earlier concepts of non-degenerate gases discussed in Sec. 2-5, wherein it was alleged that the gas became classical, or nondegenerate, at high temperatures and low particle densities (which are obtained at large volumes).

We can now develop the equation of state for our boson gas in terms of α, for small values of α where we neglect all terms higher than second order. We start by expressing the specific internal energy as the ratio of U, given by (12-24) and (12-28), to $N_m = N$, given by (12-18) and (12-19):

$$u = \frac{U}{N} = \frac{3}{2} kT \left[1 + \frac{\alpha}{2^{5/2}} + \frac{\alpha^2}{3^{5/2}} + \cdots \right] \left[1 + \frac{\alpha}{2^{3/2}} + \frac{\alpha^2}{3^{3/2}} + \cdots \right]^{-1}$$

$$u = \frac{3}{2} kT \left[1 - \frac{\alpha}{2^{5/2}} - \frac{\alpha^2}{2^4 3^{5/2}} (2^5 - 3^{5/2}) + \cdots \right] \tag{12-42}$$

With the use of (2-94) we can express the equation of state in terms of the pressure and volume as

$$PV = NkT \left[1 - \frac{\alpha}{2^{5/2}} - \frac{\alpha^2}{2^4 3^{5/2}} (2^5 - 3^{5/2}) + \cdots \right] \tag{12-43}$$

with the result that, in the classical limit, we recover the usual classical equations of state:

$$\lim_{\alpha \to 0} PV = NkT \tag{12-44}$$

and

$$\lim_{\alpha \to 0} U = \frac{3}{2} NkT \tag{12-45}$$

We can express (12-43) in terms of the parameters appearing in ξ, from (12-30), by incorporating the equality of (12-40) with the result

$$\frac{PV}{NkT} = 1 - \frac{Nh^3}{16(m\pi k)^{3/2}} \frac{1}{VT^{3/2}} - \frac{(2^5 - 3^{5/2})N^2 h^6}{2^7 3^{5/2}(m\pi k)^3} \frac{1}{V^2 T^3} + \cdots \tag{12-46}$$

which is the equation of state presaged by (2-132) in Sec. 2-5 for a weakly degenerate boson gas.

In the expression for the specific entropy in (12-37) for small α the logarithmic term will become dominant and we will be justified in neglecting the first-order term in α appearing in (12-42) when the latter is substituted into (12-37). We then find the specific translational entropy for a weakly degenerate boson gas to be given by

$$s = \frac{5}{2} k + k \ln \left[\frac{V}{N} \left(\frac{2\pi mkT}{h^2} \right)^{3/2} \right] \tag{12-47}$$

which is known (at least to professors of physics and chemistry) as the Sackur-Tetrode prescription for the translational entropy of a perfect monatomic gas of atoms having zero total angular momentum [i.e., with $j = 0$

in (12-1)], and usually derived more directly by purely classical analysis.[2] For atoms possessing a nonnull j value, a contribution of $k \ln (2j + 1)$, arising from (12-5), must be added to all the extensive thermodynamic parameters.

Case II: $\alpha \simeq 1$

When α is very nearly unity, the system will exhibit properties that are strongly quantum mechanical in nature and the boson gas will then be highly degenerate. The maximum value of $\alpha = 1$ was found in Secs. 5-3 and 12-2 to occur when the number of particles in the system just equals the number of states available to be occupied by the particles in the system. We see from (12-21) that this means that there are *no* mobile particles at all when $\alpha = 1$. Thus our condition for strong degeneracy, analogous to (12-39) for weak degeneracy, is

$$N_m = 0 \quad \left\{ \begin{array}{l} \alpha = 1 \\ \\ N = N_0 \end{array} \right. \tag{12-48}$$

However, from (12-21), which we express as

$$\frac{N_m}{N} = \frac{1}{\xi} F(1) = 0 \tag{12-49}$$

we see that ξ must be infinite, since from (12-18) and (1-31)

$$F(1) = \zeta(3/2) = 2 \cdot 612 \dots \tag{12-50}$$

where the numerical value of the Riemann zeta function may be found by direct summation (which is not recommended; since for the 100th term in the sum, the contribution is $0 \cdot 001$, indicating that the sum converges quite slowly), by recourse to the Euler-Maclaurin sum formula via the technique outlined in Sec. 1-6, or by merely looking up the value in a table[3] (in the same way one would look up sine, cosine, or logarithmic functions). The fact that $F(1)$ is finite (and not zero) whereas N_m/N must vanish, leads to the conclusion that

$$\lim_{\alpha \to 1} \xi = \infty \tag{12-51}$$

as the strong degeneracy analog to (12-41). But when we incorporate the

[2]O. Sackur, *Ann. Physik* **36**, 598 (1911); **40**, 67 (1913); H. Tetrode, *ibid.*, **38**, 434 (1912).
[3]E. Jahnke and F. Emde, *Tables of Functions with Formulae and Curves*, 4th ed. (New York: Dover Publications, 1945), Chap. 9.

definition of ξ, given by (12-30), into (12-51) we find that strong degeneracy requires

$$\lim_{\alpha \to 1} VT^{3/2} = 0 \tag{12-52}$$

which agrees with our earlier notions that the quantum system is degenerate (that is, the quantum effects become important) when the temperature is low and the particle density high (which occurs when the volume of confinement of the particle is small).

From (12-24) we find that

$$\frac{u}{T} = \frac{3}{2} k \frac{G(1)}{\xi} \tag{12-53}$$

where we can identify[3]

$$G(1) = \zeta(5/2) = 1.341 \ldots \tag{12-54}$$

by reference to (1-31) and the defining equation (12-28) [see Prob. 12-6]. Here again, by virtue of the condition (12-51), we see that

$$\lim_{\alpha \to 1} \frac{u}{T} = 0 \tag{12-55}$$

so that at low temperatures the specific internal energy vanishes faster than T. From (12-53) and the condition (12-51) the student can also show the specific heat capacity vanishes at low temperatures as $T^{3/2}$ (see Prob. 12-7). This feature of the particle gas is in direct conflict with the specific heat capacity obtained from (9-16) for the photon gas. The photon gas has a specific heat capacity which vanishes as T^3 for small values of T, although the photon is alleged to be a boson. The resolution of this conflict arises from the fact that statistics do not reveal the energy dependence of the "particles" making up the gas. The "kinetic" energy of a photon with linear momentum p, is given by (9-1) and the kinetic energy of a boson particle of mass m and momentum p, is given, nonrelativistically, by $p^2/2m$. Thus for a given energy the particle spectrum has a greater density of states than the photon spectrum (see Prob. 12-8). Since the particle density of states is greater, there are more excitation modes available to the particle than the photon at a given energy, and consequently the specific heat capacity is also greater ($T^{3/2} > T^3$ for $T \simeq 0$).

The entropy of the ideal boson gas vanishes at a temperature of absolute zero, as it should according to the third law of thermodynamics. This can easily be seen by letting $\alpha = 1$ in (12-37) so that the logarithmic term vanishes identically and when $\alpha = 1$, (12-55) may be substituted into (12-37) so that

$$\lim_{\alpha \to 1} s = 0 \tag{12-56}$$

Thus when $\alpha = 1$ all of the molecules are in the state corresponding to zero energy [and zero momentum, as we are generally interested in momentum states in the form of (12-5)] and $VT^{3/2} = 0$, which implies that for a finite volume the absolute temperature vanishes. As α decreases from unity there is a progressive escape of particles from the cell of zero energy until, at $\alpha = 0$ all of the particles are external to the cell of zero energy.

PROBLEMS

12-1. Verify that the number of bosons undergoing translation in a Bose-Einstein gas with $j = 0$ is given by (12-6).

12-2. (a) Show that $\alpha < 0 \Rightarrow N < 0$ from (12-8) and (12-9). (b) Show that if $\alpha > 1$, $F(\alpha)$ becomes unbounded and hence N becomes unbounded. (*Hint*: show that $1 \le e^x \le \infty$ and if $\alpha > 1$ there is some $x \ne 0$ at which $e^x = \alpha$.)

12-3. "Invert" (12-19) by setting

$$\alpha = \sum_{n=1}^{\infty} a_n \left(\frac{N/V}{N_c} \right)^n$$

in the r.h.s. of (12-19) and solving for the a_n. Retain terms to third order in your analysis.

12-4. Verify that the integral representation of $G(\alpha)$ in (12-23) is equivalent to the series formulation in (12-28) by supplying any steps between (12-25) and (12-28) which are not obvious to you.

12-5. (a) Show that the ratio of the characteristic temperatures of two boson gases having the same particle density, given by (12-35), is equal to the inverse ratio of the molecular masses

$$\frac{\Theta_1}{\Theta_2} = \frac{m_2}{m_1} \tag{A}$$

(b) Show that the ratio of the characteristic rotational temperatures for two diatomic gases having the same interatomic separation distance is also given by (A).

12-6. Verify the numerical values of $\zeta(3/2)$ and $\zeta(5/2)$ given by (12-50) and (12-54), respectively. [*Hint*: review the technique used in Sec. 1-6 to evaluate $\zeta(4)$.]

12-7. Show that the specific heat capacity, at low temperatures for a boson particle gas is proportional to $T^{3/2}$. [*Hint*: substitute (12-30) into (12-53) and make use of (2-10a).]

12-8. The de Broglie wavelength for a particle of mass m and energy E, is given by (5-43). The de Broglie wavelength for a photon of Energy E_k is given by

$$\lambda_\gamma = \frac{h}{p} = \frac{h}{E_k} c \tag{B}$$

(a) Show that $\lambda = \lambda_\gamma(v/2c) < \lambda_\gamma$ (b) By application of the concept involved in (5-41) show that the particle boson, with smaller de Broglie wavelength, has a greater "effective density of states" than the photon boson. (c) Show that the ratio of density of states for a particle gas to a photon gas at a specified energy E_k, given by (11-22) for each gas, is $(2c/v)^3$ where c and v are the velocity of the photon and particle respectively. (d) Use the concept involved in (6-31) to justify the particle boson having a larger heat capacity than the photon boson, at low temperatures.

12-9. Show that $F(\alpha)$ and $G(\alpha)$ are related by the conditions

$$F(\alpha) = \alpha \frac{dG}{d\alpha}$$

12-10. Show that a weakly degenerate Bose gas is more compressible than an ideal gas.

12-11. Show that if $\alpha = \exp(\beta\mu)$ is about one and the particles of a Bose gas are in the ground state ε_0 which is small, then

$$N_0 \simeq \frac{kT}{\varepsilon_0 - \mu}$$

12-12. At very low temperature in a Bose gas, a portion of the Bose particles drop into the lowest energy state $\varepsilon_0 = 0$ where they no longer contribute to the energy or pressure of the gas. Begin with equation (12-20) to show that

$$N \simeq -\frac{kT}{\mu} + \zeta(3/2)N_c V \tag{C}$$

where μ is the chemical potential (see Prob. 12-11). Also show that

$$N_0 = N\left[1 - \left(\frac{T}{T_0}\right)^{3/2}\right]$$

where T_0 is the critical temperature at which the particles first begin to enter the ground state and is determined by (C) when $N_0 = 0$. This phenomenon is called *Einstein condensation.* (*Hint*: make use of Prob. 12-11 *supra*.)

12-13. Liquid helium can be viewed as an example of Einstein condensation of a Bose-Einstein gas. At $2.2°K$, He^4 becomes a mixture of a normal fluid and a superfluid. The superfluid is composed of the He^4 atoms which have gone into the ground state. The number of particles in the condensed phase (superfluid) increases as the temperature decreases (see Probs. 12-11 and 12-12 *supra*). Calculate the critical temperature for He^4, where the density for He^4 is

$$\rho = .178 \text{ gm/cm}^3$$

and

$$\zeta(3/2) \text{ is given by } (12\text{-}50)$$

Why is your calculated value different from $2.2°K$?

12-14. Why doesn't a photon gas go into an Einstein condensed phase? [*Hint*: review the discussion following (9-4).]

13 | *The Fermi-Dirac Gas*

13-1 INTRODUCTION

The present chapter is an imperfect carbon copy of the preceding one; the imperfections arising from the difference in sign appearing in the denominator between (5-11) and (5-12). It may seem remarkable that the authors regard a simple change in sign as worthy of a whole chapter in their text. It is even more striking that this change in sign should occasion so many more words when the term affected by the sign change doesn't even appear in the description of nondegenerate systems. Thus when the condition of (5-42b) is fulfilled, both (5-11) and (5-12) reduce to (5-10). But as we learned in the previous four chapters, there are numerous situations in which a particular system will be found to be strongly degenerate, and the classical analysis will not suffice to accurately describe the system under these conditions.

One of the foremost examples of the failure of classical statistics, and the subsequent éclat of the quantum statistics, is in the description of the properties of metals (and more recently, semiconductors), especially their electrical and thermal conductivities. These properties of metals were first explained rather satisfactorily by Sommerfeld and his coworkers,[1] who assumed that the electrons in the metals existed in the state of a gas without cohesion and covolume. It is perhaps not unreasonable to make this assumption as a "first guess" in the attack on the problem of describing the properties of a metal.

At the turn of the century Drude[2] considered this avenue of approach,

---

[1] A. Sommerfeld, *Z. Physik* **47,** 1, 43 (1928); C. Eckart, *ibid.,* p. 38; W. V. Houston, *ibid.,* p. 33, and *Z. Physik* **48,** 449 (1928); A. Sommerfeld and N. H. Frank, *Rev. Mod. Phys.* **3,** 1 (1931); and A. Sommerfeld and H. Bethe, *Handbuch der Physik* XXIV/2 (1934).

[2] P. Drude, *Ann. Physik* **1,** 566 (1900); *ibid.* **3,** 369 (1900).

and although he was constrained to treat the electrons as corrected boltzons, he did arrive at a reasonable value for the Wiedemann-Franz ratio[3] of the heat conductivity to electrical conductivity of a metal which was known experimentally to be relatively independent of the type of metal and to vary directly with the absolute temperature.[4] The primary failure of Drude's theory was that it predicted a contribution of $\frac{3}{2}k$ per electron to the specific heat capacity at constant volume for the metal [cf. (6-7)]. This contribution is not observed experimentally. Sommerfeld modified Drude's theory by substituting the Fermi-Dirac statistics for the Maxwell-Boltzmann-Planck statistics and found a marked improvement in the agreement between theory and experiment.

Since the chief objective of theoretical physics is to obtain agreement between theoretical predictions and experimental results, and since such agreement arises, in the case of metals at least, only through the consideration of the mobile electrons as comprising a Fermi-Dirac gas, it may not seem unreasonable to the student to invest some time in investigating the characteristics of such a gas. Hence the reason for the existence of the instant chapter.

In discussing the Fermi-Dirac gas, without cohesion and covolume, composed of particles undergoing pure translation, we find that the total degeneracy for the system is given by (12-5):

$$g = (2j + 1)\frac{4\pi V}{h^3}p^2\,dp \qquad (12\text{-}5)$$

where the resultant angular momentum of the particles is given by jh. Since the Fermi-Dirac gas obeys the generalized Pauli principle the wave function describing the molecular system will have to be antisymmetric.

Experimental studies indicate that the conduction electrons in metals behave, in many respects, as if they were free of atomic influences. It seems natural that such electrons would be in the lowest orbital angular momentum state of $l = 0$. We limit our consideration to such electrons (or leptons in general, although most applications apply to electron systems) so that, from (12-3)

$$j = s = \tfrac{1}{2} \qquad (13\text{-}1)$$

and the fermion angular momentum degeneracy is then

$$2j + 1 = 2 = g_j \qquad (13\text{-}2)$$

From (13-2) we see that the fermion gas system has twice the degeneracy of

[3]G. Wiedemann and R. Franz, *Ann Physik* **89**, 497 (1853).

[4]See, for example, the discussions, tables, and graphs in M. W. Zemansky, *Heat and Thermodynamics*, 5th ed. (New York: McGraw-Hill Book Company, 1968), p. 96; F. Seitz, *The Modern Theory of Solids* (New York: McGraw-Hill Book Company, 1940), p. 177.

the boson gas when the respective constituent particles are in their lowest angular momentum state. We shall note other differences, resulting from the Pauli principle, as we proceed.

13-2 EVALUATION OF α

In a procedure analogous to that followed in Sec. 12-2 we can express the number of particles N, in the system occupying a volume V, from (5-12) as

$$\frac{N}{V} = g_j N_c \frac{2}{\sqrt{\pi}} \int_0^\infty \frac{\alpha x^{1/2}\, dx}{e^x + \alpha} \tag{13-3}$$

where we have made the substitution of (12-7) for x and N_c is given by (5-41). We may write (13-3) in the form of (12-9) by defining

$$F_+(\alpha) \equiv \frac{2}{\sqrt{\pi}} \int_0^\infty \frac{\alpha x^{1/2}\, dx}{e^x + \alpha} \tag{13-4}$$

in analogy with (12-8) so that

$$\frac{N}{V} = g_j N_c F_+(\alpha) \tag{13-5}$$

As we found in Chap. 12, the range of x in (13-4) is again given by (12-10)

$$0 \le x \le \infty \tag{12-10}$$

We recall that the integral (12-8), corresponding to (13-4), became unbounded when the second Lagrange undetermined multiplier exceeded unity. This led us to restrict the values of α to those permitted by (12-11) for a boson gas. We notice that this constraint does not arise in the description of the fermion gas, since (13-4) is well behaved for all nonnegative values of α. This situation can be seen more clearly, perhaps, by recourse to (5-61) which expresses α in terms of the chemical potential for the one-component system.

$$\alpha = e^{\mu/kT} \tag{5-61}$$

In Table 13-1 we have indicated the three limiting values of α and the corresponding values of the chemical potential. We see that as α goes from zero to positive infinity, the chemical potential sweeps out the entire range of real values from negative infinity through positive infinity. The extended range of α for a Fermi-Dirac gas, accompanied by the restricted range of α for the Bose-Einstein gas is accounted for by the fact that the Pauli exclusion principle forbids more than one fermion particle to occupy any one quantum state, and consequently the lowest energy state of the Femi-Dirac system is

Table 13-1. Corresponding Values of α and μ Given by (5-61)

α	μ
0	$-\infty$
1	0
∞	$+\infty$

much greater than the lowest energy state of the boltzon or Bose-Einstein gas. Indeed, for the latter two gas systems the lowest energy configuration of the system is the state $E = 0$ and *all* N particles in the system crowd into this same lowest state, in which they possess zero kinetic energy. As we have seen, this condition is precluded for the Fermi-Dirac gas by the Pauli exclusion principle, and for such a system the lowest energy is obtained when the N quantum states of lowest energy are filled with one fermion in each. The condition to be obeyed by the Bose-Einstein system is that the chemical potential must be less than the system ground-state energy, which we have taken to be $E = 0$; consequently, for such a system

$$- \infty \leq \mu \leq 0 \tag{13-6}$$

which, from (5-61) and Table 13-1, is equivalent to (12-11). The student may wish to consult other readily available texts[5] for further insight into this phenomenon.

Due to the wide range of values available to α, we shall treat the evaluation of $F_+(\alpha)$ in (13-4) in two separate states, representing the cases of small α and large α, respectively.

Case I: $0 \leq \alpha \leq 1$ (13-7)

The treatment of the fermion gas without cohesion and covolume parallels that followed for the analogous Boson system in Sec. (12-2). We multiply numerator and denominator of the r.h.s. of (13-4) by e^{-x} to obtain

$$\frac{\sqrt{\pi}}{2} F_+(\alpha) = \int_0^\infty \alpha x^{1/2} e^{-x} dx (1 + \alpha e^{-x})^{-1} \tag{13-8}$$

---

[5]See, for example, G. H. Wannier, *Statistical Physics* (New York: John Wiley & Sons, Inc., 1966), Chap. 9; T. L. Hill, *An Introduction to Statistical Thermodynamics* (Reading, Mass.: Addison-Wesley Publishing Company, Inc., 1960), Chap. 22; J. E. Mayer and M. G. Mayer, *Statistical Mechanics* (New York: John Wiley & Sons, Inc., 1940), Chap. 16.

Inasmuch as α is restricted by (13-7), the quantity αe^{-x} is never greater than unity and we can make use of the relation

$$(1 + \varepsilon)^{-1} = \sum_{n=0}^{\infty} (-\varepsilon)^n, \qquad \varepsilon < 1 \qquad (13\text{-}9)$$

which is equivalent to (12-12). We then find

$$\frac{\sqrt{\pi}}{2} F_+(\alpha) = - \sum_{n=1}^{\infty} \frac{(-\alpha)^n}{n^{3/2}} \int_0^{\infty} y^{1/2} e^{-y}\, dy \qquad (13\text{-}10)$$

where we have set the dummy integration variable

$$y = nx \qquad (13\text{-}11)$$

and interchanged the order of summation and integration in complete analogy with (12-17). The integral in (13-10) is recognized as

$$\Gamma(\tfrac{3}{2}) = \frac{1}{2}\Gamma(\tfrac{1}{2}) = \frac{\sqrt{\pi}}{2} \qquad (13\text{-}12)$$

and hence we arrive at the result, which is valid for small α,

$$F_+(\alpha) = - \sum_{n=1}^{\infty} \frac{(-\alpha)^n}{n^{3/2}} \qquad (13\text{-}13)$$

We see then, that when α is small, (13-13) may be "inverted" to yield α in terms of $N/(g_j N_c V)$ when recourse is had to the alternative definition of $F_+(\alpha)$ in (13-5).

Case II: $1 \le \alpha \le \infty$ $\qquad\qquad\qquad\qquad\qquad\qquad\qquad$ (13-14)

When α is large, as indicated by (13-14), we see that the chemical potential is not negative. It is more convenient, for purposes of mathematical analysis, to carry out the integrations of (13-3) and (13-4) in terms of the kinetic energy of the particles rather than their momentum, as we did in the case of small α (negative chemical potential). From the energy-momentum relation of (5-6) we can express

$$p^2 = 2m\varepsilon \qquad (13\text{-}15\text{a})$$

and

$$dp = \sqrt{\frac{m}{2}}\, \varepsilon^{-1/2}\, d\varepsilon \qquad (13\text{-}15\text{b})$$

which, when combined with (5-61) and (13-2) and substituted into (5-12), yields

$$dn = 4\pi V \frac{g_j}{2} \left(\frac{2m}{h^2}\right)^{3/2} \varepsilon^{1/2} \frac{1}{e^{\beta(\varepsilon - \mu)} + 1}\, d\varepsilon \qquad (13\text{-}16)$$

It is customary, in the usual course of developing an expression for the second Lagrange undetermined multiplier for an isolated, noninteracting fermion system, to define

$$f(\varepsilon) \equiv \frac{1}{e^{\beta(\varepsilon - \mu)} + 1} \tag{13-17}$$

where $f(\varepsilon)$ is physically interpreted as the probability that a quantum state with energy ε is occupied. We can then integrate (13-16) to obtain an expression for the number of particles in our system

$$\frac{N}{g_j N_c V} = F_+(\alpha) \tag{13-18}$$

where

$$F_+(\alpha) = \frac{2}{\sqrt{\pi}} \beta^{3/2} \int_0^\infty \varepsilon^{1/2} f(\varepsilon) \, d\varepsilon \tag{13-19}$$

is equivalent to (13-4) and depends on α by way of μ through (5-61) and (13-17).

Before we proceed to evaluate (13-19) it is advantageous to investigate some of the properties of $f(\varepsilon)$. The salient features of $f(\varepsilon)$ are summarized in Table 13-2 below. We note that at a temperature of absolute zero $f(\varepsilon)$

Table 13-2. Limiting Values of $f(\varepsilon)$, Given by (13-17) for $T = 0$ and $T > 0$

$T = 0$	$T > 0$	$f(\varepsilon)$
$\varepsilon < \mu$	$\varepsilon \ll \mu$	1
$\varepsilon = \mu$	$\varepsilon = \mu$	1/2
$\varepsilon > \mu$	$\varepsilon \gg \mu$	0

is discontinuous at $\varepsilon = \mu$. At nonzero temperatures the function is continuous and for different values of μ we find a series of curves which depart from the rectangular curve at $T = 0$, as shown in Fig. 13-1. However, all curves pass through the ordinate value of 0.5 at energies equal to the chemical potential. We shall soon see that the chemical potential of the system (often referred to as the Fermi energy of the system) is a function of temperature, although for many applications the temperature dependence may be ignored. Strictly speaking, however, different values of μ result in a shift of the chemical potential along the ε-axis and yield somewhat different curves which depart from the rectangular curve of $\beta = \infty$ shown in Fig. 13-1, but all such curves pass through the point $f(\varepsilon = \mu) = \frac{1}{2}$.

In the present section we are interested in values of $\alpha = e^{\beta\mu} \gg 1$. This is mathematically equivalent to the condition $\beta \to \infty$ or $T \to 0$, which is represented by the rectangular curve of Fig. 13-1. From Fig. 13-2 we see that as $\alpha \to \infty$ the derivative of $f(\varepsilon)$ approaches a negative Dirac delta function

$$\lim_{x \to \infty} \frac{df}{d\varepsilon} = -\delta(\varepsilon - \mu) \tag{13-20}$$

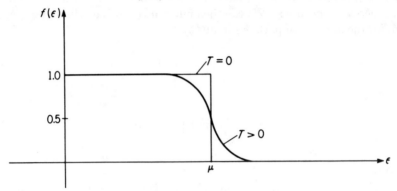

FIG. 13-1. The Fermi-Dirac distribution function $f(\varepsilon)$, given by (13–17) plotted at temperatures of $T = 0$ and at a low temperature $T > 0$.

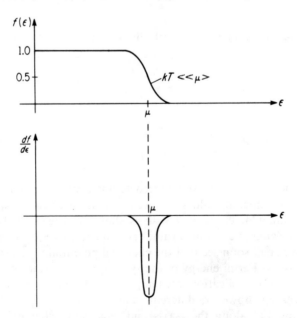

FIG. 13-2. The Fermi-Dirac distribution function and its derivative plotted for very low temperature indicating the relation of (13–20).

In the present case of α very large, but not infinite, it is convenient to change variables from ε to a dimensionless parameter y, by means of the transformation

$$y = \beta(\varepsilon - \mu) \tag{13-21}$$

so that the Fermi-Dirac distribution function becomes

$$f(\varepsilon) = f = \frac{1}{e^y + 1} \tag{13-22}$$

and

$$\frac{df}{d\varepsilon} = \frac{df\,dy}{dy\,d\varepsilon} = -\beta\frac{e^y}{(e^y + 1)^2} \tag{13-23}$$

We are now in a position to evaluate $F_+(\alpha)$ in (13-19), which we express as

$$\frac{\sqrt{\pi}}{2}F_+(\alpha) = \beta^{3/2}\frac{2}{3}\int_0^\infty f(\varepsilon)\,d(\varepsilon^{3/2})$$

An integration by parts leads to

$$\frac{\sqrt{\pi}}{2}F_+(\alpha) = \frac{2}{3}\beta^{3/2}\left[f(\varepsilon)\,\varepsilon^{3/2}\Big|_0^\infty - \int_0^\infty \varepsilon^{3/2}\frac{df}{d\varepsilon}\,d\varepsilon\right] \tag{13-24}$$

The integrated part vanishes at both limits [cf. Table 13-2 for $f(\varepsilon = \infty)$] and so we are left with

$$-\frac{3\sqrt{\pi}F_+(\alpha)}{4} = \beta^{3/2}\int_0^\infty \varepsilon^{3/2}\frac{df}{d\varepsilon}\,d\varepsilon \tag{13-25}$$

In order to utilize the previously defined relations of (13-21) through (13-23), it is convenient to expand $\varepsilon^{3/2}$ in a Taylor's series about μ as

$$\varepsilon^{3/2} = \mu^{3/2} + \frac{3}{2}\left(\frac{y}{\beta}\right)\mu^{1/2} + \frac{3}{8}\left(\frac{y}{\beta}\right)^2\mu^{-1/2} - \frac{1}{16}\left(\frac{y}{\beta}\right)^3\mu^{-3/2}$$

$$+ \frac{3}{128}\left(\frac{y}{\beta}\right)^4\mu^{-5/2} + \cdots \tag{13-26}$$

Substitution of (13-26) into (13-25) leads to

$$\frac{3\sqrt{\pi}}{4}F_+(\alpha) = \int_{-t}^\infty\left[t^{3/2} + \frac{3}{2}yt^{1/2} + \frac{3}{8}y^2t^{-1/2} - \frac{1}{16}y^3t^{-3/2}\right.$$

$$\left. + \frac{3}{128}y^4t^{-5/2} + \cdots\right]\frac{e^y}{(e^y + 1)^2}\,dy \tag{13-27}$$

where we have set

$$t = \beta\mu \tag{13-28}$$

Since t is a constant in the integral of (13-27), we can write the integral of the sum of terms as a sum of integrals of the form

$$\frac{3\sqrt{\pi}}{4} F_+(\alpha) = t^{3/2} I_0 + \frac{3}{2} t^{1/2} I_1 + \frac{3}{8} t^{-1/2} I_2$$

$$- \frac{1}{16} t^{-3/2} I_3 + \frac{3}{128} t^{-5/2} I_4 + \cdots \qquad (13\text{-}29)$$

where

$$I_n = \int_{-t}^{\infty} \frac{y^n e^y \, dy}{[1 + e^y]^2}$$

$$= \int_{-\infty}^{\infty} \frac{y^n e^y \, dy}{[1 + e^y]^2} - \int_{-\infty}^{-t} \frac{y^n e^y \, dy}{[1 + e^y]^2} \qquad (13\text{-}30)$$

Now when $t = \beta\mu \to \infty$ the second integral approaches zero. This will occur for $\alpha \to \infty$ or $T \to 0$ or $\mu \to \infty$. For large, but noninfinite t, the second integral will have a value of the order of $(-t)^n e^{-t}$. It is well to keep this result in mind.[6]

We note that the quantity $e^y/(1 + e^y)^2$ is an even function of y, since

$$\frac{e^{-y}}{(1 + e^{-y})^2} = \frac{e^{-y} e^{2y}}{e^{2y}(1 + e^{-y})^2} = \frac{e^y}{(e^y + 1)^2} \qquad (13\text{-}31)$$

and consequently we can express (13-30) in the form

$$I_{2p+1} = 0 \qquad (13\text{-}32\text{a})$$

$$I_{2p} = 2 \int_0^{\infty} \frac{y^{2p} e^y \, dy}{(1 + e^y)^2} \qquad (13\text{-}32\text{b})$$

where we have ignored terms of the order of $t^n e^{-t}$.

We can easily evaluate I_{2p} in terms of known (to the student who has studied Sec. 1-2 of this text) functions. We begin by incorporating (13-31) into (13-32b) to yield

$$I_{2p} = 2 \int_0^{\infty} y^{2p} e^{-y} (1 + e^{-y})^{-2} \, dy \qquad (13\text{-}33)$$

and expanding

$$(1 + e^{-y})^{-2} = \sum_{n=0}^{\infty} (-)^n (n + 1) e^{-ny} \qquad (13\text{-}34)$$

---

[6]The student is invited to read the scathing criticism of this type of derivation by R. Weinstock, *Am. J. Phys.* **37**, 1273 (1969).

by means of the binomial expansion, which is valid for $e^{-y} < 1$, to obtain

$$I_{2p} = -2 \int_0^\infty y^{2p} \sum_{n=0}^\infty (-)^{n+1}(n+1)e^{-(n+1)y}\, dy \qquad (13\text{-}35)$$

We now relabel our sum beginning with $m \equiv n + 1 = 1$ and interchange the order of summation and integration so that

$$I_{2p} = -2 \sum_{m=1}^\infty \frac{(-)^m}{m^{2p}} \int_0^\infty e^{-my}(my)^{2p}\, d(my)$$

$$= +2\Gamma(2p+1) \sum_{m=1}^\infty \frac{(-)^{m+1}}{m^{2p}}$$

$$= 2(2p)!\, \eta(2p) \qquad (13\text{-}36)$$

where recourse has been had to (1-1), (1-4), and (1-80).

The Riemann zeta function is more commonly tabulated than the eta function, and to take advantage of this situation, we can use (1-81b) to express

$$I_{2p} = 2(2p)![1 - 2^{(1-2p)}]\zeta(2p) \qquad (13\text{-}37)$$

From Sec. 1-2 and the fact that[7]

$$\eta(0) = -\zeta(0) = \frac{1}{2} \qquad (13\text{-}38)$$

we see that

$$I_0 = 1; \quad I_2 = \frac{\pi^2}{3}; \quad I_4 = \frac{7\pi^4}{15} \qquad (13\text{-}39)$$

We find, after substituting (13-32) and (13-39) into (13-29), that

$$\frac{3\sqrt{\pi}}{4} F_+(\alpha) = t^{3/2} + \frac{\pi^2}{8} t^{-1/2} + \frac{7\pi^4}{640} t^{-5/2} + O(t^4 e^{-t}) \qquad (13\text{-}40)$$

where α is related to t by means of (13-28) and (5-61).

When (13-40) is substituted into (13-18) we obtain an expression for the number of particles in the system as a function of the chemical potential. Put in other terms, this means that we have an expression for the chemical potential, and consequently for the second Lagrange undetermined multiplier, which after all, is the goal of this section. When (13-28) is also incorporated we find

$$\frac{N}{g_j N_c V \beta^{3/2}} = \frac{4}{3\sqrt{\pi}} \mu^{3/2} \left[1 + \frac{\pi^2}{8}\left(\frac{kT}{\mu}\right)^2 + \frac{7\pi^4}{640}\left(\frac{kT}{\mu}\right)^4 + \cdots \right] \qquad (13\text{-}41)$$

where terms of the order $(\mu/kT)^4 e^{-\mu/kT}$ have been neglected.

[7]M. Abramowitz and I. Stegun (eds.), *Handbook of Mathematical Functions*, N.B.S. Applied Mathematics Series 55 (Washington, D.C.: Government Printing Office, 1964), p. 807.

In dealing with fermion systems (particularly electron systems) it has become customary to refer to the chemical potential as the *Fermi energy* of the system. We see from (13-41) (and we will demonstrate more explicitly below) that the Fermi energy is a function of the absolute temperature. However; at any given temperature the Fermi energy is a constant, dependent only on the value at absolute zero temperature. We shall denote the value of the chemical potential or Fermi energy at a temperature of absolute zero by μ_0. From (13-41) we see that at a temperature of absolute zero

$$\mu_0^{3/2} = \frac{3\sqrt{\pi}N}{4g_jN_cV\beta^{3/2}} \tag{13-42}$$

which can be expressed as (see Prob. 13-2)

$$\mu_0 = \frac{\hbar^2}{2m}\left[\frac{6\pi^2}{g_j}\frac{N}{V}\right]^{2/3} \tag{13-43}$$

with g_j given by (13-2) for the fermion system.

In analogy with (12-35), we can define a characteristic temperature for our fermion system known as the *Fermi temperature*, Θ_F, by means of

$$\mu_0 = k\Theta_F \tag{13-44}$$

or, from (13-43)

$$\Theta_F = \frac{\hbar^2}{2mk}\left[\frac{6\pi^2}{g_i}\frac{N}{V}\right]^{2/3} \tag{13-45}$$

which is a function of the particle density and of the mass of the molecules in the system. Similarly, we see that the quantity

$$\beta\mu_0 = \frac{\Theta_F}{T} = \left[\frac{3\sqrt{\pi}}{4g_j}\frac{N}{N_cV}\right]^{2/3} \tag{13-46}$$

is a measure of the degeneracy of the system. When the particle density is much less than the effective density of states, the temperature of the system is much greater than the Fermi temperature and the system is nondegenerate, in accordance with our discussion in Sec. 2-5 *supra*:

$$\frac{N}{V} \ll N_c \Rightarrow T \gg \Theta_F \;;\quad \text{nondegenerate} \tag{13-47}$$

On the other hand, when

$$\frac{N}{V} \gg \frac{1}{\Lambda^3} = N_c \Rightarrow T \ll \Theta_F \;;\quad \text{degenerate} \tag{13-48}$$

Consequently the Fermi temperature represents that temperature of the system below which the system is degenerate and above which the system is nondegenerate. Consistent with this fact, the Fermi temperature is often referred to as the *degeneracy temperature* of the system.

At high temperatures and low particle densities we should expect that The Fermi-Dirac gas will resemble a classical Maxwell-Boltzmann-Planck gas system. We shall see in the following section that this prophecy is indeed fulfilled.

At the low temperatures and high particle densities the system will be strongly degenerate and quantum effects will play an important role in determining the properties of the system. In this region, the quantity $\beta\mu_0$ will be quite large, and consequently

$$s = \frac{1}{t_0} = \frac{1}{\beta\mu_0} \ll 1 \tag{13-49}$$

so that a power series in s can be expected to converge rather rapidly.

We first rewrite the relation between the Fermi energy at temperature T and the Fermi energy at absolute zero temperature, (13-41), in terms of (13-42) and (13-28), as

$$\left(\frac{\mu_0}{\mu}\right)^{3/2} = 1 + \frac{\pi^2}{8}t^{-2} + \frac{7\pi^4}{640}t^{-4} + O(t^4 e^{-t}) \tag{13-50}$$

and then expand $1/\mu$ in terms of $1/\mu_0$ according to

$$t^{-1} = s + a_1 s^2 + a_2 s^3 + a_3 s^4 + \cdots \tag{13-51}$$

where the coefficient a_i are to be determined. We shall retain terms up to fourth order in s. From (13-51) we see that

$$\frac{\mu_0}{\mu} = \frac{t^{-1}}{s} = 1 + a_1 s + a_2 s^2 + a_3 s^3 + a_4 s^4 + \cdots \tag{13-52}$$

Now by virtue of (13-49), we can apply the binomial expansion to the r.h.s. of (13-52) retaining terms to fourth order in s, to express

$$\left(\frac{\mu_0}{\mu}\right)^{3/2} = 1 + \frac{3}{2}a_1 s + \frac{3}{8}(a_1^2 + 4a_2)s^2 + \frac{3}{48}(24a_3 + 12a_1 a_2 - a_1^3)s^3$$

$$+ \frac{3}{128}(a_1^4 - 8a_1^2 a_2 + 32a_1 a_3 + 16a_2^2 + 64a_4)s^4 + \cdots \tag{13-53}$$

From (13-51) we can write

$$t^{-2} = s^2 + 2a_1 s^3 + (a_1^2 + 2a_2)s^4 + \cdots \tag{13-54a}$$

and

$$t^{-4} = s^4 + \cdots \tag{13-54b}$$

Substitution of (13-53) and (13-54) into the l.h.s. and r.h.s. of (13-50), respectively, and equating the coefficients of the like powers of s on each side of the resulting equation, leads to the following values of

$$a_1 = 0$$

$$a_2 = \frac{\pi^2}{12}$$

$$a_3 = 0 \qquad\qquad (13\text{-}55)$$

$$a_4 = \frac{7\pi^4}{360}$$

With the aid of (13-55) we can write (13-52) in the form

$$\mu = \mu_0 \left[1 + \frac{\pi^2}{12} s^2 + \frac{7\pi^4}{360} s^4 + \cdots \right]^{-1} \qquad (13\text{-}56)$$

which is amenable to the binomial expansion so that we reach our final form of

$$\mu = \mu_0 \left[1 - \frac{\pi^2}{12}\left(\frac{kT}{\mu_0}\right)^2 - \frac{\pi^4}{80}\left(\frac{kT}{\mu_0}\right)^4 + \cdots \right] \qquad (13\text{-}57)$$

We can gather some idea of the magnitude of

$$\frac{kT}{\mu_0} = \frac{T}{\Theta_F} = s \qquad\qquad (13\text{-}58)$$

in (13-57) and compare this to the terms of the order of $t^4 e^{-t}$ which we have neglected in obtaining (13-57) and (13-41). From (13-45) we can write the Fermi temperature for electrons as

$$\Theta_F = \frac{\lambda_c^2 E_0}{2k} \left[\frac{3}{4\pi g_j} \frac{N}{V} \right]^{2/3} \qquad (13\text{-}59)$$

where the Compton wavelength and the electron rest energy are given by[8]

$$\lambda_c = \frac{hc}{E_0} = 2.426 \times 10^{-10} \text{ cm} \qquad (13\text{-}60a)$$

and

$$E_0 = mc^2 = 510 \times 10^3 \text{ eV} \qquad (13\text{-}60b)$$

respectively, and c is the speed of light in vacuo. Planck's constant has the value

$$k = 8.62 \times 10^{-5} \frac{\text{eV}}{\text{molecule-}^\circ K} \qquad (13\text{-}61)$$

[8]R. R. Roy and R. D. Reed, *Interactions of Photons and Leptons with Matter* (New York: Academic Press, Inc., 1968), p. 185.

and g_j is given by (13-2). Substitution of these constants into (13-59) yields

$$\Theta_F = 4.24 \times 10^{-11} \left(\frac{N}{V}\right)^{2/3} \text{cm}^2\text{-deg} \tag{13-62}$$

for the electron degeneracy temperature, which as we see, depends only on the electron density in the gas (the mass dependency has been explicitly accounted for by means of (13-60) for electrons). We can substitute (13-62) into (13-57) to obtain the Fermi energy as a function of the absolute temperature and the number of electrons per unit volume.

In the case of monovalent metals, the number of free electrons per cm^3 ought to be equal to the number of atoms per cm^3, which we can express as

$$\frac{N}{V} = N_0 \frac{\rho}{M} \tag{13-63}$$

where

$$N_0 = 6.025 \times 10^{23} \frac{\text{atoms}}{\text{gm-mole}} \tag{13-64}$$

and ρ and M are the density and molecular mass of the metal, respectively. From Table 13-3 we see that for monovalent metals the quantity ρ/M lies between about $\frac{1}{7}$ and $\frac{1}{25}$, and typically we might take $\rho/M \simeq \frac{1}{10}$ to get a representative value for the degeneracy temperature. With these values then, we find

$$\left(\frac{N}{V}\right)^{2/3} \simeq 15 \times 10^{14} \text{ cm}^{-2} \tag{13-65}$$

so that (13-62) yields

$$\Theta_F \simeq 65,000°\text{K} \tag{13-66}$$

so that at all temperatures below the boiling point, the electron gas in metals is highly degenerate. Thus the conduction electrons in metals will have to

Table 13-3. Values of ρ/M for Representative Monovalent Metals.

Metal	ρ (gm/cm^3)	M (gm/mole)	ρ/M (gm-mole/cm^3)
Lithium	0.534	6.94	0.077
Sodium	0.971	23	0.042
Copper	8.93	63.54	0.14
Silver	10.50	107.88	0.098

be treated with quantum statistics and we should not expect them to behave in the manner of boltzons.

At room temperature we find that

$$\frac{T}{\Theta_F} \simeq \frac{300}{65000} \simeq \frac{1}{220} \tag{13-67}$$

so that (13-49) is indeed valid. Even at a temperature of 377°C. $s = 1/100$ and thus

$$\frac{\pi^2}{12}\left(\frac{kT}{\mu_0}\right)^2 \simeq 8.24 \times 10^{-5} \tag{13-68a}$$

and

$$\frac{\pi^4}{80}\left(\frac{kT}{\mu_0}\right)^4 \simeq 1.2 \times 10^{-8} \tag{13-68b}$$

Thus we see that the third term in the square brackets of (13-57) is generally quite negligible and, in fact, is usually omitted from consideration.[9] On the other hand, we see from (13-68) that μ does not differ appreciably from μ_0 at ordinary temperatures, and consequently the terms we have neglected at these temperatures have the values

$$t^4 e^{-t} \simeq (\beta\mu_0)^4 e^{-\beta\mu_0} = 10^8 e^{-100} \simeq 10^{-35} \tag{13-69}$$

which is indeed much less than the third term in the square brackets of (13-57); and thus the approximations we made in obtaining (13-57) are generally justified at ordinary temperatures.

13-3 INTERNAL ENERGY AND ENTROPY

Case I: $0 \le \alpha \le 1$ $\qquad\qquad\qquad\qquad\qquad\qquad$ (13-7)

In this case of weak degeneracy we may proceed as in Sec. 12-3 for our fermion gas without cohesion and covolume, under the assumption that the energy of the particles is due only to their translational motion. In analogy with (12-22) we can express the internal energy of the system as

$$U = \frac{2g_j}{\sqrt{\pi}} V N_c kT \int_0^\infty \frac{\alpha x^{3/2}\, dx}{e^x + \alpha} \tag{13-70}$$

---

[9]See, for example, C. Kittel, *Elementary Statistical Physics* (New York: John Wiley & Sons, Inc., 1958), p. 94; or K. Huang, *Statistical Mechanics* (New York: John Wiley & Sons, Inc., 1963), p. 228. But compare the slightly different approach in J. E. Mayer and M. G. Mayer, *Statistical Mechanics* (New York: John Wiley & Sons, Inc., 1940), p. 384, where the third term in the square brackets of (13-57) is retained.

where x is given by (12-7). We can put this in the form of (12-24) by writing

$$U = \frac{3}{2}kTg_jVN_cG_+(\alpha) \tag{13-71}$$

where

$$G_+(\alpha) = \frac{4}{3\sqrt{\pi}} \int_0^\infty \frac{\alpha x^{3/2}\, dx}{e^x + \alpha} \tag{13-72}$$

Actually, since no assumptions have yet been made concerning the range of values for α, both (13-71) and (13-72) are completely general and valid for all values of α. The particular range of values of α will determine the procedure to be used in the evaluation of $G_+(\alpha)$. For the weakly degenerate system, governed by the condition of (13-7), we follow the prescription of multiplying numerator and denominator under the integral sign in (13-72) by e^{-x} and incorporate (13-9) and (13-11) to obtain

$$G_+(\alpha) = \frac{-4}{3\sqrt{\pi}} \sum_{n=1}^\infty \frac{(-\alpha)^n}{n^{5/2}} \int_0^\infty e^{-y}y^{3/2}\, dy \tag{13-73}$$

where y is given by (13-11). We recognize the integral to be

$$\Gamma\left(\frac{5}{2}\right) = \frac{3\sqrt{\pi}}{4} \tag{13-74}$$

and hence

$$G_+(\alpha) = -\sum_{n=1}^\infty \frac{(-\alpha)^n}{n^{5/2}} \tag{13-75}$$

Combining (13-75) with (13-71) leads to the following expression for the internal energy of the weakly degenerate fermion gas

$$U = \frac{3}{2}kTg_jN_cV\alpha\left[1 - \frac{\alpha}{2^{5/2}} + \cdots\right] \tag{13-76}$$

The number of particles in the system is given by (13-5) and (13-13) as

$$N = g_jN_cV\alpha\left[1 - \frac{\alpha}{2^{3/2}} + \cdots\right] \tag{13-77}$$

When α is much less than unity it may be neglected in the brackets of (13-77) and we find, in this case,

$$\alpha \simeq \frac{N}{g_jN_cV} \tag{13-78}$$

We may divide (13-76) by (13-77) to obtain an expression for the mean energy per particle as

$$
\begin{aligned}
\frac{U}{N} &= \frac{3}{2} kT \left(1 - \frac{\alpha}{2^{5/2}} \right) \left[1 - \frac{\alpha}{2^{3/2}} \right]^{-1} \\
&= \frac{3}{2} kT \left(1 - \frac{\alpha}{2^{5/2}} \right) \left[1 + \frac{\alpha}{2^{3/2}} + \cdots \right] \\
&= \frac{3}{2} kT \left[1 + \alpha \left(\frac{1}{2^{3/2}} - \frac{1}{2^{5/2}} \right) + \cdots \right] \\
&= \frac{3}{2} kT \left[1 + \frac{\alpha}{2^{5/2}} + \cdots \right]
\end{aligned}
\tag{13-79}
$$

where we have used the binomial expansion and retained only the first-order terms in α. With the help of (2-94) and (13-78) we find the equation of state for the weakly degenerate fermion system to be given by

$$
PV = NkT \left[1 + \frac{Nh^3}{16 g_j (m\pi k)^{3/2}} \frac{1}{VT^{3/2}} + \cdots \right]
\tag{13-80}
$$

when N_c is expressed in terms of (5-41).

If the fermion particles comprising the system possessed zero spin (which, of course, is a contradiction in terms) g_j, given by (13-2), would be unity and (13-80) is, for this hypothetical system, equivalent to (2-133).

The entropy of a fermion gas is given by (5-54) as

$$
S = \frac{5}{3} \frac{U}{T} - Nk \ln \alpha
\tag{5-54}
$$

and when $\alpha \ll 1$ the logarithmic term will dominate and we are then justified in neglecting $\alpha/2^{5/2}$ in comparison with unity in (13-79). Under this condition the specific translational entropy for the weakly degenerate Fermi-Dirac gas becomes

$$
s = \frac{S}{N} = \frac{5}{2} k - k \ln \left(\frac{N}{g_j N_c V} \right)
\tag{13-81}
$$

which is the Sackur-Tetrode equation for the system. Again, for a spinless (and consequently academic) fermion gas (13-81) becomes identical to (12-47).

Note that the weakly degenerate quantum mechanical perfect gases become identical to the classical gas when spin is neglected. But of course the intrinsic spin angular momentum quantum numbers, and the restricted values they may assume, are precisely what distinguish the quantum systems from their classical counterparts. Thus we see that the corrections to the classical perfect-gas law, appearing in (12-46) and (13-80) are due to quantum effects and not to any molecular interactions between the particles.

Case II: $1 \leq \alpha \leq \infty$ (13-14)

At low temperatures and high particle densities (13-14) and (13-48) become equivalent and the Fermi-Dirac gas system becomes highly degenerate. We may, under this condition, proceed to evaluate the internal energy in the manner employed in the preceding section to evaluate N, which led us to (13-41). We may still obtain the internal energy of the system from (13-71) except we write (13-72), for the degenerate gas, in the form

$$G_+(\alpha) = \frac{4\beta^{5/2}}{3\sqrt{\pi}} \int_0^\infty \varepsilon^{3/2} f(\varepsilon)\, d\varepsilon \tag{13-82}$$

in analogy with (13-19), and the Fermi-Dirac distribution function is given by (13-17). We see that the integral in (13-82) differs from that in (13-19) only by the exponent of ε, and consequently the former may be evaluated by the procedure used to evaluate the latter in the preceding section.

$$\frac{3\sqrt{\pi}}{4\beta^{5/2}} G_+(\alpha) = \frac{2}{5} \int_0^\infty f(\varepsilon)\, d(\varepsilon^{5/2})$$

$$= \frac{2}{5} \left[f(\varepsilon)\varepsilon^{5/2} \Big|_0^\infty - \int_0^\infty \varepsilon^{5/2} \frac{df}{d\varepsilon}\, d\varepsilon \right]$$

$$+ \frac{15\sqrt{\pi}}{8} G_+(\alpha) = \int_0^\infty (\beta\varepsilon)^{5/2} \frac{e^y}{(e^y + 1)^2}\, d(\beta\varepsilon) \tag{13-83}$$

Where we have expressed $df/d\varepsilon$ in terms of (13-23). We now expand $(\beta\varepsilon)^{5/2}$ in a Taylor's series about μ to take advantage of the change in variable offered by (13-21)

$$(\beta\varepsilon)^{5/2} = (\beta\mu)^{5/2} + \frac{5}{2}(\beta\mu)^{3/2} y + \frac{15}{8}(\beta\mu)^{1/2} y^2 + \frac{5}{16}(\beta\mu)^{-1/2} y^3$$

$$- \frac{5}{128}(\beta\mu)^{-3/2} y^4 + \frac{3}{256}(\beta\mu)^{-5/2} y^5 - \cdots \tag{13-84}$$

which, with the aid of (13-30), (13-32), and (13-39), leads to (see Prob. 13-7)

$$G_+(\alpha) = \frac{8}{15\sqrt{\pi}} \left[t^{5/2} + \frac{5\pi^2}{8} t^{1/2} - \frac{7\pi^4}{384} t^{-3/2} + O(t^4 e^{-t}) \right] \tag{13-85}$$

When (13-85) is substituted back into (13-71) we find that

$$U = \left(\frac{4}{5\sqrt{\pi}} \right) \beta^{3/2} \mu^{5/2} g_j N_c V \left[1 + \frac{5\pi^2}{8} t^{-2} - \frac{7\pi^4}{384} t^{-4} + O(t^{3/2} e^{-t}) \right] \tag{13-86}$$

We can now use the binomial expansion on (13-57) to obtain

$$\mu^{5/2} = \mu_0^{5/2} \left[1 - \frac{5\pi^2}{24} s^2 - \frac{7\pi^2}{384} s^4 + \cdots \right] \qquad (13\text{-}87)$$

and from (13-54) and (13-55) we find

$$t^{-2} = s^2 + \frac{\pi^2}{6} s^4 \qquad (13\text{-}88a)$$

and

$$t^{-4} = s^4 \qquad (13\text{-}88b)$$

When (13-87) and (13-88) are substituted into (13-86) we see that the internal energy of the fermion gas can be expressed in terms of the Fermi energy at zero temperature as

$$U = \frac{3}{5} N\mu_0 \left[1 + \frac{5}{12} \pi^2 \left(\frac{T}{\Theta_F} \right)^2 - \frac{\pi^4}{16} \left(\frac{T}{\Theta_F} \right)^4 + \cdots \right] \qquad (13\text{-}89)$$

which clearly shows that the internal energy of the Fermi-Dirac ideal gas does not vanish at the temperature of absolute zero, in sharp contrast to the classical [cf. (2-103) or (5-23)] and the Bose-Einstein [cf. (12-55)] gases. Of course the specific heat capacity at constant volume goes to zero as the absolute temperature tends towards zero, for all perfect gases; and the fermion gas is no exception as we can see by differentiating (13-89) w.r.t. T

$$c_v = \frac{du}{dT} = \frac{\pi^2}{2} k \left(\frac{T}{\Theta_F} \right) - \cdots \qquad (13\text{-}90)$$

Thus the Fermi-Dirac gas has a specific heat capacity which approaches zero linearly with the temperature; again in contrast to the Maxwell-Boltzmann-Planck gas [for which c_v does not vanish at $T = 0$; cf. (5-23)] and the photon and particle boson gases [see the discussion below (12-55)].

By incorporating (2-94) into (13-89) we can express the equation of state of the highly degenerate monatomic fermion gas without cohesion and covolume as

$$PV = \frac{2}{5} N\mu_0 \left[1 + \frac{5}{12} \pi^2 \left(\frac{T}{\Theta_F} \right)^2 - \frac{\pi^4}{16} \left(\frac{T}{\Theta_F} \right)^4 + \cdots \right] \qquad (13\text{-}91)$$

We see that the ideal Fermi-Dirac gas must be constrained by externally fixed walls, even at absolute zero temperature, since the pressure exerted by the system does not vanish. This condition is a direct consequence of the Pauli exclusion principle, which precludes more than one particle from having zero momentum. The remaining $N - 1$ particles are thus required to have a finite (and different) momentum which gives rise (in the manner discussed in Sec. 2-5) to the nonvanishing zero-point pressure.

In the preceding section we saw that at a temperature of $377°C = 650°K$,

$$s = \frac{kT}{\mu_0} = \frac{1}{100}$$

from which we find that

$$\mu_0 \simeq 5.6\,eV = 3.5 \times 10^{-12}\,\text{erg} \tag{13-92}$$

for conduction electrons in a typical monovolent metal. From (13-92) and (13-65) we see that (13-91) yields a zero-point pressure of

$$P_0 \simeq 14 \times 10^{10}\,\frac{\text{dyne}}{\text{cm}^2} \tag{13-93}$$

which is about 140,000 atmospheres – a fairly substantial pressure! (For a more detailed discussion of the zero-point pressure of the ideal fermion gas, see the texts by Mayer and Mayer or Hill in Ref. 5).

The entropy of the degenerate Fermi-Dirac gas is still given by (5-54), into which we can substitute (5-61) and (13-89) to obtain

$$S = \frac{N\mu_0}{T}\left[1 + \frac{5}{12}\pi^2\left(\frac{T}{\Theta_F}\right)^2 - \frac{\pi^4}{16}\left(\frac{T}{\Theta_F}\right)^4 + \cdots\right] - \frac{N\mu}{T} \tag{13-94}$$

We can now express μ in terms of μ_0 from (13-57) and write

$$S = \frac{\pi^2}{2}N\mu_0\frac{T}{\Theta_F{}^2}\left[1 - \frac{\pi^2}{10}\left(\frac{T}{\Theta_F}\right)^2 + \cdots\right] \tag{13-95}$$

from which we see that the entropy of the degenerate fermion gas vanishes at the temperature of absolute zero; and in fact is quite small for all ordinary temperatures in light of (13-66).

PROBLEMS

13-1. Show that $I_0 = 1$ or alternatively that $\zeta(0) = -\frac{1}{2}$ directly by evaluating I_0 of (13-32b). [*Hint*: Write I_0 of (13-32b) in the form

$$I_0 = 2\int_0^\infty \frac{e^y\,dy}{(1 + e^y)^2} = -2\int_0^\infty d\left(\frac{1}{1 + e^y}\right)]$$

13-2. Show that the Fermi energy at absolute zero is given by (13-43). [*Hint*: begin with (13-42) and make use of (4-29), (5-41), and (2-130).]

13-3. Find the ratio of the "characteristic temperature" for a boson system to that for a fermion system [i.e., that given by (12-35) to that given by (13-45)], which is larger? Can you account for this physically?

13-4. Supply any steps which are not transparent to you in the derivation of (13-57) and particularly verify (13-55).

13-5. (a) Show that (13-59) is equivalent to (13-45) for an electron system. (b) Evaluate Θ_F given by (13-62) for the monovolent metals of Table 13-3 and verify that the value of Θ_F in (13-66) is fairly typical for an electron gas.

13-6. Follow the derivation of (13-80) beginning with (13-70) and supply any mathematical steps which are not intuitively obvious to you.

13-7. Do problem 13-4 again by replacing (13-57) by (13-89) and substituting (13-85) for (13-55) in the statement of that problem.

13-8. Evaluate the specific heat capacity at constant volume, given by (13-90), for a degenerate electron gas in a monatomic metal at a temperature of $377°C$ (well above room temperature) and reconcile your result with the fact that, at high temperatures, the principle of equipartition of energy (Sec. 6-2) requires the electrons to contribute $3/2\,k$ in addition to the value of $3\,k$ predicted by the Einstein [cf. (7-38)] or Debye [cf. (8-84)] theory of solids. (*Hint*: reconsider the meaning of a "high" temperature.)

13-9. Show that for *very* large t (large chemical potential or low temperature) (13-40) can be obtained from (13-25) in one step by incorporating (13-20) into (13-25).

13-10. In the band theory of semiconductors, the energy of the electron is separated into three regions: the valence energy band, the forbidden energy band, and the conduction energy band. At $T = 0$, the electrons are in the ground state or the valence band. As the temperature increases, the electrons are thermally excited. Since the electrons can not have energy values which lie in the forbidden energy region which separate the valence and conduction band, the electrons must be thermally excited to the conduction band (the electrons obey Fermi-Dirac statistics). When an electron is excited to the conduction band, it leaves a vacancy in the valence band. The properties of the valence band can be accounted for by assuming the vacancy left by the electron acts like a particle of charge $+e$ and effective mass m_h^*. This particle is called a "hole." The probability of a hole occupying an energy level E is the same as that of an electron not occupying the energy level E. Derive an expression for the probability of a hole occupying an energy level E.

13-11. Show that a weakly degenerate ideal Fermi gas is less compressible than an ideal classical gas. [*Hint*: make use of (2-6a) for both gases and compare.]

13-12. As a first approximation, the conduction electrons of the atoms making up a metal can be viewed as moving freely within the metal, and these electrons are taken to be a Fermi-Dirac gas. Calculate the Fermi energy (chemical potential) for silver at $T = 0$ if the conduction electron density is 5.76×10^{22} electrons/cm^3.

13-13. When electrons are evaporated off a metal filament, it is found that the velocity distribution of the electrons is Maxwellian (that is, classical). The electrons inside the metal obey Fermi-Dirac statistics. The minimum energy, ε_0, required to remove an electron from the metal is greater than the chemical potential, μ, by an amount ϕ, where ϕ is called the work function, and $\varepsilon_0 - \mu = \phi$. What is the condition on ϕ for this to be true?

13-14. At very low temperatures, the electronic specific heat capacity of a metal (taken as a Fermi gas) is approximately

$$c_v = \gamma T$$

where γ can be determined by experiment. Use (13-90) to determine the Fermi energy of gold, for which it is found that $\gamma = 7.3 \times 10^3$ erg/mole-deg^2. Compare this result to the value obtained from the free electron approximation (see Prob. 13-12),

$$\varepsilon_f = 8.7 \times 10^{-12} \text{ erg}$$

What would the effective mass, m^*, of an electron have to be in the free electron approximation in order that the Fermi energy be equal to that calculated in this problem? Explain why this difference in the values of the Fermi energy occurs.

14 Applications — Electron Theory of Metals

14-1 INTRODUCTION

The authors now draw their text to a close with a topic that experience has shown, alas, has often been given insufficient time and coverage. This is often due to shortened course time available, e.g., alloting three rather than four hours per week class time, or switching to a quarter system from a semester system; or to an instructor's desire to cover the "fundamentals" adequately; or simply to a lack of foresight in planning the course work. Whatever the cause, the effect is often a jejune feeling on the part of the student who fails to find any relevancy between the endless string of mathematical formulas and any field of physics.

In the hope of alleviating this situation somewhat the authors have, in the Preface, urged the instructor to make a concerted effort to cover the material in this chapter in some detail in order to instill some feeling of accomplishment in the student who has followed, if not mastered, the preceding thirteen chapters, and to indicate farther horizons for the student to pursue. To confine the present chapter within reasonable bounds only one particular application is treated, namely the free-electron theory of metals. Even this restricted topic is not exhausted by the considerations herein.

The chapter should be sufficiently amenable to self-study that the student who has actively participated in the previous thirteen chapters will be prepared to work his way through in the absence of an instructor.

Under the aegis of electron theory of metals the student will find discussed transport phenomena of physical quantities in one dimension, including steady-state conditions and mean free path. The electric current density and heat flux in a metal are deduced, culminating in the Wiedemann-Franz ratio of thermal to electrical conductivity of the metal. Also considered in this section is the topic of thermoelectricity, in terms of the

Thomson, Peltier, and Seebeck effects, with attention drawn to the relations among the three effects.

The treatment of the selected applications of statistical physics in the chapter is intended to be illustrative, not exhaustive. It is hoped that the student will perceive the actual and potential utility of statistical physics to the many disciplines within the breadth of what is commonly called "physical science," and indeed, the need to employ statistical physics to gain an accurate description and awareness of our physical environment.

14-2   ELECTRON THEORY OF METALS

In the present section we develop the Sommerfeld model of a metal. Recall from Sec. 13-1 that Drude[1] presented the first theoretical derivation of the empirical Wiedemann-Franz[2] law by assuming that a metal contained free electrons which behaved somewhat like an ideal "electron gas." Lorentz[3] applied the classical Maxwell-Boltzmann-Planck statistics to the Drude theory of noninteracting electrons comprising the supposed gas, and thus improved the Drude model; but the Lorentz model could hardly be called satisfactory.[4] Parameters appearing in the Lorentz theory cannot be simultaneously fit, by means of experimental data, to give reasonable agreement for the specific heat capacity, the electrical and thermal conductivities, the Lorenz number, and the Hall coefficient.

In the ensuing discussion we shall envision an electron gas for which the local conditions (defined by the two Lagrange undetermined constants $\alpha = e^{\beta\mu}$ and $\beta = 1/kT$) are considered as functions of x alone and independent of y and z. We shall also assume that the distribution of electron speeds is not isotropic, but is biased somehow in the x-direction due to the possible existence of thermal temperature gradients or of impressed electric fields. This is then a departure from the cases considered in the preceding chapters where the distribution of particles was assumed to be homogeneous in x, y, z, and isotropic in the components of momentum p_x, p_y, p_z.

In Sec. 5-1 we saw that the volume of a single cell in phase space is equal

[1]P. Drude, *Ann. Physik* **1**, 566 (1900); *ibid.,* **3**, 369 (1900).

[2]G. Wiedemann and R. Franz, *Ann. Physik* **89**, 497 (1853).

[3]H. A. Lorentz. *Proc. Acad. Sci. Amst.* **7**, 438, 588, 684 (1904–5). This reference is given in a footnote on page 10 of the following eminently readable book: H. A. Lorentz, *The Theory of Electrons* (New York: Dover Publications, Inc., 1952). For a recent historical review of Lorentz' theory of electrons see S. Goldberg, *Amer. J. Phys.* **37**, 982 (1969).

[4]For an historical essay on the early theoretical models of metals see A. H. Wilson, *The Theory of Metals*, 2nd ed. (London: Cambridge University Press, 1953), Chap. 1.

to h^3. Thus the number of cells in the volume V corresponding to particles with an uncertainty in their momentum components of dp_x, dp_y, dp_z is given by

$$g(p) = \frac{V \, dp_x \, dp_y \, dp_z}{h^3} \tag{14-1}$$

If we now let ξ, η, and ζ be the components of the electron speed, the number of cells corresponding to a small volume element

$$dV = dx \, dy \, dz \tag{14-2}$$

will be given by

$$g(p) = \left(\frac{m}{h}\right)^3 d\xi \, d\eta \, d\zeta \, dx \, dy \, dz \tag{14-3}$$

In analogy with (5-12) we write the number of electrons to be found in the volume element of (14-2) and the momentum element

$$d\mathbf{p} = m^3 \, d\xi \, d\eta \, d\zeta \tag{14-4}$$

as

$$dn = \left(\frac{m}{h}\right)^3 \frac{g_j}{e^{\beta(\varepsilon - \mu)} + 1} \, d\xi \, d\eta \, d\zeta \, dx \, dy \, dz \tag{14-5}$$

where g_j is given by (13-2). In analogy with (13-17) let us represent the equilibrium distribution function as

$$f_0 = \frac{g_j}{e^{\beta(\varepsilon - \mu)} + 1} \tag{14-6}$$

We now define the equilibrium velocity distribution function for the electron gas as

$$\phi_0(\xi, \eta, \zeta) = \left(\frac{m}{h}\right)^3 f_0 \tag{14-7}$$

so that the equilibrium number of electrons in the system, given by (14-5), takes the form

$$dn_0 = \phi_0(\xi, \eta, \zeta) \, d\xi \, d\eta \, d\zeta \, dV \tag{14-8}$$

with the aid of (14-2).

It is now necessary to modify the distribution of (14-8) to take into account the spatial heterogeneity and the velocity anisotropy. The spatial heterogeneity can be introduced in a simple way by assuming that $\alpha \, [= e^{\beta\mu}]$ and $\beta \, [= 1/kT]$ are functions of x; or in other words, by assuming that the chemical potential and the absolute temperature may vary with position in the preferred direction x. We shall account for the anisotropy in ξ, η, ζ, by adding a perturbation term which explicitly depends on the direction of motion of the electrons. We now require that this perturbation term be odd in ξ and even in η and ζ. We take as the form of this perturbation term the following

$$\xi\chi(v, x) \tag{14-9}$$

Where $\chi(v, x)$ is isotropic in ξ, η, ζ and the electron speed is given by

$$v = \sqrt{\xi^2 + \eta^2 + \zeta^2} \tag{14-10}$$

We thus have as the number of electrons with velocities in the range $d\xi \, d\eta \, d\zeta$ to be found within the volume element of (14-2)

$$dn = [\phi_0(v, x) + \xi\chi(v, x)] \, d\xi \, d\eta \, d\zeta \, dV \tag{14-11}$$

where ϕ_0 and χ are isotropic in ξ, η, ζ and are functions of x through μ and T (or, equivalently, through the Lagrange undetermined multipliers α and β).

A.   Transport Phenomena of Physical Quantities in One Dimension

The existence of the perturbation term in (14-11) permits us to treat the transport by the electrons, in the x-direction, of various physical quantities, giving rise to such phenomena as electric current, internal pressure, and the flow of heat in metals.

Since we are now not dealing with equilibrium conditions within the metal we will find that at some arbitrary point x_0, the average value of the x component of the electron velocity will not, in general, vanish. Rather, the average (i.e., the mean, not the root-mean-square value of ξ will be given by

$$\langle \xi \rangle = \frac{\int \xi \, dn}{\int dn} \tag{14-12}$$

which, in terms of (14-11), takes the form

$$\langle \xi \rangle = \frac{\iiint[\phi_0(v, x_0) + \xi\chi(v, x_0)]\xi \, d\xi \, d\eta \, d\zeta \iiint dV}{\iiint[\phi_0(v, x_0) + \xi\chi(v, x_0)] \, d\xi \, d\eta \, d\zeta \iiint dV} \tag{14-13}$$

since the velocity and displacement components are independent. The integration over spatial components have the same value in the numerator and denominator and thus cancel.

By virtue of (14-10) we can transform the velocity integration from Cartesian to polar coordinates in the form

$$d\xi \, d\eta \, d\zeta = 4\pi v^2 \, dv \tag{14-14}$$

Also ϕ_0 is an even function of ξ so that $\xi\phi_0$ is an odd function; likewise χ

is an even function of v, being isotropic in ξ, η, ζ, so that $\xi\chi$ is an odd function of ξ. Thus the first term in the numerator and the second term in the denominator vanish from symmetry considerations, and we are left with

$$\langle \xi \rangle = \frac{\int \xi^2 \chi(v,x_0) v^2 \, dv}{\int \phi_0(v,x_0) v^2 \, dv} \tag{14-15}$$

Making use of the relation (14-10) and the fact that $\chi(v,x_0)$ is isotropic in ξ, η, ζ, allows us to express

$$\iiint \xi^2 \chi(v,x_0) \, d\xi \, d\eta \, d\zeta = \frac{1}{3} \iiint (\xi^2 + \eta^2 + \zeta^2)\chi(v,x_0) \, d\xi \, d\eta \, d\zeta \tag{14-16}$$

$$4\pi \int \xi^2 \chi(v,x_0) v^2 \, dv = \frac{4\pi}{3} \int v^2 \chi(v,x_0) v^2 \, dv \tag{14-17}$$

which, when substituted back into (14-15), leads to

$$\langle \xi \rangle = \frac{1}{3} \frac{\int \chi(v,x_0) v^4 \, dv}{\int \phi_0(v,x_0) v^2 \, dv} \tag{14-18}$$

The denominator in (14-18) can be evaluated, since ϕ_0 is given by (14-7) and (14-6), and has the value (see Prob. 14-2)

$$\int \phi_0(v,x_0) v^2 \, dv = \begin{cases} \dfrac{1}{4\pi} g_j N_c F_+(\alpha) \\[2ex] \dfrac{1}{4\pi} \dfrac{N}{V} \end{cases} \tag{14-19}$$

where $F_+(\alpha)$ is defined by (13-18) and (13-19). Of course the actual value of $F_+(\alpha)$ will depend on the value of α, which is determined by μ, which in turn we have assumed depends on the particular location x_0. Thus in our example of the average velocity of electrons in the x-direction, we find that

$$\langle \xi \rangle = \frac{4\pi}{3} \frac{V}{N} \int \chi(v,x_0) v^4 \, dv \tag{14-20}$$

where, of course, the integral can be evaluated only after we have identified the perturbation particle density function $\chi(v,x_0)$.

Now let us examine the transport, by electron flow, of any mechanical or electrical quantity, q, associated with the movement of electrons in a metal. We shall take the direction of motion of the electrons to be along the x-direction and consider an element of area

$$dA_\perp = dy \, dz \tag{14-21}$$

perpendicular to the direction of motion. Typically the nonequilibrium steady-state flow of the electrons will be due to such phenomena as an impressed electric field or thermal gradient applied to the metal. The amount of the quantity q carried by the electrons across the normal area of (14-21) in time dt is equal to the product of the spatial density of electrons, the area, the time, the component of the velocity of the electrons in the direction of motion, and the physical quantity which is being transported by the movement of the electrons:

$$d^3Q = \frac{dn}{dV} dA_\perp \, dt \, \xi q \qquad (14\text{-}22)$$

More generally we are interested in the amount of q which is transported across unit area per unit time, or in other words, the *flux* of q, which we shall denote by Φ. From the definition of flux and from (14-22) we have

$$\frac{d^3Q}{dA_\perp \, dt} \equiv d\Phi = \frac{dn}{dV} \xi q \qquad (14\text{-}23)$$

The total flux is found by substituting dn/dV from (14-11) and integrating over all the velocity components

$$\Phi = \int q\xi(\phi_0 + \xi\chi) \, d\xi \, d\eta \, d\zeta \qquad (14\text{-}24)$$

We shall have occasion to use (14-24) several times before we conclude this chapter. For the present it will suffice if we note that when the quantity of interest q is the charge on the electron, the flux of charge is the charge transported per unit time through unit area normal to the direction of flow of the charge, or more commonly, the electric current density, **j**. If q represents the momentum of the electron, the flux is known as the pressure exerted by the electrons on the end surfaces of the metal. When q is taken to be the kinetic energy of the electrons, the energy flux can be identified with the heat flux through the metal. We shall pursue these ideas in greater depth *infra*, but now we turn our attention to the criteria for steady-state transport conditions to exist.

In previous chapters we have contented ourselves with average properties of the substance such as mean energy and mean velocities. These average properties, however, are not sufficient to treat transport problems. We must now consider the electron distributions with respect to both position and velocity. In other words, we must consider the electron motion in terms of a six-dimensional phase space, analogous to that discussed in Sec. 1-4,

$$dV \, d\tau = dx \, dy \, dz \, d\xi \, d\eta \, d\zeta \qquad (14\text{-}25)$$

where dV is given by (14-2) and $d\tau$ is equal to $d\mathbf{p}/m^3$ from (14-4). We can safely assume that at some time t the electrons under consideration occupy some element of volume dV and have their velocities lying in the range $d\tau$.

After the passage of some time dt these electrons will occupy a volume element dV' about the point x',y',z' which is related to the original point x,y,z, by

$$x' = x + \xi\,dt$$
$$y' = y + \eta\,dt \tag{14-26}$$
$$z' = z + \zeta\,dt$$

But (14-26) must be only an approximation, since the electrons will not only have changed their location but their velocity components may also be changed by the action of some external force **F**. Thus we will find that after some time dt has elapsed, the velocities of the electrons will lie in some different region $d\tau'$ about ξ',η',ζ'. These velocity components will be related to the initial velocity components by means of

$$\xi' = \xi + \frac{F_x}{m}\,dt$$

$$\eta' = \eta + \frac{F_y}{m}\,dt \tag{14-27}$$

$$\zeta' = \zeta + \frac{F_z}{m}\,dt$$

The situation is further complicated by the fact that during the time dt some electrons which were originally in the element of phase space $dV\,d\tau$ will suffer collisions with the atoms of the metal (we can generally ignore collisions between electrons) and be scattered elsewhere than into $dV'\,d\tau'$. Similarly, there will be electrons which were initially in some other region of phase space than $dV\,d\tau$, that will be scattered into the region $dV'\,d\tau'$ by atomic collisions taking place within the time dt.

From (14-5) through (14-7) we can write for the number of electrons leaving the region $dV\,d\tau$ of phase space

$$dn_{\text{leaving}} = \phi\,dV\,d\tau \tag{14-28}$$

As these electrons peregrinate through the phase space toward the region $dV'\,d\tau'$ in time dt, there will be some number

$$dn_{\text{out}} = B\,dV\,d\tau\,dt \tag{14-29}$$

which are scattered elsewhere than into $dV'\,d\tau'$ by collisions with the atoms of the metal. During this same time dt, there will be likewise a number of electrons which were originally without $dV\,d\tau$, which are scattered into $dV'\,d\tau'$

$$dn_{\text{in}} = A\,dV'\,d\tau'\,dt \tag{14-30}$$

Hence the net influx into $dV'\,d\tau'$ during the time dt is the sum of those electrons which were initially in $dV\,d\tau$ plus those which are scattered into the region from without $dV\,d\tau$ less those which were in $dV\,d\tau$ but are scattered elsewhere than into $dV'\,d\tau'$.

$$dn_{\text{net}} = \phi dV\,d\tau + \left[AdV'\,d\tau' - BdV\,d\tau\right]dt \qquad (14\text{-}31)$$

Note that the A and B in (14-31) assume the role of creation and annihilation operators, suggestive of the Einstein A and B coefficients appearing in the theory of radiative transitions. They represent the number of electrons scattered in and out of the "volume" of phase space $dV\,d\tau$, per unit "volume" and per unit time.

Steady-state conditions will be assured if the number of electrons arriving in $dV'\,d\tau'$ is the same as the number which initially were found in the region $dV\,d\tau$. Thus the requirement of study state (nonequilibrium) motion of the electron takes the form

$$dV = dV'$$

$$(14\text{-}32)$$

$$d\tau = d\tau'$$

We can arrive at the same conclusion expanding dV' or $d\tau'$ in a Taylor's expansion about dV or $d\tau$ and neglecting higher-order terms. This is justified because the velocities and accelerations of all the electrons which are scattered into the region $dV'\,d\tau'$, irrespective of their origin, are approximately the same. Of course, even though the *size* of the initial and final phase volumes are the same, these two regions are taken about different points of the phase space.

Substitution of (14-32) into (14-31) leads to

$$dn_{\text{net}} = \left[\phi(x, y, z; \xi, \eta, \zeta) + (A - B)\,dt\right]dV\,d\tau \qquad (14\text{-}33)$$

as the net number of electrons finally arriving into the region $dV'\,d\tau'$ of phase space after time dt. But in analogy with the equilibrium distribution of (14-8), the net occupation of the region $dV'\,d\tau'$ ought to be capable of representation by ·

$$dn = \phi(x', y', z'; \xi', \eta', \zeta')\,dV'\,d\tau' \qquad (14\text{-}34)$$

We can now expand the distribution function of (14-34), representing the density of electrons within the volume dV' and having velocities within the region $d\tau'$, in a Taylor's series about $dV\,d\tau$, with the aid of (14-26) and (14-27), retaining only first-order terms:

$$\phi(x', y', z'; \xi', \eta', \zeta') = \phi\left(x + \xi\,dt, y + \eta\,dt, z + \zeta\,dt; \right.$$

$$\left.\xi + \frac{F_x}{m}\,dt, \eta + \frac{F_y}{m}\,dt, \zeta + \frac{F_z}{m}\,dt\right) \qquad (14\text{-}35)$$

$$\phi(x', y', z'; \xi', \eta', \zeta') = \phi(x, y, z; \xi, \eta, \zeta) + \left[\xi \frac{\partial \phi}{\partial x} + \eta \frac{\partial \phi}{\partial y} + \zeta \frac{\partial \phi}{\partial z} \right.$$

$$\left. + \frac{F_x}{m} \frac{\partial \phi}{\partial \xi} + \frac{F_y}{m} \frac{\partial \phi}{\partial \eta} + \frac{F_z}{m} \frac{\partial \phi}{\partial \zeta} \right] dt + \cdots \qquad (14\text{-}36)$$

When (14-36) and (14-32) are substituted in (14-34) and the result compared with (14-33), we recognize the net number of electrons scattered by collisions with the metallic atoms into the phase region $dV'\, d\tau'$ in the time dt as

$$A - B = \xi \frac{\partial \phi}{\partial x} + \eta \frac{\partial \phi}{\partial y} + \zeta \frac{\partial \phi}{\partial z} + \frac{F_x}{m} \frac{\partial \phi}{\partial \xi} + \frac{F_y}{m} \frac{\partial \phi}{\partial \eta} + \frac{F_z}{m} \frac{\partial \phi}{\partial \zeta} \qquad (14\text{-}37)$$

when steady-state conditions prevail. By hypothesis we have assumed that ϕ is independent of y and z; and the only impressed force which we shall consider is that arising from an electric field in the x-direction. Under these circumstances

$$\frac{\partial \phi}{\partial y} = \frac{\partial \phi}{\partial z} = F_y = F_z = 0$$

$$F_x = -eE \qquad (14\text{-}38)$$

and the steady-state Boltzmann equation for the distribution function, represented by (14-37), takes the simplified form

$$A - B = \xi \frac{\partial \phi}{\partial x} - \frac{e}{m} E \frac{\partial \phi}{\partial \xi} \qquad (14\text{-}39)$$

The Boltzmann transport equation is treated at length in many texts dealing with statistical mechanics and solid state physics,[5] where the quantity $A - B$ is frequently designated by

$$A - B = \left(\frac{\partial f}{\partial t} \right)_{\text{coll}} \qquad (14\text{-}40)$$

in which the particular distribution function f to be used is determined by the particles whose motion is to be described, and is not necessarily limited to the Fermi-Dirac function of (14-6) which is, of course, applicable to electrons in metals.

Let us now turn our attention to the average or *"mean" free path* of electrons in a metal between collisions with the atoms of the metal. The mean free path can be defined in various ways and the student should be cognizant of the different meanings assigned to the term by different authors.

[5]See, for example, K. Huang, *Statistical Mechanics* (New York: John Wiley & Sons, Inc., 1963), Chap. 3; A. H. Wilson, Ref. 4, *supra*.

The approach to be followed herein is neither unique, nor quite generally followed by writers in the field. We begin by considering a beam of particles having the same direction and sense. This beam may be weakened or attenuated as the particles traverse some distance ds. The loss of particles from the beam, by collisions with atoms or ions in the metallic lattice, in traveling a distance ds is proportional to the number of particles existing prior to the trek across the distance ds and to the path length ds itself:

$$dn_{\text{out}} = -\frac{1}{l} n_0 \, ds \tag{14-41}$$

The minus sign in (14-41) arises because the number of particles in the beam decreases with increasing path length. The quantity l appearing in (14-41) is defined to be the *mean free path between collisions*, of the electrons, with the metallic ions in the lattice.

Now in time dt the electrons, having speed v given by (14-10), will traverse the distance

$$ds = v \, dt \tag{14-42}$$

so that (14-41) takes the form

$$dn_{\text{out}} = -\frac{v}{l} n_0 \, dt \tag{14-43}$$

From (14-28) we see that the number of electrons existing prior to their voyage through the path ds is given by

$$n_0 = \phi dV \, d\tau \tag{14-44}$$

and hence

$$dn_{\text{out}} = -\frac{v}{l} \phi \, dV \, d\tau \, dt \tag{14-45}$$

If we compare (14-45) with (14-29) we see that the annihilation operator takes the form

$$B = -\frac{v}{l} \phi = -\frac{\phi}{T} \tag{14-46}$$

where T represents the mean time between collisions, not the absolute temperature (the student should experience no confusion in this respect as there is no similarity between the dimensions of time and temperature), and is related to the mean free path by

$$l = vT \tag{14-47}$$

The mean free path between collisions – or alternatively, the mean time between collisions – depends on the velocity of the electrons, as well as the local conditions determined by the temperature and the chemical potential.

In order to make further progress we must make a supplementary hypothesis that we alluded to with respect to (14-9) and (14-11), viz.,

$$\phi = \phi_0 + \xi\chi \qquad (14\text{-}48)$$

In the absence of external fields and inhomogeneities we see that

$$\frac{\partial\phi}{\partial x} = 0 = E \qquad (14\text{-}49)$$

and, from (14-39) we find that

$$A_0 - B_0 = 0 \qquad (14\text{-}50)$$

which implies that the nondisturbed values of

$$A_0 = B_0 = -\frac{v}{l}\phi_0 \qquad (14\text{-}51)$$

when use is made of (14-46).

Now the electrons which are scattered into the beam along the path *ds* are emitted by the atoms in the metallic lattice. This emission by the atoms may be a function of the local conditions through x (which itself may be a function of the temperature of the lattice) but it is independent of the speed of the electrons [in other words, the emission is the same with or without the anisotropic term $\xi\chi$ in (14-48)], hence

$$A = A_0 = -\frac{v}{l}\phi_0 \qquad (14\text{-}52)$$

On the other hand, the electrons which disappear from the beam are absorbed by the atoms which collide with the electrons (under this hypothesis we implicitly ignore electron-electron collisions and consider only the collisions between electrons and atoms), and this absorption may depend not only on the electron speed, but on the local conditions of the atoms as well. Thus

$$A - B = A_0 - B$$

$$= -\frac{v}{l}\phi_0 + \frac{v}{l}\phi$$

$$A - B = -\frac{v}{l}(\phi_0 - \phi) \qquad (14\text{-}53)$$

when reference is made to (14-52) and (14-46). If we now substitute (14-48) into (14-53) and equate the result to (14-39), we find

$$\xi\chi = \frac{l}{v}\left(\xi\frac{\partial\phi}{\partial x} - \frac{eE}{m}\frac{\partial\phi}{\partial\xi}\right) \qquad (14\text{-}54)$$

The perturbing term, $\xi\chi$, in (14-48) is assumed to be small so that as a first approximation we may take $\phi = \phi_0$ in (14-54) with the result that[6]

$$\frac{\partial\phi}{\partial x} = \frac{\partial\phi_0}{\partial x} \tag{14-55a}$$

$$\frac{\partial\phi}{\partial\xi} = \frac{\partial\phi_0}{\partial\xi} = \frac{\partial\phi_0}{\partial v}\frac{\partial v}{\partial\xi} = \frac{\xi}{v}\frac{\partial\phi_0}{\partial v} \tag{14-55b}$$

where the last term follows directly from (14-10). Substitution of (14-55) into (14-54) leads to

$$\chi = \frac{l}{v}\left(\frac{\partial\phi_0}{\partial x} - \frac{eE}{mv}\frac{\partial\phi_0}{\partial v}\right) \tag{14-56}$$

We can make use of the kinetic-energy relation

$$\varepsilon = \frac{mv^2}{2}$$
$$d\varepsilon = mv\,dv \tag{14-57}$$

to transform the last term in (14-56) to the form

$$\chi = \frac{l}{v}\left(\frac{\partial\phi_0}{\partial x} - eE\frac{\partial\phi_0}{\partial\varepsilon}\right) \tag{14-58}$$

which we take as the form of our perturbation term. From (14-6), (14-7), and (13-31) we see that χ is an even function of v and, from (14-10), is also an even function of ξ which was required by (14-9).

In our discussion of the mean free path (or the mean time) between collisions, we commented on the fact that l is not uniquely defined by various workers in the subject. In fact one can define different mean free paths for different interaction mechanisms of the electrons in metals, and of course there will be different mechanisms for insulators or semiconductors than for metals.[7] We have generally assumed that the mechanism whereby the electrons are scattered into and out of the path ds is one of diffusion by the ions in the lattice. All of the electrons have been assumed to be free and their mutual collisions have been ignored. We then assumed that they are diffused into and out of the path ds by the lattice of ions that they encounter on their voyage.

We mentioned earlier in conjunction with (14-24) that if q represents

---

[6]For a slightly different approach to this development see J. L. Olsen, *Electron Transport in Metals* (New York: Interscience Publishers, 1962), Chap. 1.

[7]Cf. Chap. 4 of J. L. Olsen, Ref. 6 *supra* and N. F. Mott and R. W. Gurney, *Electronic Processes in Ionic Crystals* (New York: Dover Publications, Inc., 1964), p. 104.

the momentum transported across unit surface area per unit time, the flux, Φ, is then the time rate of change of momentum per unit area, or the force exerted per unit area, or more commonly, the pressure exerted on the container of the gas of electrons. Thus we may write for the pressure

$$P = \int m\xi\xi \, (\phi_0 + \xi\chi) \, d\xi \, d\eta \, d\zeta \tag{14-59}$$

and, since the perturbation term, χ, is an even function of ξ, the contribution to the second integral in (14-59) vanishes by means of

$$m\int \xi^3 \chi d\xi = 0 \tag{14-60}$$

inasmuch as the three cartesian components of the velocity are independent. Thus the pressure within the metal arising from the transport of momentum through the lattice of the metal by the electrons takes the form

$$P = \int m\xi^2 \frac{dn_0}{dV} \tag{14-61}$$

when (14-8) is substituted into (14-59). If we now integrate both sides of (14-61) over the three-dimensional volume, dV, we find that

$$PV = \int m\xi^2 \, dn_0 = \frac{1}{3}\int mv^2 \, dn_0$$

$$= \frac{2}{3}\int \frac{mv^2}{2} \, dn_0$$

or

$$PV = \frac{2}{3} U \tag{2-94}$$

when use is made of the isotropy of the electron velocity [cf. (14-16)] and the definition of internal energy for a structureless non-interacting point-particle given by (2-93). The student should not be surprised to find that we have recovered the formula first deduced from the virial back in Chap. 2. The internal energy of the fermion system is still given by (13-89) so that the pressure obtained in (2-94) is equivalent to (13-91).

B. *The Wiedemann-Franz Ratio*

The Wiedemann-Franz ratio is the ratio of thermal to electrical conductivities which, experimentally, is found to be approximately constant at a given temperature for different metals; and for a given metal it is proportional to the absolute temperature.

Since the electrical conductivity is mathematically easier to compute, we shall obtain an expression for it first. To begin with, we recall that if q in (14-24) denotes the electron charge, $-e$, the flux Φ, is just the current (time rate of transport of charge) flowing across unit area, or more commonly, the current density, which we shall denote by j,

$$j = -e\int \xi(\phi_0 + \xi\chi)d\tau \tag{14-62}$$

When (14-58) is substituted into (14-62) we obtain

$$j = -e\int \left[\xi\phi_0 + \frac{l}{v}\xi^2 \left(\frac{\partial\phi_0}{\partial x} - eE\frac{\partial\phi_0}{\partial\varepsilon} \right) \right] d\tau \tag{14-63}$$

Now from (14-6), (14-7), and (14-57) we recall that ϕ_0 is an even function of ξ, so that $\xi\phi_0$ is an odd function of ξ, and consequently the integral of $\xi\phi_0$ over all values of ξ vanishes from the symmetry conditions. Likewise, when describing the phenomenon known as Ohm's law in a metal we usually deal with a homogeneous conductor at a constant temperature, so that

$$\frac{\partial\phi_0}{\partial x} = 0, \quad \text{Ohm's law conductor} \tag{14-64}$$

and we then express the current density in the metal as

$$j = e^2E\int \xi^2 \frac{l}{v}\frac{\partial\phi_0}{\partial\varepsilon}d\tau \tag{14-65}$$

We can incorporate (14-16) into (14-65) to transform the ξ^2 to $v^2/3$ and then use (14-14), (14-25) and (14-57) to convert $d\tau$ into a differential element of the kinetic energy so that (14-65) becomes

$$j = \frac{8\pi e^2 E}{3m^2}\int l\varepsilon \frac{\partial\phi_0}{\partial\varepsilon}d\varepsilon \tag{14-66}$$

We can then write the integral in terms of the fermi function by means of the definition (14-7) so that

$$j = \frac{8\pi e^2 mE}{3h^3}\int l\varepsilon \frac{df_0}{d\varepsilon}d\varepsilon \tag{14-67}$$

In Sec. 13-2 we discovered that at ordinary temperatures the electron gas in metals is very highly degenerate [cf. (13-66)]. In the same section we also found that for such highly degenerate systems, the derivative of the fermi function acts like a negative delta function with the singularity at the fermi energy [cf. (13-20)]. In such a situation we should expect to find

$$j = \frac{-16\pi e^2 mE}{3h^3}l\mu \tag{14-68}$$

where l is the mean free path of the electrons having kinetic energies equal to the chemical potential or the fermi energy. Note that the extra factor of 2 comes about by the term $g_j(= 2$ for electrons) which appears in (14-6) but is absent in (13-17). We saw in the preceding chapter that the fermi energy at finite temperature is very nearly equal to the fermi energy at zero temperature, given by

$$\mu \simeq \mu_0 = \frac{h^2}{8\pi^2 m}(3\pi^2 n)^{2/3} \qquad (13\text{-}43)$$

where

$$n = \frac{N}{V} \qquad (14\text{-}69)$$

is the density of electrons. When (13-43) is substituted into (14-68) we obtain the following expression for the electrical conductivity of the metal:

$$\sigma = \frac{j}{E} = \frac{-2e^2\bar{l}}{h}\left(\sqrt{\frac{\pi}{3}}\,n\right)^{2/3} \qquad (14\text{-}70)$$

where the minus sign tells us that electron current is directed opposite to the electric field. From (13-43) we can write

$$\mu_0^{1/2} = \sqrt{\frac{m}{2}}\,\bar{v} = \frac{h}{2\sqrt{2m}}\left(\frac{3n}{\pi}\right)^{1/3} \qquad (14\text{-}71)$$

which permits (14-70) to be written in the form

$$\sigma = \frac{-ne^2\bar{l}}{m\bar{v}} = \frac{-ne^2}{m}\bar{T} \qquad (14\text{-}72)$$

in which the mean time between collisions is given by (14-47). The velocity of electrons having kinetic energy equal to the fermi energy at a temperature of absolute zero is denoted by $\bar{v}$ and the corresponding mean time between collisions is denoted by $\bar{T}$. From (14-70) and (14-72) the student can easily obtain an expression for the average drift velocity and mobility of the electrons in the metal[8] [see Prob. 14-6].

The mean free path $\bar{l}$, or equivalently, the mean time between collisions may depend on the absolute temperature as well as on the fermi energy — which for our discussion above we took to be μ_0. The quantity $\bar{v}$, defined above, is independent of the absolute temperature, being defined in terms of μ_0 from (14-71). Thus if the electrical conductivity depends on temperature, this can come about only by means of the temperature influence on n and l; but we generally assume that n is relatively independent of temperature so that the quantities $\bar{l}$ and $\bar{T}$ must be strongly temperature dependent. Thus, for a complete description of σ it would be necessary for us to know the functional dependence of $\bar{l}$ or $\bar{T}$ on the temperature, the fermi energy, and on $\bar{v}$.

[8] For a discussion of the electrical properties of metals see A. F. Ioffe, *Physics of Semiconductors* (New York: Academic Press, Inc., 1960), Chap. 2.

At ordinary temperatures the electrical conductivity is inversely proportional to the temperature, and so $\bar{l}$ and $\bar{T}$ ought to be inversely proportional to the temperature as well. From experimental measurements of σ and knowing the values of e, m, n (one generally assumes that the density of electrons is equal to the density of atoms in a monatomic metal), and $\bar{v}$ [from (14-71)] the value of $\bar{l}$ can be calculated. At ordinary temperatures it is found that $\bar{l}$ is of the order of a few hundred lattice spacings, and so an electron would then travel, on the average, a few hundred interatomic distances before being scattered by the ions composing the metallic crystal lattice. This statistical nature of the electron-ion collisions leads us to think that it is not a classical mechanism which removes electrons from the beam, but rather a quantum mechanical mechanism which is responsible for the electrical conductivity of metals. This is made even more plausible by the fact that (14-72) is in reasonable agreement with experiment and was obtained from the quantum-mechanical (i.e., highly degenerate) Fermi-Dirac distribution function.[9]

To calculate the heat flow, carried by the electrons, along the x-direction we let q in (14-24) represent the kinetic energy carried by the electrons, $mv^2/2$, and Φ then becomes the heat flux which we denote by

$$\mathscr{Q} = \int \frac{mv^2}{2} \xi(\phi_0 + \xi\chi) \, d\xi \, d\eta \, d\zeta \tag{14-73}$$

Once again we recall that ϕ_0 is an even function of ξ, and of course, from (14-10), so is v^2, so that we are left with

$$\mathscr{Q} = \frac{2\pi m}{3} \int v^6 \chi \, dv \tag{14-74}$$

when we make use of (14-14) and (14-17). We may now substitute (14-57) and (14-58) into (14-74) to obtain

$$\mathscr{Q} = \frac{8\pi}{3m^2} \int l\varepsilon^2 \left(\frac{\partial \phi_0}{\partial x} - eE \frac{\partial \phi_0}{\partial \varepsilon} \right) d\varepsilon \tag{14-75}$$

At this point the student might be tempted to set $E = 0$ in (14-75) just as we set $\partial\phi_0/\partial x = 0$ in (14-63). However, the heat flux is usually measured under experimental conditions such that there is no electric current density. This means that j in (14-63) must be zero under the conditions when $\partial\phi_0/\partial x \neq 0$. Consequently there must be an electric field set up by the temperature gradient within the metal just as the same temperature gradient is responsible for the heat flux within the metal. The integral over $d\tau$ of $\xi\phi_0$ in (14-63) must still vanish by symmetry requirements, as it did earlier, irrespective of

---

[9]For a different approach leading to (14-72) see C. Kittel, *Introduction to Solid State Physics*, 3rd ed. (New York: John Wiley & Sons, Inc., 1966), p. 215.

external electric fields and temperature gradients. Hence (14-62) becomes

$$j = -e \int \frac{l}{v} \xi^2 \left(\frac{\partial \phi_0}{\partial x} - eE \frac{\partial \phi_0}{\partial \varepsilon} \right) d\tau = 0 \tag{14-76}$$

We can write (14-75) and (14-76) in a more explicit manner in terms of what are now somewhat standard integrals. Before doing this, however, we must express $\partial \phi_0 / \partial x$ in a more definite form. We have assumed herein that both the temperature and the chemical potential of the metal may be functions of position. The chemical potential is generally considered to depend upon position through the temperature, so that we write

$$\frac{\partial \phi_0}{\partial x} = \frac{\partial \phi_0}{\partial \beta} \frac{\partial \beta}{\partial T} \frac{\partial T}{\partial x} + \frac{\partial \phi_0}{\partial \mu} \frac{\partial \mu}{\partial T} \frac{\partial T}{\partial x} \tag{14-77}$$

From (4-29) we readily see that

$$\frac{\partial \beta}{\partial T} = -\frac{\beta}{T} \tag{14-78}$$

and from (14-6) and (14-7) the student can easily show that

$$\frac{\partial \phi_0}{\partial \beta} = \frac{-(\varepsilon - \mu) \phi_0}{e^{-(\varepsilon - \mu)} + 1} \tag{14-79}$$

and

$$\frac{\partial \phi_0}{\partial \mu} = \frac{\beta \phi_0}{e^{-\beta(\varepsilon - \mu)} + 1} \tag{14-80}$$

so that (14-77) takes the form

$$\frac{\partial \phi_0}{\partial x} = \frac{\beta \phi_0}{e^{-\beta(\varepsilon - \mu)} + 1} \left[\frac{\varepsilon}{T} + T \frac{\partial}{\partial T} \left(\frac{\mu}{T} \right) \right] \frac{\partial T}{\partial x} \tag{14-81}$$

We next recall from (14-6) and (14-7) that

$$\frac{\beta \phi_0}{e^{-\beta(\varepsilon - \mu)} + 1} = -\frac{\partial \phi}{\partial \varepsilon}_0 \tag{14-82}$$

so that we finally reach the result that

$$\frac{\partial \phi_0}{\partial x} = -\frac{\partial T}{\partial x} \left[\frac{\varepsilon}{T} + T \frac{\partial}{\partial T} \left(\frac{\mu}{T} \right) \right] \frac{\partial \phi_0}{\partial \varepsilon} \tag{14-83}$$

When (14-44), (14-17), (14-57), and (14-83) are all inserted into (14-76) we obtain the rather formidable expression for the electric current density of

$$j = e \left[eE + T \frac{\partial T}{\partial x} \frac{\partial}{\partial T} \left(\frac{\mu}{T} \right) \right] K_1 + e \left[\frac{1}{T} \frac{\partial T}{\partial x} \right] K_2 = 0 \tag{14-84}$$

where we have defined the K_1 and K_2 from[10]

$$K_n \equiv \frac{8\pi}{3m^2} \int l\varepsilon^n \frac{\partial \phi_0}{\partial \varepsilon} \, d\varepsilon \qquad (14\text{-}85)$$

In a similar manner, when (14-83) is substituted into (14-75), we find that the heat flux generated by a temperature gradient in the metal is of the form

$$-\mathcal{Q} = \left[eE + T\frac{\partial T}{\partial x}\frac{\partial}{\partial T}\left(\frac{\mu}{T}\right) \right] K_2 + \left[\frac{1}{T}\frac{\partial T}{\partial x} \right] K_3 \qquad (14\text{-}86)$$

As we mentioned previously, the heat flux is generally measured experimentally in the absence of an electric current density; thus we may utilize the right-hand equality of (14-84) to evaluate.

$$\left[eE + T\frac{\partial T}{\partial x}\frac{\partial}{\partial T}\left(\frac{\mu}{T}\right) \right] = -\frac{K_2}{K_1}\left[\frac{1}{T}\frac{\partial T}{\partial x} \right]; \quad \mathbf{j} = 0 \qquad (14\text{-}87)$$

which can then be inserted into (14-86) to yield

$$\mathcal{Q} = \left[\frac{K_2^2 - K_1 K_3}{K_1 T} \right] \frac{\partial T}{\partial x} \qquad (14\text{-}88)$$

The thermal conductivity of the metal is defined to be the heat flux divided by the temperature gradient, so we have

$$\kappa \equiv \frac{\mathcal{Q}}{\left(\frac{\partial T}{\partial x}\right)} = \frac{K_2^2 - K_1 K_3}{K_1 T} \qquad (14\text{-}89)$$

expressed in terms of the three integrals K_1, K_2, and K_3 which are given by (14-85)

We can evaluate

$$K_n = \frac{16\pi m}{3h^3} \int_0^\infty l\varepsilon^n \frac{\partial f}{\partial \varepsilon} \, d\varepsilon \qquad (14\text{-}90)$$

where the Fermi-Dirac function $f(\varepsilon)$ is given by (13-17), as a special case of the more general integral

$$J(\psi) \equiv \int_0^\infty \psi(\varepsilon) \frac{\partial f}{\partial \varepsilon} \, d\varepsilon \qquad (14\text{-}91)$$

which we can evaluate by following the procedure utilized in the preceding chapter to evaluate the integral in (13-25). We change the variable of integration from the energy, ε, to the dimensionless variable, y, given by (13-21).

---

[10]The reader will notice a great deal of similarity between the development herein of the Wiedemann-Franz ratio and that given by F. Seitz, *The Modern Theory of Solids*, (New York: McGraw-Hill Book Company, 1940), Chap. 4.

We then expand the function $\psi(\varepsilon)$ in a Taylor's series about the chemical potential, which is equivalent to a Maclaurin expansion when ψ is expressed in terms of the new variable y,

$$\psi(y) = \sum_{n=0}^{\infty} \frac{y^n}{n!}\left(\frac{d^n\psi}{dy^n}\right)\bigg|_{y=0} \tag{14-92}$$

When (14-92) is introduced into (14-91) and the variable change effected, we obtain

$$J(\psi) = -\sum_{n=0}^{\infty} \frac{1}{n!}\left(\frac{d^n\psi}{dy^n}\right)\bigg|_{y=0} I_n \tag{14-93}$$

when the order of summation and integration is reversed, and we recognize the resulting integral as I_n, given by (13-30). The general form of I_n is given by (13-32) and (13-37), with the first three nonvanishing values given by (13-39). This allows us to write

$$-J(\psi) = \psi(\varepsilon = \mu) + \frac{\pi^2}{6\beta^2}\frac{d^2\psi}{d\varepsilon^2}\bigg|_{\varepsilon=\mu} + \frac{7\pi^4}{360\beta^4}\frac{d^4\psi}{d\varepsilon^4}\bigg|_{\varepsilon=\mu} + \cdots \tag{14-94}$$

In order to evaluate K_n we let the corresponding function

$$\psi(\varepsilon) = \bar{l}\varepsilon^n \tag{14-95}$$

from which the student can verify in a straightforward manner [see Prob. 14-7] that

$$\psi(\varepsilon = \mu) = \bar{l}\mu^n \tag{14-96a}$$

$$\frac{d^2\psi}{d\varepsilon^2}\bigg|_{\varepsilon=\mu} = \bar{l}'\mu^n + 2n\bar{l}'\mu^{n-1} + n(n-1)\bar{l}\mu^{n-2} \tag{14-96b}$$

$$\frac{d^4\psi}{d\varepsilon^4}\bigg|_{\varepsilon=\mu} = \bar{l}^{\text{IV}}\mu^n + 4n\bar{l}^{\text{III}}\mu^{n-1} + 6n(n-1)\bar{l}''\mu^{n-2}$$

$$+ 4n(n-1)(n-2)\bar{l}'\mu^{n-3} + n(n-1)(n-2)(n-3)\bar{l}\mu^{n-4} \tag{14-96c}$$

where the superscripts on l indicates differentiation with respect to ε and the bar overhead denotes that the quantity is to be evaluated at $\varepsilon = \mu$.

From (14-90), (14-91), (14-94), (14-95), and (14-96) we can express

$$K_1 = \frac{-16\pi m}{3h^3}\left[\bar{l}\mu + \frac{\pi^2}{3\beta^2}\bar{l}^1 + \frac{\pi^2}{6\beta^2}\bar{l}''\mu + \frac{7\pi^4\bar{l}^{\text{III}}}{90\beta^4} + \frac{7\pi^4}{360\beta^4}\bar{l}^{\text{IV}}\mu + \cdots\right] \tag{14-97a}$$

$$K_2 = -\frac{16\pi m}{3h^3}\left[\bar{l}\left(\mu^2 + \frac{\pi^2}{3\beta^2}\right) + \frac{2\pi^2\bar{l}'\mu}{3\beta^2} + \frac{\pi^2\bar{l}''}{6\beta^2}\left(\mu^2 + \frac{7\pi^2}{5\beta^2}\right)\right.$$

$$\left. + \frac{7\pi^4\bar{l}^{\text{III}}\mu}{45\beta^4} + \frac{7\pi^4\bar{l}^{\text{IV}}\mu}{360\beta^4} + \cdots\right] \tag{14-97b}$$

and

$$K_3 = -\frac{16\pi m}{3h^3}\left[\overline{l}\mu\left(\mu^2 + \frac{\pi^2}{\beta^2}\right) + \frac{\pi^2\overline{l}^{\mathrm{I}}}{\beta^2}\left(\mu^2 + \frac{7\pi^2}{15\beta^2}\right)\right.$$

$$\left. + \frac{\pi^2\overline{l}^{\mathrm{II}}\mu}{6\beta^2}\left(\mu^2 + \frac{21}{5}\frac{\pi^2}{\beta^2}\right) + \frac{7\pi^4}{30\beta^4}\overline{l}^{\mathrm{III}}\mu^2 + \frac{7\pi^4\overline{l}^{\mathrm{IV}}\mu^3}{360\beta^4} + \cdots\right] \qquad (14\text{-}97c)$$

when all the terms in (14-96) are retained. In fact, however, we do not need nearly so many terms to evaluate the thermal conductivity in (14-89). We know that at ordinary temperatures the electrons in the metal constitute a highly degenerate gas, or, in other words

$$\frac{1}{\beta} \ll \mu \quad \text{for} \quad T < 6500°\text{K} \qquad (14\text{-}98)$$

and furthermore $\overline{l}$ is assumed to be a rather smooth function of energy so that $\overline{l}^{\mathrm{I}}$ and the higher derivatives of the mean free path should be quite small compared to $\overline{l}$ itself. Thus, as a first approximation, let us retain only terms in $\overline{l}$ and ignore all of the derivatives in evaluating (14-89). It is easy (the student will readily admit) to show that the result is then

$$\kappa = \frac{16\pi^3 m\overline{l}\mu}{9h^3\beta^2 T}\left(1 - \frac{\pi^2}{3\beta^2\mu^2}\right) \qquad (14\text{-}99)$$

and, from (14-98) we may disregard the second term in the parentheses of (14-99). When use is made of (13-43), (14-69), and (14-71), we can express the thermal conductivity of the metal in a form similar to (14-72) for the electrical conductivity

$$\kappa = \frac{\pi^2 k^2 T n\overline{l}}{3m\overline{v}} \qquad (14\text{-}100)$$

When we divide (14-100) by (14-72), the result is the Wiedemann-Franz ratio

$$\frac{\kappa}{\sigma} = \frac{\pi^2}{3}\left(\frac{k}{e}\right)^2 T \qquad (14\text{-}101)$$

which is independent of the nature of the material and proportional to the absolute temperature. The early and approximate theory of Drude gave a similar result with the numerical factor of 3 rather than $\pi^2/3$. The Lorentz theory[4] utilizing the classical statistics gave the factor as 2. The numerical factor given by the Sommerfeld model is in excellent agreement with the results obtained from experiments with samples of Al, Fe, Ni, Cu, Zn, Pd, Ag, Cd, Sn, W, Pt, Au, and Pb carried out near room temperature.[11] The

---

[11]See, for example, J. S. Blakemore, *Solid State Physics* (Philadelphia: W. B. Saunders Company, 1969), p. 139.

agreement of (14-101) with experiment is truly remarkable and the success can be attributed to the fact that the mean free path disappears from the ratio. The expressions (14-72) and (14-100) for the electrical and thermal conductivity separately are not so satisfactory, however; as they each contain the mean free path, which can be evaluated only by means of hypotheses supplementary to the Sommerfeld theory. The very close agreement between the Drude result and (14-101) which, as we have seen, is in good agreement with experiment was one of the strong points in favor of the early proponents of the classical Drude theory. Since Planck's constant does not appear in the Wiedemann-Franz ratio, we are not too surprised that it can be accounted for by a classical theory.

C. *Thermoelectrical Phenomena*

In this subsection we shall be interested in considering electrical and thermal currents propagating along the x-direction in a metalic wire of constant cross-section. We know from more elementary courses in physics that such an ohmic conductor is characterized by the linear relation between the electrical current density and the electric field given by (14-70). Furthermore such a conductor will dissipate energy in accordance with Joule's law which we express as

$$\Delta_e = \mathbf{j} \cdot \mathbf{E} = j_x E_x = jE \tag{14-102}$$

wherein Δ_e represents the time rate of dissipation of energy, by the electrical current in the wire, per unit volume of the conductor; or, in other words, Δ_e is the power density dissipated by electrical means in the wire. We may safely omit the subscripts on j and E, since we are treating a one-dimensional situation in which the component of the electric field and current density perpendicular to the direction of flow of electrons are identically zero.

We recall that the electric current density arose from (14-24) as the meaning of the flux Φ when the quantity being transported was the electron charge $-e$. The electric current density obeys the equation of continuity,[12] which is just a statement of the conservation of charge, and can be written

$$-\partial_t \rho_e = \nabla \cdot \mathbf{j} = \partial_x j_x + \partial_y j_y + \partial_z j_z \tag{14-103a}$$

in general, and in particular for our special case under consideration, we have

$$-\partial_t \rho_e = \partial_x j \tag{14-103b}$$

where ρ_e is the electrical charge density (measured e.g., in coulombs per cubic meter).

[12]R. Becker and F. Sauter, *Electromagnetic Fields and Interactions* (Waltham, Mass.: Blaisdell Publishing Company, 1964), Chap. C1, or consult most any classical electricity text.

In our illustration we have assumed the existence of thermal currents as well as electrical. A thermal current will transport energy (kinetic energy of translation) which we will perceive as heat. This heat energy will also be accumulated in the wire in much the same manner as the joule heat (although we shall presently see that part of this heat flow may be reversible, unlike the joule heating). Since heat is merely one form of energy, the statement of the conservation of heat energy can also be expressed in terms of the equation of continuity for one-dimensional flow. Thus if we let ρ_T be the heat energy density (measured, say, in calories or joules per cubic meter) flowing into some volume of the wire, then the power density brought into the volume via thermal currents is

$$\Delta_T = \partial_t \rho_T = -\partial_x \left(\frac{\text{heat current}}{\text{unit area}} \right) \qquad (14\text{-}104\text{a})$$

But the heat current per unit area is just the quantity we have called $\mathcal{Q}$ in (14-73), so we may write

$$\Delta_T = -\partial_x \mathcal{Q} \qquad (14\text{-}104\text{b})$$

Hence the total power density accumulated in the wire due to both electric and thermal currents is the sum of Δ_e and Δ_T

$$\Delta = jE - \partial_x \mathcal{Q} \qquad (14\text{-}105)$$

From the l.h.s. of (14-84) we can write

$$eE + T\partial_x \left(\frac{\mu}{T} \right) = \frac{j}{eK_1} - \frac{K_2}{K_1 T} \partial_x T \qquad (14\text{-}106)$$

where we have written

$$\partial_x \left(\frac{\mu}{T} \right) = \partial_T \left(\frac{\mu}{T} \right) \partial_x T \qquad (14\text{-}107)$$

We can use (14-106) to express $\mathcal{Q}$ from (14-86) in terms of j, rather than E, as

$$-\mathcal{Q} = \frac{j}{e} \frac{K_2}{K_1} - \frac{K_2^2}{K_1 T} \partial_x T + \frac{K_3}{T} \partial_x T \qquad (14\text{-}108)$$

and to solve expressly for E,

$$E = \frac{j}{e^2 K_1} - \frac{K_2}{K_1 eT} \partial_x T - \frac{T}{e} \partial_x \left(\frac{\mu}{T} \right) \qquad (14\text{-}109)$$

We now multiply numerator and denominator of the r.h. term in (14-108) by K_1 factor the term $\partial_x T$ and insert (14-89) to obtain

$$-\mathcal{Q} = \frac{j}{e} \frac{K_2}{K_1} - K \partial_x T \qquad (14\text{-}110)$$

From (14-70) and (14-84) we see that the conductivity of an ohmic metal is given by

$$\sigma = e^2 K_1; \quad \text{ohmic metal} \tag{14-111}$$

which can be inserted into (14-109). When (14-109), (14-110), and (14-111) are introduced into (14-105) we find

$$\Delta = \frac{j^2}{\sigma} - \partial_x(K\partial_x T) + \left\{\partial_x\left(\frac{j}{e}\frac{K_2}{K_1}\right) - \frac{j}{e}\left[\frac{K_2}{K_1 T}\partial_x T + T\partial_x\left(\frac{\mu}{T}\right)\right]\right\} \tag{14-112}$$

By straightforward differentiation the student can show that the quantity in braces appearing in (14-112) can be written in the form

$$\frac{j}{e} T\partial_x\left[\frac{K_2}{K_1 T} - \frac{\mu}{T}\right] + \frac{K_2}{K_1}\partial_x\left(\frac{j}{e}\right) = \partial_x\left(\frac{j}{e}\frac{K_2}{K_1}\right)$$
$$- \frac{j}{e}\left[\frac{K_2}{K_1 T}\partial_x T + T\partial_x\left(\frac{\mu}{T}\right)\right] \tag{14-113}$$

which wouldn't be much of an advantage except for the fact that we opened this subsection by confining our attention to wires of constant cross section, in which case the electric current density may be taken as constant along the direction of the wire, and the second term on the l.h.s. of (14-113) may then be safely neglected. Consistent with this assumption, then, we may express (14-112) as

$$\Delta = \frac{j^2}{\sigma} - \partial_x(\kappa\partial_x T) + \frac{j}{e} T\partial_x\left[\frac{K_2}{K_1 T} - \frac{\mu}{T}\right] \tag{14-114}$$

The student will recognize the first term as being the usual power density arising from Joule heating. (In our illustration, $j = I/A$ where I is the current through the wire and A is the cross sectional area of the wire. Similarly, for such a simple conductor of length L, $E = V/L$ where V is the voltage across the wire. Thus $j^2/\sigma = jE = IV/AL$, which is the Joule power loss per unit volume.) The second is easily seen to arise from thermal currents resulting from a temperature gradient.

Since the Joule heating is proportional to j^2, a positive and negative current both give rise to the generation of heat and similarly, because of the second x-differentiation, the thermal current always gives rise to the generation of heat, irrespective of the direction of the temperature gradient. The last term in (14-114) however, is linear in both the electrical and thermal currents and ought, therefore, to allow the possibility of reversible reactions i.e., either heat emission or heat absorption.

Indeed, it is found that there are three well-known experimental phenomena which can be accounted for by the last term in (14-114) based on the Sommerfeld model of a metal.

The first phenomenon to be discussed is the so-called *Thomson effect*, which is the observed evolution or absorption of heat that occurs in a metal when the metal is subjected to a temperature gradient at the same time that an electrical current is passing through the metal. The heat which is generated or absorbed can be expressed in terms of an *effective electric field, E'*, existing within the metal which is customarily expressed as

$$E' = \sigma \partial_x T \tag{14-115}$$

in which σ is referred to as the *Thomson coefficient* after Sir William Thomson (later Lord Kelvin) who discovered this phenomenon in 1856; it should not be confused with the electrical conductivity.

If we substitute (14-115) into the third term of (14-114) we may write the reversible contribution to the power density within the metal as

$$\Delta_{\text{rev}} = \frac{j}{e} T \partial_T \left[\frac{K_2}{K_1 T} - \frac{\mu}{T} \right] \partial_x T$$

$$= -\sigma j \partial_x T$$

$$= -jE' \tag{14-116}$$

and the Thomson coefficient may be written as

$$\sigma = -\frac{T}{e} \partial_T \left[\frac{1}{T} \left(\frac{K_2}{K_1} - \mu \right) \right] \tag{14-117}$$

in terms of the integrals evaluated by (14-97). The student should be able to demonstrate that [see Prob. 14-12]

$$\frac{1}{T} \left(\frac{K_2}{K_1} - \mu \right) \simeq \frac{\pi^2 k^2 T}{3\mu} \left[1 + \frac{\bar{l}'}{\bar{l}} \mu \left(1 + \frac{\pi^2}{3\beta^2 \mu^2} \right) + \cdots \right] \tag{14-118}$$

to first order in $\bar{l}'$. We note that the second term in the parentheses of (14-118) is identical (other than sign) to the term appearing in parentheses in (14-99), and consequently may be neglected here for the same reason it was neglected there (and what reason is that?).

We may then insert (14-118) into (14-117), perform the indicated operations and arrive with the following expression for the Thomson coefficient:

$$\sigma = -\frac{\pi^2 k^2 T}{3\mu} \left(1 + \frac{\bar{l}'}{\bar{l}} \mu \right) \tag{14-119}$$

The quantity $\bar{l}'/l$ cannot be evaluated until a supplementary hypothesis is advanced concerning the mean-free-path dependence on the chemical potential. Frequently this ratio is determined by using experimentally measured values of σ as known quantities on the l.h.s. of (14-119), since the other parameters are considered to be known.

The *Thomson electromotive force* ε_T set up in a metal of length L and having its ends at temperatures T_1 and T_2, respectively, is given by

$$
\begin{aligned}
\varepsilon_T &= \int_0^L E'\, dx \\
&= \int_0^L \sigma \partial_x T\, dx \\
&= \int_{T_1}^{T_2} \sigma\, dT
\end{aligned}
\tag{14-120}
$$

The reversible nature of the Thomson effect has been experimentally verified. When the electric current and ε_T are in opposite directions the electrical energy is converted into heat and when the electric current and the temperature gradient are oppositely directed, the heat energy is converted into electrical energy (note that the Thomson emf is directed oppositely to the temperature gradient for negative values of σ).

The second phenomenon of interest is the *Peltier effect*, discovered in 1834 by Jean C. Peltier (1785–1845), which is usually identified as an emf which occurs at the junction between two dissimilar metals at a constant temperature when an electric current passes through the junction.

The Peltier electric field set up between the two metals, A and B, at the constant temperature T can be defined in a manner analogous to (14-116) in terms of the reversible contribution to the power density at the junction between the metals and the electric current passing through the junction

$$
\Delta_{\text{rev}\,\pi} = j\frac{T}{e}\partial_x\left[\frac{K_2}{K_1 T} - \frac{\mu}{T}\right] = -jE_\pi
\tag{14-121}
$$

$$
E_\pi = -\frac{T}{e}\partial_x\left[\frac{K_2}{K_1 T} - \frac{\mu}{T}\right]
\tag{14-122}
$$

It is experimentally more convenient to measure the emf set up in the junction between the metals, A and B, at the temperature T which we designate by $\Pi_{AB}(T)$ and which is known as the *Peltier emf* or the *Peltier coefficient*. Since the emf is given by the line integral over the electric field, we may utilize (14-122) to obtain

$$
\Pi_{AB}(T) = -\frac{T}{e}\int_A^B \partial_x\left[\frac{K_2}{K_1 T} - \frac{\mu}{T}\right] dx
$$

or

$$
\Pi_{AB}(T) = -\frac{T}{e}\left[\left(\frac{K_2}{K_1 T} - \frac{\mu}{T}\right)_B - \left(\frac{K_2}{K_1 T} - \frac{\mu}{T}\right)_A\right]
\tag{14-123}
$$

The student can easily show [see Prob. 14-13] that the Peltier emf and the Thomson coefficients of the two metals are related by

$$\partial_T \left[\frac{\Pi_{AB}(T)}{T} \right] = \frac{\sigma_B - \sigma_A}{T} \tag{14-124}$$

We see from (14-123) that the Peltier emf satisfies

$$\Pi_{AB}(T) = -\Pi_{BA}(T) \tag{14-125}$$

as, of course, it must from elementary physical considerations. It is also experimentally verified that the Peltier effect is reversible, resulting in a cooling of the junction when the current and the emf are in the same direction.

Again (14-118) can be used in conjunction with (14-123) to evaluate the mean free path in the metals, but because of (14-124) such an evaluation is not independent of that obtained by means of the Thomson coefficient.

We shall conclude this chapter (and the main text) with a brief discussion of the *Seebeck effect*, discovered between 1822 and 1826 by Thomas J. Seebeck

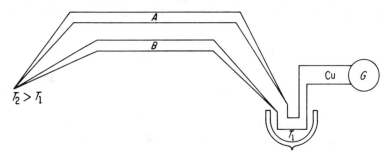

FIG. 14-1. Typical thermocouple application of the Seebeck effect.

(1770–1831). Like the two effects discussed previously, this effect is manifested experimentally as an emf, which in this case is set up in an open circuit formed by two different metals A and B when the two junctions are at different temperatures T_1 and T_2. This arrangement is shown in Fig. 14-1 in a typical thermocouple application.

Apparently the Seebeck effect is a combination of the Thomson effect, since there is a temperature gradient in both metals A and B, and the Peltier effect, since there are dissimilar metals at both temperatures T_1 and T_2. In Fig. 14-1 it is assumed that temperature T_2 is to be measured and temperature $T_1 < T_2$ is some known temperature which might be maintained by melting ice in a Dewar flask. It has also been assumed that the ends of metal A and B at temperature T_1 are connected by means of an intermediate metal, e.g., copper wire, to a high resistance copper wire galvanometer, or a potentiometer. The Seebeck emf is given by the algebraic sum of the Thomson and

Peltier emfs around the circuit shown in Fig. 14-1, and is denoted by $\sigma_{AB}(T_2, T_1)$:

$$\sigma_{AB}(T_2, T_1) = \Pi_{AB}(T_2) + \int_{T_2}^{T_1} \sigma_B \, dT + \Pi_{BCu}(T_1)$$

$$+ \int_{T_1}^{T_1} \sigma_{Cu} \, dT + \Pi_{CuA}(T_1) + \int_{T_1}^{T_2} \sigma_A \, dT \qquad (14\text{-}126)$$

We see that the integral of σ_{Cu} vanishes, since the endpoints are the same; the other two remaining integrals may be combined, as may the Peltier emfs at the reference temperature, so that (14-126) may be written as

$$\sigma_{AB}(T_2, T_1) = \int_{T_1}^{T_2} (\sigma_A - \sigma_B) \, dT + \Pi_{AB}(T_2)$$

$$+ [\Pi_{BCu}(T_1) + \Pi_{CuA}(T_1)] \qquad (14\text{-}127)$$

It has been experimentally demonstrated that the Peltier emf between all possible pairs of metals satisfies the following rule of combination, sometimes referred to as the *law of intermediate metals*[13]

$$\Pi_{AX}(T) + \Pi_{XB}(T) = \Pi_{AB}(T) \qquad (14\text{-}128)$$

Thus if the Peltier emf is known for several metals relative to some standard metal X, the relative Peltier emf between the two metals in question can be determined from (14-128).

Taking X to represent copper we can insert (14-128) and (14-125) into (14-127) to obtain the Seebeck emf for the thermocouple circuit of Fig. 14-1 as

$$\sigma_{AB}(T_2, T_1) = \Pi_{AB}(T_2) - \Pi_{AB}(T_1) + \int_{T_1}^{T_2} (\sigma_A - \sigma_B) \, dT \qquad (14\text{-}129)$$

If we insert (14-124) into (14-129) and carry out an integration by parts we find that we can express

$$\sigma_{AB}(T_2, T_1) = \int_{T_1}^{T_2} \frac{\Pi_{AB}(T)}{T} \, dT \qquad (14\text{-}130)$$

We see that the three effects we have been discussing are not independent, but are related by means of (14-124) and (14-130), so that if any one of the quantities σ_A, $\Pi_{AB}(T)$, or $\sigma_{AB}(T_1, T_2)$ are known, the others may be readily found. The relations (14-124) and (14-130) may be obtained on the basis of

[13]See, for example, B. L. Worsnop and H. T. Flint, *Advanced Practical Physics for Students*, 5th ed. (London: Methuen & Company Limited., 1939), 540; E. U. Condon and H. Odishaw, *Handbook of Physics* (New York: McGraw-Hill Book Company, 1958), Part 4, Chap. 6.

purely thermodynamical reasoning, independently of any particular model for the metal.[14]

As a final note, the student may be see references to the *absolute thermo-electric power*, which is not a measure of power at all, but is defined as the derivative of the Seebeck emf with respect to absolute temperature, and denoted herein as

$$S_{AB} = S_A - S_B \equiv \frac{d\sigma_{AB}}{dT}(T_1, T_2) = \frac{\Pi_{AB}}{T} \qquad (14\text{-}131)$$

where the second equality follows directly from (14-130). We see then that the Peltier emf is equal to the product of the thermoelectric power and the absolute temperature

$$\Pi_{AB}(T) = S_{AB}T \qquad (14\text{-}132)$$

and the Seebeck emf is the integral over the temperature of the difference in thermoelectric powers of the two metals

$$\sigma_{AB}(T_1, T_2) = \int_{T_1}^{T_2} [S_A - S_B]\, dT \qquad (14\text{-}133)$$

We can employ (14-124) and (14-131) to express the Thomson coefficients in terms of the thermoelectric power as

$$\sigma_B - \sigma_A = T\frac{dS_{AB}}{dT} \qquad (14\text{-}134)$$

[14]For discussions of thermoelectric effects the student should consult any solid-state physics or statistical physics textbook under the headings of *thermoelectric effects, free-electron theory of metals, transport properties*, and the like. In addition to Wilson and Seitz cited *supra*, the following specific references are suggested: J.-P. Jan, "Galvanomagnetic and Thermomagnetic Effects in Metals," in F. Seitz and D. Turnbull (eds.), *Solid State Physics*, Vol. 5 (New York: Academic Press, Inc., 1957); S. N. Levine, *Quantum Physics of Electronics* (New York: The Macmillan Company, 1965), Chap. 7; F. W. Sears, *Electricity and Magnetism* (Reading, Mass.: Addison-Wesley Publishing Company, Inc., 1951), Chap. 6; J. M. Ziman, *Principles of the Theory of Solids* (London: Cambridge University Press, 1965), Chap. 7.

PROBLEMS

14-1. Let ξ, η, ζ, lie along three mutually orthogonal cartesian axes. Make use of (14-10) and show that the polar form of $d\xi$, $d\eta$, $d\zeta$ is equivalent to $v\, dv\, v \sin\theta\, d\phi\, d\theta$ where ϕ and θ are the usual longitude and colatitude angles, respectively. Since $\phi_0(v, x_0)$ and $\chi(v, x_0)$ in (14-13) are independent of angle, integrate over ϕ and θ and obtain (14-14) and (14-15).

14-2. Verify (14-19). [*Hint*: refer back to Chap. 13 and remember that the limits of the integral in (14-19) are zero and infinity (relativistic effects have been ignored in this chapter).]

14-3. Let ϕ_0 depend on x only through β and μ in (14-6) and differentiate ϕ_0 w.r.º t. x, and ε and show explicitly that χ in (14-58) is an even function of v and ζ as is required by the form of (14-9).

14-4. Make use of the symmetry afforded by the immediately preceding problem to verify the veracity of (14-60).

14-5. Obtain (14-72) from (14-62) by filling in any steps which are not intuitively obvious to you.

14-6. Many textbooks define the electric current density to be $j = - nev_D$ where $-v_D$ is average drift velocity of the electrons in the direction of the electric field. From (14-70) and (14-72) obtain an expression for v_D in terms of the applied electric field, the charge and mass of the electron, and the mean time between collisions of the electrons with the lattice ions. Also find the electron mobility in the metal which is defined as the average drift velocity of the charge carrier per unit electric field.

14-7. Verify (14-96) by differentiating (14-95).

14-8. Verify (14-97) by substituting (14-96) into (14-94) and using (14-90) and (14-91).

14-9. Show that the mean value of the x-component of the electron velocity, given by (14-20), can be written as

$$\langle \xi \rangle = \frac{\bar{l}}{m\bar{v}}\left[eE + T\frac{\partial}{\partial T}\left(\frac{\mu}{T}\right) + \frac{\mu}{T}\frac{\partial T}{\partial x} \right]$$

when the value of χ given by (14-58) is introduced into (14-20). [*Hint*: use (14-57) and (14-83) and follow the procedure used to obtain the thermal conductivity with the aid of (13-43) and (14-71).]

14-10. Evaluate the Lorenz number, defined as $\kappa/\sigma T$, as predicted by the Drude and the Sommerfeld models. [*Hint*: use (14-101).]

14-11. Verify the veracity of (14-113).

14-12. Obtain (14-118) with the aid of (14-97).

14-13. Make use of the defining equation (14-117) and (14-123) to obtain (14-124).

14-14. Make use of (14-129) to show.

(a) $\sigma_{AB}(T_1, T_2) + \sigma_{BC}(T_1, T_2) = \sigma_{AC}(T_1, T_2)$

(b) $\sigma_{AB}(T_1, T_2) + \sigma_{AB}(T_2, T_3) = \sigma_{AB}(T_1, T_3)$

14-15. Obtain (14-130) from (14-124) and (14-129) by the procedure suggested in the text.

14-16. Show that the thermal conductivity of an electron gas at low temperature is $K = ncv\bar{l}\ 3$.

14-17. Calculate the mean free path of electrons at the Fermi surface of copper for both room temperature and liquid helium temperature if the electrical conductivities are respectively $5 \times 10^{17}\ \text{sec}^{-1}$ and $5 \times 10^{22}\ \text{sec}^{-1}$ (ESU), where the electron velocity at the Fermi surface is to be taken as $v_f = 1.6 \times 10^8$ cm/sec.

14-18. The mechanical vibrations of the ion cores about the lattice equilibrium sites in a metal are described in the quantum mechanical picture by phonons. The phonons act like particles and obey Bose-Einstein statistics. When a temperature gradient is applied across the metal, heat is not only transported by the electrons, but a small amount is transported by phonons. How is the general form of the Boltzmann transport equation for phonons expected to compare to that of the electron? Explain.

14-19. If the emf of a copper and constantan thermocouple is known between the temperatures T_1 and T_2, and the emf is known between the temperatures T_1 and T_3, what is the emf for the thermocouple between temperatures T_2 and $T_3 (T_1 < T_2 < T_3)$?

14-20. If the emf of copper and constantan thermocouple is known between the temperatures T_1 and T_2, and if the emf of a gold-iron and copper thermocouple is known between the temperatures T_1 and T_2, what is the emf of a constantan and gold-iron thermocouple between the temperatures T_1 and T_2?

Fourier Series Representation of an Arbitrary Function

The student is well aware of the fact that two or more waves of a particular kind may traverse a given region simultaneously, and independently of one another. Thus at a cocktail party, waves originating from N independent sources may impinge on the ear of a guest, who is still able, by diligence, to screen out the background of $N - 1$ of the sources and concentrate his attention on the waves emanating from a particular source. This principle, whereby the resultant disturbance is equivalent to the sum of the individual disturbances, is called the *principle of superposition*, and is valid when the equations governing the wave motion are linear. Hence when the super-position principle is valid, one can analyze a very complicated wave motion as a linear combination of simple waves. The French mathematician Joseph Fourier (1768–1830) in his analysis of heat conduction showed that the most general form of a periodic (physically realizable) wave could be synthesized from a linear combination of simple harmonic waves.[1] Thus if $y(t)$ is the mathematical description of a periodic wave with period T, it can be written, according to the Fourier formulation of the principle of superposition, as a linear combination of simple harmonic waves:

$$y(t) = \sum_{n=0}^{\infty} [a_n \cos n\omega t + b_n \sin n\omega t] \tag{1}$$

where

$$\omega = 2\pi f = \frac{2\pi}{T} \tag{2}$$

is the angular frequency of the wave. We can easily see that

[1] J. Fourier, *Theorie Analytique de la Chaleur*. Edition of 1878. English trans. by Dover Publications (New York: 1966).

$$y(t + T) = \sum_{n=0}^{\infty} [a_n \cos (n\omega t + n2\pi) + b_n \sin (n\omega t + n2\pi)]$$

$$= \sum_{n=0}^{\infty} \cos n2\pi [a_n \cos n\omega t + b_n \sin n\omega t]$$

$$y(t + T) = y(t) \tag{3}$$

is indeed periodic with period T. Mathematicians have investigated the Fourier series of (1) to determine the conditions which must be imposed[2] upon the arbitrary function, $y(t)$, to insure that the r.h.s. indeed converges to $y(t)$. The conditions which $y(t)$ must satisfy, sometimes called the Dirichlet conditions, are fulfilled by practically all of the functions which are of interest to workers in the physical sciences. The function $y(t)$ must be a bounded periodic function which, in any one period, has at most a finite number of local maxima and minima, and only a finite number of points of discontinuity. These conditions are obviously mathematical rather than physical in nature, and if fulfilled by $y(t)$ the Fourier series of $y(t)$ will converge to $y(t)$ at all points where $y(t)$ is continuous.[3] If $y(t)$ is a discontinuous function, it can be shown (and, in fact is shown in other textbooks[4]) that the Fourier series converges to the arithmetic mean of the right-hand and left-hand limits of $y(t)$ at the point where $y(t)$ has a finite jump. Thus if $y(t)$ has a discontinuity at the point $t = \xi$ and if $y(\xi +)$ and $y(\xi -)$ are the right-hand and left-hand limits of the function at the point of discontinuity, respectively, then the Fourier series will converge to the value

$$y(\xi) = \frac{y(\xi +) + y(\xi -)}{2}$$

at the point of discontinuity. Note that if $y(t)$ is continuous at the point $t = \xi$, then the Fourier series converges to $y(\xi)$ as $y(\xi +) = y(\xi -)$ at a point of continuity. If $y(t)$ is *discontinuous* at the point $t = \xi$ the *continuous* Fourier series will be incapable of exactly matching $y(\xi)$ and reacts pathologically by *overshooting* the right- and left-hand values of the function at the discontinuity. This situation is known as the *Gibbs phenomenon*, after J. W. Gibbs, who discovered this feature of the Fourier series representation empirically at the turn of the present century.[5] The Gibbs phenomenon

[2] See, for example, M. J. Lighthill, *Introduction to Fourier Analysis and Generalized Functions* (London: Cambridge University Press, 1958).

[3] R. D. Stuart, *An Introduction to Fourier Analysis* (New York: Barnes & Noble, 1961), Chap. 1.

[4] L. Brand, *Advanced Calculus* (New York: John Wiley & Sons, Inc., 1955), Chap. 12.

[5] J. W. Gibbs, *Nature* **59**, 200, 606 (1899). See also the discussion in Ref. 4 *supra*.

occurs when a discontinuous function is represented as a linear combination of any complete orthonormal set of functions [e.g., Legendre polynomials, Bessel functions, Mathieu functions, Tchebycheff polynomials, etc., as well as the sine and cosine functions of (1)]. The amount by which the Fourier series exceeds the function at the point of discontinuity depends on the particular form of the function to be represented, as well as the choice of orthonormal expansion functions. For the series of (1) the overshoot amounts to about 9 percent of the magnitude of the jump discontinuity in the function $y(t)$ at the point of discontinuity.[6] The student should investigate with care the effect of the Gibbs phenomenon on the Fourier series representation of a discontinuous function at points of discontinuity. There is a wealth of information available concerning the Gibbs phenomenon and techniques that can be employed to suppress it.[7]

Returning our attention to (1), we will find it convenient to choose our origin such that the independent variable is defined over the interval

$$-\frac{T}{2} \le t \le \frac{T}{2} \tag{4}$$

We recall that the Dirichlet conditions were applied to a periodic function. If we are interested in a nonperiodic function, defined over a finite range $a \le t \le b$, we can label $b - a = T$ and shift the axis so that (4) holds. Then the nonperiodic function may also be represented by (1), with the ancillary result that outside the interval in which the nonperiodic function is defined, the r.h.s. of (1) will represent a periodic extension of the function.

It is apparent that if we know the form of all the expansion coefficients, a_n and b_n, in (1) we will be in a position to express the Fourier representation of $y(t)$. It is equally apparent that, since there are an infinite number of the a_n and b_n, it would be impractical to attempt to write all the coefficients in tabular form. It would be much more convenient to have a general equation, involving the index n, to tell us how to evaluate any of the a_n or b_n. Fortunately such a general formula exists, and we shall now proceed to identify it. A little thought leads us to the conclusion that the form of the coefficients

[6]R. Courant and D. Hilbert, *Methods of Mathematical Physics* (New York: Interscience Publishers, Inc., 1963), p. 105, and references contained herein.

[7]In addition to the above references, see G. Arfken, *Mathematical Methods for Physicists* (New York: Academic Press, 1966), p. 520; H. S. Carslaw, *Theory of Fourier's Series and Integrals* (London: Macmillan & Company, 1930), Chap. 9; R. V. Churchill, *Fourier Series and Boundary Value Problems* (New York: McGraw-Hill Book Company, 1941), p. 86; E. A. Kraut, *Fundamentals of Mathematical Physics* (New York: McGraw-Hill Book Company, 1967), p. 186; C. Lanczos, *Applied Analysis* Englewood Cliffs, N.J.: Prentice-Hall, Inc., 1956), p. 225; E. T. Whittaker and G. N. Watson, *A Course of Modern Analysis*, 4th ed. (London: Cambridge University Press, 1927), Chap. 9.

will strongly depend on the function, $y(t)$, being represented; the coefficients describing a sawtooth wave must differ from those describing a square wave.

To evaluate the a_n we multiply both sides of (1) by cos $m\omega t$ and integrate with respect to t over the complete period from $-T/2$ to $+T/2$; we assume m is an integer. Since the integral of a sum of terms is equal to the sum of the individual integrals (for a finite sum at least, see Ref. 8 for further discussion of this point) we can write

$$\int_{-T/2}^{T/2} y(t) \cos m\omega t \, dt = \sum_{n=0}^{\infty} \left\{ a_n \int_{-T/2}^{T/2} \cos n\omega t \cos m\omega t \, dt \right.$$

$$\left. + b_n \int_{-T/2}^{T/2} \sin n\omega t \cos m\omega t \, dt \right\} \qquad (5)$$

We now proceed to evaluate the two integrals on the r.h.s. of (5). The first integral can be written as

$$I_{nm} = \int_{-T/2}^{T/2} \cos n\omega t \cos m\omega t \, dt \qquad (6a)$$

$$= \frac{1}{m\omega} \int_{-T/2}^{T/2} \cos n\omega t \, d[\sin m\omega t]$$

$$= \frac{1}{m\omega} \left\{ [\cos n\omega t \sin m\omega t] \Big|_{-T/2}^{T/2} - \int_{-T/2}^{T/2} \sin m\omega t [-n\omega \sin n\omega t \, dt] \right\} \quad (6b)$$

From (2) we see that

$$\frac{\omega T}{2} = \pi \qquad (2a)$$

and thus the integrated term vanishes at both limits, and we have

$$I_{nm} = -\frac{n}{m^2\omega} \int_{-T/2}^{T/2} \sin n\omega t \, d[\cos m\omega t]$$

$$= -\frac{n}{m^2\omega} \left\{ [\sin n\omega t \cos m\omega t] \Big|_{-T/2}^{T/2} - n\omega \int_{-T/2}^{T/2} \cos m\omega t \cos n\omega t \, dt \right\}$$

$$I_{nm} = +\frac{n^2}{m^2} I_{nm} \qquad (6c)$$

The only way for (6c) to be satisfied is for I_{nm} to be null or for $n^2 = m^2$. Since n was restricted to be a nonnegative integer in (1), this means that

$$n = m \neq 0 \qquad (7)$$

[8] E. W. Hobson, *Theory of Functions of a Real Variable and the Theory of Fourier's Series*, 2nd ed. (New York: Dover Publications, Inc., 1957), Vol. II, p. 482.

With the relation of (7) we can express

$$I_{mm} = \int_{-T/2}^{T/2} \cos^2 m\omega t \, dt = 2 \int_0^{T/2} \cos^2 m\omega t \, dt \qquad (8)$$

and by means of the trigonometric identity

$$\cos 2\theta = \cos^2\theta - \sin^2\theta = 2\cos^2\theta - 1 \qquad (9)$$

(8) becomes

$$I_{mm} = \int_0^{T/2} \left[\cos 2m\omega t + 1 \right] dt$$

$$I_{mm} = \frac{1}{2m\omega} \sin 2m\omega t \Big|_0^{T/2} + t \Big|_0^{T/2} = T/2 \qquad (10)$$

The remaining condition, when $m = n = 0$, can be evaluated as

$$I_{00} = \int_{-T/2}^{T/2} 1 \cdot 1 \; dt = T \qquad (11)$$

and thus we can write

$$I_{mn} = \frac{T}{2} \delta_{mn} \qquad m \neq 0$$

$$I_{00} = T \qquad (12)$$

where the Kronecker delta function is null if the two indices differ and is unity if they are the same.

The second integral in (5) can similarly be defined and evaluated by a repeated integration by parts (see Prob. AI-1):

$$J_{nm} = \int_{-T/2}^{T/2} \sin n\omega t \cos m\omega t \, dt \qquad (13a)$$

$$= \frac{n^2}{m^2} J_{nm} \qquad (13b)$$

The interpretation of (13b) is the same as that of (6c): if $n \neq m$, J_{nm} must vanish. We now will show that even if n and m are identical, J_{nm} is still null. It is obvious from the definition of (13a) that when $m = n = 0$,

$$J_{00} = 0 \qquad (14a)$$

and

$$J_{mm} = \frac{1}{m\omega} \int_{-T/2}^{T/2} \sin m\omega t \, d \left[\sin m\omega t \right]$$

$$= \frac{1}{2m\omega} \sin^2 m\omega t \Big|_{-T/2}^{T/2} = 0 \qquad (14b)$$

so, for all values of m and n,

$$J_{mn} = 0 \tag{15}$$

We can now substitute (12) and (15) into (5) to obtain

$$\int_{-T/2}^{T/2} y(t) \cos m\omega t \, dt = a_0 T \delta_{m0} + \sum_{n=1}^{\infty} a_n \frac{T}{2} \delta_{mn} \tag{16}$$

All the terms on the r.h.s. of (16) are identically zero, except one, for a given value of m, due to the presence of the Kronecker delta functions. Thus we see that cosine coefficients are given by

$$a_0 = \frac{1}{T} \int_{-T/2}^{T/2} y(t) \, dt$$

$$a_m = \frac{2}{T} \int_{-T/2}^{T/2} y(t) \cos m\omega t \, dt \tag{17}$$

The b_n can be evaluated by a procedure analogous to that used to determine the a_n. We multiply both sides of (1) by $\sin m\omega t$ (where m is an integer) and integrate over one period. This leads to

$$\int_{-T/2}^{T/2} y(t) \sin m\omega t \, dt = \sum_{n=0}^{\infty} a_n J_{mn}$$

$$+ \sum_{n=1}^{\infty} b_n \int_{-T/2}^{T/2} \sin n\omega t \sin m\omega t \, dt \tag{18}$$

where the second sum on the r.h.s. has been started with $n = 1$, rather than $n = 0$, since the sine term vanishes when $n = 0$, and the first sum is identically zero by (15). The integral on the r.h.s. of (18) could be evaluated by the repeated process of integration by parts used *supra*, but it is quicker to recognize the trigonometric identity

$$\cos(m + n)\omega t = \cos m\omega t \cos n\omega t - \sin m\omega t \sin n\omega t \tag{19}$$

which leads to

$$\int_{-T/2}^{T/2} \sin m\omega t \sin n\omega t \, dt = I_{mn} - \int_{-T/2}^{T/2} \cos[(m + n)\omega t] \, dt$$

$$= I_{mn} \tag{20}$$

When we substitute (20) and (12) into (18), we have

$$\int_{-T/2}^{T/2} y(t) \sin m\omega t \, dt = \sum_{n=1}^{\infty} b_n \frac{T}{2} \delta_{mn}$$

and thus

$$b_m = \frac{2}{T} \int_{-T/2}^{T/2} y(t) \sin m\omega t \, dt \tag{21}$$

We are now in a position to justify our earlier procedure of defining our range of variable by means of (4). Any function may be defined in terms of the sum of an even and an odd function such as

$$y(t) = \left\{ \frac{y_{(t)} + y_{(-t)}}{2} \right\} + \left\{ \frac{y_{(t)} - y_{(-t)}}{2} \right\}$$

$$= y_e(t) + y_o(t) \tag{22}$$

independent of any intrinsic symmetry properties of $y(t)$. Now if an odd function is integrated over an interval which is symmetrical about the origin, the integral vanishes (see Prob. AI-2). When (22) is substituted into (21), we see that

$$b_m = \frac{2}{T} \left\{ \int_{-T/2}^{T/2} y_e(t) \sin m\omega t \, dt + \int_{-T/2}^{T/2} y_0(t) \sin m\omega t \, dt \right\} \tag{23}$$

The product of an even function $[y_e(t)]$ and an odd function $[\sin mt]$ is odd, and thus the first integral in (23) is identically null. The product of an odd function $[y_o(t)]$ with an odd function results in an even function and so we find

$$b_m = \frac{2}{T} \int_{-T/2}^{T/2} y_o(t) \sin m\omega t \, dt$$

$$= \frac{4}{T} \int_{0}^{T/2} y_o(t) \sin m\omega t \, dt \tag{24}$$

The student can now easily show (see Prob. AI-3) that the coefficients of the even cosine terms are given by

$$a_0 = \frac{2}{T} \int_{0}^{T/2} y_e(t) \, dt$$

$$a_m = \frac{4}{T} \int_{0}^{T/2} y_e(t) \cos m\omega t \, dt \tag{25}$$

Hence from (24) and (25) we see that if the function $y(t)$ is neither intrinsically even nor intrinsically odd, it will be necessary to use both the sine and cosine terms in (1) to represent $y(t)$, and the a_n and b_n will be given by (17) and (21) or by (24) and (25). However, if $y(t)$ is an even (odd) function, then $y_0(t)$ $[y_e(t)]$ will be identically zero, as can be seen from (22), and b_m $[a_m]$ will also be identically zero for all m, and the even (odd) function, $y(t)$, will be represented by only the even (odd) cosine (sine) terms in (1). It seems natural that an even (odd) function should be capable of representation by a sum of even (odd) functions.

The nodding acquaintance with Fourier series, which the student may have obtained in this brief appendix, should be sufficient to enable the student to follow the Fourier series arguments made in the corpus of this text; however, a cursory excursion into the references should reveal to the student a wealth of topics pertaining to Fourier analysis which have been omitted from discussion herein.

PROBLEMS

1. Show that (13b) follows directly from the definition of (13a). [*Hint*: follow the procedure used to go from (6a) to (6c).]

2. Show that, if $y_o(t) = - y_o(-t)$,

$$\int_{-a}^{a} y_o(t)\, dt = 0 \qquad - a \le t \le a$$

3. Verify (25) by substituting (22) into (17).

4. From the definition of a_0 in (17), show that a_0 may be interpreted as the mean value of $y(t)$, averaged over one period.

5. In the testing of wide band (video) amplifiers, it is common practice to employ a square-wave signal. Consider a square wave defined by

$$y(t) = \begin{cases} -V_0 & -\dfrac{T}{2} < t < 0 \\[2mm] 0 & t = 0,\ \pm\ T/2 \\[2mm] +V_0 & 0 < t < T/2 \end{cases}$$

(a) Graph $y(t)$ over several periods (b) What is the intrinsic symmetry property of $y(t)$? (c) Obtain all the Fourier expansion coefficients for $y(t)$.

6. Consider a function defined by

$$y(t) = \begin{cases} -V_0 & -\dfrac{T}{2} \le t < -T/4 \\[2mm] +V_0 & -\dfrac{T}{4} < t < +T/4 \\[2mm] -V_0 & \dfrac{T}{4} < t \le T/2 \\[2mm] 0 & t = \pm\ T/4 \end{cases}$$

(a) What relation does this function bear to the wave in Prob. 5? (b) Graph this function over several periods. (c) Obtain all the Fourier coefficients for this function. (d) Contrast your results with those obtained for Prob. 5.

7. Discuss the Gibbs phenomenon with respect to the discontinuity in the wave function of Prob. 5 or 6. (This is discussed at length in the references.)

II | *Complex Variables*

A complex number z can be defined as an ordered pair of two real numbers x and y which obeys certain laws of combination. It is customary to write

$$z = x + iy \tag{1}$$

where

$$i = + \sqrt{i^2} = + \sqrt{-1} \tag{2}$$

is termed the *imaginary unit* (the student may recognize that frequently engineers, particularly electrical engineers, designate $\sqrt{-1}$ by j, rather than i, which is the conventional symbol used by mathematicians, physicists, and chemists). The real numbers x and y are known as the *real* and *imaginary* parts (or components) of the complex number z, and are often designated by

$$\text{Re } (z) = x$$

and

$$\text{Im } (z) = y \tag{3}$$

respectively.

If $x = 0$, the number $z = 0 + iy$ is often termed a *pure imaginary* number, whereas if $y = 0$, the number $z = x + 0$ reduces to an ordinary *real* number. Thus real numbers are a subclass of complex numbers. It follows from definition (1) that two complex numbers can be equal to each other if and only if their real and imaginary parts are each, respectively, equal.

The sum or difference of two complex numbers z_1 and z_2 is a complex number whose real and imaginary parts are the sum or difference of the real and imaginary parts of z_1 and z_2

$$z_1 = x_1 + iy_1$$
$$z_2 = x_2 + iy_2$$
$$\overline{z_1 \pm z_2 = (x_1 \pm x_2) + i(y_1 \pm y_2)} \tag{4a}$$
$$z_3 = x_3 + iy_3 \tag{4b}$$

The product of two complex numbers can similarly be found by merely applying the algebraic rules of multiplication:

$$z_1 z_2 = (x_1 + iy_1)(x_2 + iy_2)$$

$$= (x_1 x_2 - y_1 y_2) + i(x_1 y_2 + x_2 y_1) \tag{5a}$$

$$z_3 = x_3 + iy_3 \tag{5b}$$

similarly, one complex number may be divided by another complex number:

$$z_3 = \frac{z_1}{z_2} = \frac{x_1 + iy_1}{x_2 + iy_2} \tag{6a}$$

However, the result of (6a) is not in the form of a complex number. This defect can easily be remedied by multiplying numerator and denominator by the *complex conjugate* of z_2, defined by

$$z_2^* = x_2 - iy_2 \tag{7}$$

The complex conjugate of a complex number is obtained by replacing i in the complex number by $-i$, and may be interpreted, geometrically, as the reflection of z about the x-axis. Applying (7) to (6a), we have

$$z_3 = \frac{z_1 z_2^*}{z_2 z_2^*} = \frac{(x_1 x_2 + y_1 y_2)}{x_2^2 + y_2^2} + i\frac{(x_2 y_1 - x_1 y_2)}{x_2^2 + y_2^2} \tag{6b}$$

$$= x_3 + iy_3 \tag{6c}$$

Since there is a one-to-one correspondence between the ordered pairs of real numbers (x, y) and the complex numbers z, given by (1), it makes sense to associate the complex number with the point whose rectangular cartesian coordinates are (x, y) in the x-y plane. When used in this connection, the x-y plane is frequently referred to as the *Argand diagram*, or sometimes simply as the complex plane, or the z-plane. In Fig. AII-1 the complex number is pictured as a vector drawn from the origin to the point having coordinates (x, y). With this interpretation, we see that the point (x, y) may be labeled (r, θ) where the polar coordinates are related to the rectangular cartesian coordinates by

$$r = \sqrt{x^2 + y^2} = |z| = \sqrt{zz^*}$$

$$\theta = \tan^{-1}\frac{y}{x} \tag{8}$$

with the inverse relations given by

$$x = r\cos\theta$$

and

$$y = r\sin\theta \tag{9}$$

The interpretation of r as the magnitude of the complex number is consistent with (6b). With the use of (9), we can write (1) in the form

$$z = r[\cos \theta + i \sin \theta] \tag{10}$$

and from (1-32) and (1-33) we note that the sum in the square brackets of (10) can be written as

$$e^{i\theta} = \cos \theta + i \sin \theta \tag{11}$$

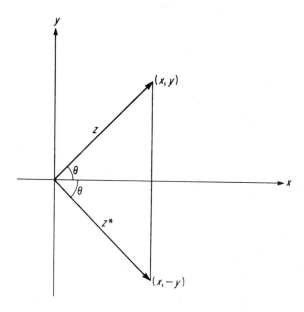

FIG. AII-1.

which is known as the *Euler formula* (not to be confounded with the *Euler equations* or the *Euler-Lagrange equations*). Incorporating (11) into (10) we see that the complex number may be expressed simply as

$$z = re^{i\theta} \tag{12}$$

In this form the complex conjugate may be formed as

$$z^* = re^{-i\theta} \tag{13}$$

from which the first equation in (8) follows trivially. We note that (12) is well suited for expressing powers of a complex number

$$z^n = r^n e^{in\theta} \tag{14}$$

as well as products and quotients of complex numbers

$$z_3 = z_1 z_2 = r_1 r_2 \, e^{i(\theta_1 + \theta_2)} = r_3 e^{i\theta_3} \tag{15}$$

$$z_3 = \frac{z_1}{z_2} = \frac{r_1}{r_2} e^{i(\theta_1 - \theta_2)} = r_3 e^{i\theta_3} \tag{16}$$

It is often convenient to consider the functional dependence of many functions on complex variables z. In general a function of a complex variable will be complex [consider the exponential dependence on an imaginary variable, given by (11)] and so write

$$f(z) = u(z) + iv(z) \tag{17}$$

where the *real* functions, u and v, may be considered as functions of x and y from (1). The complex function may possess a derivative, which is defined in the same manner as the derivative of a function of a real variable

$$f'(z) = \frac{df}{dz} = \lim_{\Delta z \to 0} \frac{f(z + \Delta z) - f(z)}{\Delta z} \tag{18}$$

where, from (1),

$$\Delta z = \Delta x + i\Delta y \tag{19}$$

The function $f(z)$ is said to be *analytic* (although the words *regular*, *holomorphic*, and *monogenic* are often used synonomously) in some region of the complex plane if it possesses a unique derivative everywhere within the region, independent of the method whereby Δz approaches zero. The function is said to be analytic at the point z_0, when it possesses a unique derivative at every point within some small circle about the point $z = z_0$. If the function possesses a unique derivative at some point, the derivative will be the same, independent of the manner in which Δz of (19) approaches zero. Let us assume that $f(z)$ is analytic over a certain domain in the complex plane, then

$$\frac{df}{dz} = f'(z) = \frac{\partial f}{\partial x}\frac{dx}{dz} + \frac{\partial f}{\partial y}\frac{dy}{dz} \tag{20}$$

approaches a definite limit as Δz approaches zero in any manner. Let us choose two particularly convenient methods for Δz to approach zero: first, along a line parallel to the real axis ($y = $ const) and second, along a line parallel to the imaginary axis ($x = $ const). In the first case $dz = dx$ and $dy = 0$ so that

$$\frac{dx}{dz} = 1; \qquad \frac{dy}{dz} = 0 \tag{21a}$$

and (20) takes the form, with the use of (17),

$$f'(z) = \left[\frac{\partial u}{\partial x} + i \frac{\partial v}{\partial x} \right] \times (1) \tag{22a}$$

In the second case $dz = idy$ and $dx = 0$, or

$$\frac{dx}{dz} = 0; \qquad \frac{dy}{dz} = \frac{1}{i} \tag{21b}$$

and when (21b) is substituted into (20) we find

$$f'(z) = \left[\frac{\partial u}{\partial y} + i \frac{\partial v}{\partial y} \right] \times \left(\frac{1}{i} \right)$$

$$f'(z) = \frac{\partial v}{\partial y} - i \frac{\partial u}{\partial y} \tag{22b}$$

Since the function $f'(z)$ is assumed to be analytic, the l.h.s. of (22a) and (22b) have the same value and thus the r.h.s. of (22a) and (22b) must also be equal, and this can be so only if the real and imaginary parts are respectively equal. Thus we find the relations

$$\frac{\partial u}{\partial x} = \frac{\partial v}{\partial y}; \qquad \frac{\partial u}{\partial y} = -\frac{\partial v}{\partial x} \tag{23}$$

which are known as the Cauchy-Riemann conditions, after the French mathematician A. L. Cauchy (1789–1857), and the German mathematician G. F. B. Riemann (1826–66). Our little demonstration has indicated that the Cauchy-Riemann conditions of (23) are necessary conditions for the existence of the derivative of the function given by (17). It is shown, in textbooks dealing with the theory of functions of a complex variable,[1] that in order to ensure that the function $f(z) = u(x, y) + iv(x, y)$ has a derivative at every point in some region of the complex plane [i.e., the single-valued function (17) is analytic in the region], it is both necessary and sufficient that the four partial derivatives appearing in (23), exist, are continuous, and satisfy the Cauchy-Riemann differential equations of (23) at every point within the region. Notice that more is demanded of a function, for it to be analytic, than just that (23) be obeyed (see Prob. AII-4).

The Cauchy-Riemann equations tell us that we cannot obtain an analytic function from a combination of two *arbitrary* differentiable functions. The real and imaginary parts of an analytic function *must* be related to each other by (23). We can now demonstrate that both the real and

---

[1]See, for example, R. V. Churchill, *Introduction to Complex Variables and Applications* (New York: McGraw-Hill Book Company, 1948), Chap. 2; L. L. Pennisi, *Elements of Complex Variables* (New York: Holt, Rinehart and Winston, Inc., 1963), Chap. 3.

imaginary parts, $u(x, y)$ and $v(x, y)$ obey the same (second-order) differential equation, and consequently *neither* u nor v can be chosen in a completely arbitrary manner. To do this we differentiate the first equation of (23) with respect to x, and the second with respect to y:

$$\frac{\partial^2 u}{\partial x^2} = \frac{\partial^2 v}{\partial x \partial y}$$

$$-\frac{\partial^2 u}{\partial y^2} = \frac{\partial^2 v}{\partial y \partial x} \tag{24}$$

If the second derivatives exist and are continuous [which will be the case in any region where $f(z)$ is analytic[1]] the order of differentiation will be immaterial and the right-hand sides of (24) will be equal, and consequently by subtracting the two equations, we will find

$$\nabla^2 u \equiv \Delta u \equiv \frac{\partial^2 u}{\partial x^2} + \frac{\partial^2 u}{\partial y^2} = 0 \tag{25}$$

which is known as *Laplace's equation*. Any function which has continuous second-order partial derivatives and which obeys Laplace's equation, is called an *harmonic function*. Thus if the function of (17) is analytic, its real and imaginary parts are (sometimes referred to as *conjugate*) *harmonic functions* (see Prob. AII-6).

We may not only differentiate a complex function but may also integrate the complex function over some region of the complex plane. In general, the value of an integral, having definite (complex) limits will depend not only on the values of those limits, but also on the path chosen to evaluate the integral. In Fig. AII-2 we see that the two points α and β may be con-

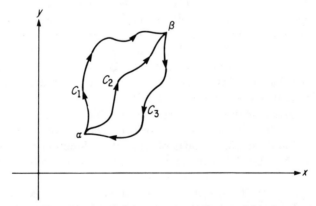

FIG. AII-2.   Line integrals between two points α and β in the complex plane generally depend on the path chosen to evaluate the integral

nected by an infinite number of curves, or paths, and, in general, $f(z)$ will take differing values along the various paths. The definite integral

$$I(\alpha, \beta, C, f) = \int_{C}^{\beta} f(z) \, dz \tag{26}$$

will, in general, be dependent not only on the limits of integration, but also on the path chosen to evaluate the integral. Such an integral as (26) is known as a *line integral*. As an example of a path-dependent line integral, consider the function

$$f(z) = \frac{1}{z - z_0} \tag{27}$$

which is analytic throughout the complex plane except at the isolated point z_0, where the function becomes unbounded. Since the derivatives of $f(z)$ exist in every neighborhood of z_0, but not at the point z_0 itself, this point is called a *singular point*, or a *singularity* of the function. To make our example more concrete, let us choose the singular point to be

$$z_0 = 1 + i = (1,1) \tag{28}$$

Also let the function $f(z)$ be integrated from the origin to the point (4,2), and we shall choose two paths of integration: first we take the path along the abscissa from the origin to $x = 4$, followed by the path from $y = 0$ to $y = 2$, along $x = 4$; the second path we shall follow is along the ordinate from the origin to $y = 2$, and then from $x = 0$ to $x = 4$ along the line $y = 2$. The two choices of path are shown in Fig. AII-3, as well as the point of singularity for $f(z)$ given by (27).

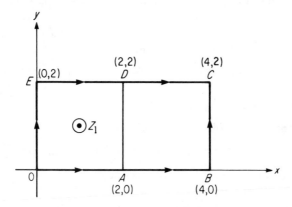

FIG. AII-3. Two possible paths to evaluate the integral of $f(z)$, given by (27), between the points (0, 0) and (4,2) are: along $OABC$ and along $OEDC$.

Along the first path we can express our integral as

$$I = \int_{\substack{x=0 \\ (y=0)}}^{4} f(z)\,dz + \int_{\substack{y=0 \\ (x=4)}}^{2} f(z)\,dz = I_1 + I_2 \tag{29}$$

where $f(z)$ can be expressed as a complex number, in the form of (1), as

$$f(z) = \frac{(x - x_0) - i(y - y_0)}{(x - x_0)^2 + (y - y_0)^2} \tag{30}$$

with $x_0 = y_0 = 1$. \hfill (31)

To evaluate I_1 along the abscissa, we note that since $y = 0$, $dz = dx$, and thus

$$I_1 = \int_{x=0}^{4} \frac{(x - x_0) + iy_0}{(x - x_0)^2 + y_0^2}\,dx$$

$$= \frac{1}{2}\int_0^4 \frac{2(x - x_0)d(x - x_0)}{(x - x_0)^2 + y_0^2} + i\int_0^4 \frac{d\!\left(\dfrac{x - x_0}{y_0}\right)}{1 + \left(\dfrac{x - x_0}{y_0}\right)^2}$$

$$= \frac{1}{2}\ln\left[(x - x_0)^2 + y_0^2\right]\Big|_0^4 + i\tan^{-1}\left(\frac{x - x_0}{y_0}\right)\Big|_0^4$$

or, making use of (31), we finally obtain

$$I_1 = \tfrac{1}{2}\ln 5 + i\left[\tan^{-1}3 + \tan^{-1}1\right] \tag{32}$$

Similarly to evaluate I_2, we note that since $x = 4$, $dz = i\,dy$, and

$$I_2 = \frac{1}{2}\int_0^2 \frac{2(y - y_0)\,d(y - y_0)}{(y - y_0)^2 + (x - x_0)^2} + i\int_0^2 \frac{d\!\left(\dfrac{y - y_0}{x - x_0}\right)}{1 + \left(\dfrac{y - y_0}{x - x_0}\right)^2}$$

$$I_2 = i\,2\tan^{-1}\left(\tfrac{1}{3}\right) \tag{33}$$

Adding (33) and (32) to obtain (29), we find

$$I = \tfrac{1}{2}\ln 5 + i\left[\tan^{-1}3 + \tan^{-1}1 + 2\tan^{-1}\left(\tfrac{1}{3}\right)\right] \tag{34}$$

We now express the integral over the second choice of path as

$$J = \int_{\substack{y=0 \\ (x=0)}}^{2} f(z)\,dz + \int_{\substack{x=0 \\ (y=2)}}^{4} f(z)\,dz = J_1 + J_2 \tag{35}$$

where we again make use of (30) and (31). To evaluate J_1, along the ordinate axis, we make use of $dz = idy$ and write

$$J_1 = \frac{1}{2} \int_0^2 \frac{2(y - y_0)d(y - y_0)}{(y - y_0)^2 + x_0^2} - i \int_0^2 \frac{d\left(\dfrac{y - y_0}{x_0}\right)}{1 + \left(\dfrac{y - y_0}{x_0}\right)^2}$$

$$J_1 = -i\,2\tan^{-1} 1 \tag{36}$$

And in a similar manner we can [but don't, (see Prob. AII-7)] show that

$$J_2 = \tfrac{1}{2} \ln 5 - i[\tan^{-1} 3 + \tan^{-1} 1] \tag{37}$$

which when combined with (36) and (35) leads to

$$J = \tfrac{1}{2} \ln 5 - i[\tan^{-1} 3 + 3\tan^{-1} 1] \tag{38}$$

We now notice a curious result, which the student may have observed in the course of other classwork – that the complete line integral from the origin back to the origin, along the path $OABCDEO$, does not vanish! The value of this integral is just

$$\oint_{OBCEO} f(z)dz = I + (-J) = I - J \tag{39}$$

where the symbol $\oint$ means that the integral is evaluated over a *closed* path, which does not intersect itself, usually in a counter-clockwise manner, back to the starting point. In general the *particular* path followed must be specified; as in the instant case the path $OBCEO$ is designated. From (34) and (38) we see that

$$I - J = i\,2\{[\tan^{-1} 3 + \tan^{-1} (\tfrac{1}{3})] + 2\tan^{-1} 1\} \tag{40}$$

The term $\tan^{-1} 1$ obviously has the value of $\pi/4$, and the sum in the square brackets can easily be evaluated by drawing a small triangle as shown below,

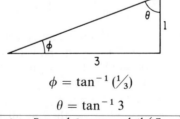

where

$$\phi = \tan^{-1} (\tfrac{1}{3})$$

$$\theta = \tan^{-1} 3$$

$$\overline{\theta + \phi = [\tan^{-1} 3 + \tan^{-1} (\tfrac{1}{3})] = \pi/2}$$

from the well-known theorem that the sum of the interior angles in a triangle is equal to two right angles. Thus we see that, instead of vanishing,

$$\oint_{OBCEO} f(z)dz = 2\pi i \tag{41}$$

The student can easily show [see Prob. AII-9] that the same result is obtained when the integral is evaluated over the path $OADEO$ (or, as we shall see later, when *any closed path which encloses the point z_0 is traversed*). On the other hand, the result is null when the integral is evaluated over the closed path $ABCDA$ (which path does not encircle the singular point z_0).

The results of this example can be easily obtained from an application of one of several tools used in complex analysis to evaluate simple, closed contour integrals, and to which the name of Cauchy is traditionally appended. The first of these tools, all of which will be enounced without proof, is the *Cauchy-Goursat theorem* which can be stated as: If a function $g(z)$ is single-valued and analytic everywhere on and within a simple, closed, "smooth" (having only a finite number of sharp corners, as in the paths of Fig. AII.3) curve C, then

$$\oint_C g(z)\, dz = 0 \tag{42}$$

The utility of the Cauchy-Goursat theorem becomes readily apparent, for example, in evaluating the integral of (26), with $f(z)$ given by (27), around the closed [simple, and smooth] curve $ABCDA$ of Fig. AII.3. On and within the curve $ABCDA$ the function to be integrated is single-valued and analytic, and hence from (42) the line integral vanishes, in accord with the result of Prob. AII-9.

Since the function of (27) is not analytic everywhere within the curve $OADEO$ [nor the curve $OABCDEO$], we may not apply the Cauchy-Coursat theorem to the evaluation of (26) along this curve. We may, however, resort to a second tool for evaluating line integrals, the *Cauchy integral formula*: If $g(z)$ is single-valued and analytic everywhere on and within a simple, closed, "smooth" curve C, and if z_0 is any point interior to C, then

$$\oint_C \frac{g(z)}{z - z_0}\, dz = 2\pi i g(z_0) \tag{43}$$

We note that by taking $g(z) = 1$ (which is analytic *everywhere* in the entire complex plane), and choosing C to be the path $OABCDEO$, the left-hand side of (43) is just the integral in (41). It is not too surprising then that the r.h.s. of (43) is the same as the r.h.s. of (41).

If the function $f(z)$ is analytic at all points interior to some circle C_0, of radius r_0 and with center located at z_0, then at all points within C_0, the function can be expanded in a Taylor's series about the point z_0. More interesting however, is the generalization of the Taylor's series, known as the *Laurent series*, given by

$$f(z) = \sum_{n=0}^{\infty} a_n(z - z_0)^n + \sum_{n=1}^{\infty} b_n(z - z_0)^{-n} \tag{44}$$

If C_1 and C_2 are two concentric circles with center at z_0, and if $f(z)$ is analytic on C_1 and C_2 and in the region bounded by C_1 and C_2, then at each point between C_1 and C_2 $f(z)$ can be represented by the convergent series of (44). The coefficient b_1 of the term $1/(z - z_0)$ is called the *residue of* $f(z)$ at $z = z_0$. If *all* the b's are zero, $f(z)$ is analytic at $z = z_0$, and the point z_0 is called a *regular point*. If a particular $b_n \neq 0$, but all the $b_m = 0$ for $m > n$, $f(z)$ is said to have a pole of order n at $z = z_0$. If b_1 is the only nonzero b coefficient, $f(z)$ is said to have a simple pole. If there are an infinite number of nonzero b's, the point z_0 is said to be an essential singularity of $f(z)$.

The third tool, frequently used to evaluate complex contour integrals, is the *Couchy residue theorem*, which can be stated as

If $f(z)$ is analytic on and within a simple, closed, smooth contour C, except at a finite number of singular points z_1, z_2, ..., z_n located in the interior of C, then

$$\oint_C f(z)\, dz = 2\pi i \sum_{k=1}^{n} b_{1k} \tag{45}$$

where b_{1k} is the residue of $f(z)$ at the point z_k.

We see that (45) can be used to evaluate the integral (41) when $f(z)$ is given by (27), and C is the path $OABCDEO$. In this case $f(z)$ has a simple pole at $z = z_0$ [since all the $b_n \equiv 0$ except for $n = 1$, also all the $a_n \equiv 0$] and b_1 is (trivially) found from (27) to be given by $b_1 = 1$. Hence (45) becomes identical to (41) in this case. Also, since $f(z)$ is analytic on and within the contour $ABCDA$, there is no residue of $f(z)$ in this region and the line integral of $f(z)$ around this contour must vanish.

Since we will generally be interested in finding the residue at the point where $f(z)$ has a simple pole, we conclude this appendix with a discussion of another method for finding the residue b_1 (other than expressing the function in its Laurent series about the point z_0 and determining b_1 from inspection). We begin by multiplying (44) by $(z - z_0)$ to obtain

$$(z - z_0)f(z) = \sum_{n=0}^{\infty} a_n(z - z_0)^{n+1} + b_1 \tag{46}$$

since, for a function having only a simple pole, b_1 is the only nonzero b in (44) Thus all the terms in the infinite sum on the r.h.s. of (46) become zero at $z = z_0$, and hence we find the residue at a simple pole to be given by

$$b_1 = \lim_{z \to z_0} (z - z_0)f(z) \tag{47}$$

PROBLEMS

1. Show that (11) follows as a direct result of (1-32) and (1-33).

2. From (11) and (14) deduce *De Moivre's theorem*:
$$[\cos \theta + i \sin \theta]^n = \cos n\theta + i \sin n\theta$$

3. By equating real and imaginary parts, use De Moivre's theorem to evaluate the trigonometric identities for $\cos 2\theta$, $\sin 2\theta$, $\cos 3\theta$, and $\sin 3\theta$.

4. Consider the function defined by
$$f(z) = \begin{cases} u(x, y) + iv(x, y); & z \neq 0 \\ 0 & ; \quad z = 0 \end{cases}$$
where
$$u(x, y) = \frac{x^3 - y^3}{x^2 + y^2} \quad \text{and} \quad v(x, y) = \frac{x^3 + y^3}{x^2 + y^2}$$

(a) Show that this function satisfies the Cauchy-Riemann equation at the origin. (b) Show that this function does not satisfy the Cauchy-Riemann equation at the origin. (c) Is the function $f(z)$ analytic at the origin? (d) Why? [*Hint*: investigate the derivatives in the manner of
$$u_x(0, 0) = \lim_{x \to 0} u_x(x, 0) \quad \text{and} \quad u_x(0, 0) = \lim_{y \to 0} u_x(0, y)]$$

5. By means of (9) we can express $f(z) = u(r, \theta) + iv(r, \theta)$. Obtain the Cauchy-Riemann equations in polar form. [*Hint*: follow the procedure in the text and evaluate $f'(z)$ along $\theta = $ const. and also along $r = $ const.]

6. Show that if $f(z)$ is analytic in some region, the imaginary part is a harmonic function.

7. Write the problem of evaluating
$$\int_c \frac{1}{z - z_0} \, dz$$
over the curves $OABC$ and $OEDC$ in Fig. AII-3, in great detail; supply all the missing steps which are not intuitively obvious to you between (29) and (41).

8. Show that the result of integrating $f(z)$, given by (27), from (4,2) to (0,0) along the path $CDEO$ is just the negative of J, given by (38).

9. Evaluate the integral of $f(z)$, given by (27), around the closed path: (a) $OADEO$, and (b) $ABCDA$, of Fig. AII-3.

10. Let C be a circle of radius ρ with center at z_0 so that $z - z_0 = \rho e^{i\theta}$ on C. (a) Show and clearly label C for an arbitrary z_0 on an Argand diagram. (b) Evaluate
$$I_n = \oint_c \frac{dz}{(z - z_0)^n}$$
for all n. (c) Use (b) to determine the a_n and b_n of (44) for all n.

Appendix III | *Lagrange's and Hamilton's Equations*

The basic equation of elementary mechanics, describing the motion of a particle acted upon by an external unbalanced force $\mathbf{F}$, is

$$\mathbf{F} = \frac{d\mathbf{p}}{dt} \equiv \dot{\mathbf{p}} \tag{1}$$

where $\mathbf{p}$ is the (vector) momentum of the particle. The student recognizes (1) as the vector statement of Newton's second law of motion, and since the components of a vector obey the same equations as the vector itself obeys, we can write (1) in component form as

$$F_i = \dot{p}_i, \qquad i = 1, 2, 3 \tag{2}$$

If there are N particles, rather than just a single particle, (1) and (2) will hold for each and every particle. By changing our point of view slightly we can interpret (2) in a somewhat different manner. Rather than thinking of the N particles requiring (2) to be written N times for the description of the motions of N particles, with three components each (in a three-dimensional space) we can think of our *single system*, composed of N particles, and requiring $3N$ coordinates to completely specify the state of motion of the single system. From this vantage point, (2) will still describe the motion of the system, but i will now run from 1 to $3N$. In other words, our collection of N particles in a three-dimensional space can be considered to be mathematically equivalent to a single particle in a $3N$-dimensional space, since both are described by the same equations of motion.

It may happen that all N particles are not independent of each other, or that the motion of even a single particle is restricted. In the case of a system composed of N particles in the configuration of a rigid body the particles are constrained such that the distances between particles must remain unchanged. This constraint can be expressed by equations of the form

$$(\mathbf{r}_i - \mathbf{r}_j)^2 = (x_i - x_j)^2 + (y_i - y_j)^2 + (z_i - z_j)^2 = c_{ij}^2 \tag{3}$$

where i and j take all values from 1 to N. By expanding the range of i and j to $3N$, the equations can be written

$$(x_i - x_j)^2 = d_{ij}^2, \qquad i, j = 1, \ldots, 3N \tag{4}$$

A single particle may be constrained to move on a plane, which we may take to be the x-y plane. Clearly the equation of constraint may be written as

$$dz = 0, \quad \text{or} \quad z = \text{const} \tag{5}$$

and we may take the constant to be zero and thus the motion will take place in the $z = 0$ plane at all time. A single particle may be further constrained in planar motion; e.g., a simple pendulum consisting of a mass at the end of an inextensible string of length l with the point of suspension at $\mathbf{r}_0$ has for its equation of constraint

$$(\mathbf{r} - \mathbf{r}_0)^2 = l^2 \tag{6}$$

where $\mathbf{r}$ is the location of the pendulum bob.

The conditions of constraint (3) through (6) are all of the form

$$\phi(\mathbf{r}_1, \mathbf{r}_2, \ldots, t) = 0 \tag{7}$$

where ϕ is some function, and $\mathbf{r}_i$ is the vector locating the ith particle. Constraints of the form (7) are known as *holonomic constraints*, which means that there exist algebraic relations between some or all of the space and time coordinates of the particles of the system. There are systems, however, for which such algebraic relations do not exist, or cannot be found without in fact solving the entire problem. Examples of this type of constraint are found when particles are confined to a particular region of space, as a particle confined to the interior or exterior of a sphere of radius a, for which the equations of constraint take the form

$$r^2 \leq a^2 \quad \text{or} \quad r^2 \geq a^2 \tag{8}$$

respectively. The constraint equation (8), cannot be recast in the form of (7) and consequently, such systems are said to be *nonholonomic*. Nonholonomic constraints are frequently encountered in connection with bodies which roll without slipping.

The algebraic relations between coordinates, given by (7), constitute such relations that the coordinates appearing in (7) become dependent coordinates, and the holonomic constraint equations can be used to eliminate these dependent coordinates from the equations of motion. Consequently, since these dependent coordinates can be eliminated, a formal solution can always be found for problems involving holonomic constraints; and for this reason we shall confine our attention to such holonomic systems.

Constraints in which the time appears explicitly are sometimes referred to as *rheonomous*, and those constraints which are independent of time are termed *scleronomous*; both designations apply to holonomic and non-holonomic constraints as well.

When a system is subjected to constraints, the forces associated with the constraints are generally not known a priori but must be obtained from the solution of the problem which, from (2), is to be found in terms of the unknown constraint forces. To circumvent this circular approach to the solution of the problem we shall consider a formulation of the laws of mechanics in such a manner that the forces of constraint are not involved and do not appear in the equations to be solved. In such a formulation only the known, applied, external forces acting on the system will be required for the solution.

In setting up the equations to be solved for a system subject to holonomic constraints, we run into the difficulty impressed on us by the fact that all $3N$ cartesian coordinates are not independent. If there were no constraints acting on the system of N particles, all $3N$ coordinates would be independent and the system would then be said to possess $3N$ *degrees of freedom*. If the system is subjected to holonomic constraints such that n of the $3N$ coordinates are dependent coordinates, then the n constraint equations in the form of (7) can be used to eliminate these n coordinates, leaving then $3N - n$ *independent* coordinates, and the system is said to possess $3N - n$ degrees of freedom. We can effect the elimination of the n-dependent coordinates in another manner by replacing the cartesian coordinates with a set of $3N - n$ *generalized coordinates*, $q_1, q_2, \ldots, q_{3N-n}$. In many instances the choice of the generalized coordinates will be suggested by the symmetry, or some other characteristic of the system under consideration. In general, each and every one of the $3N - n$ generalized coordinates will be a function of all $3N$ cartesian coordinates and, if moving coordinate frames are involved, they will depend on the time as well; thus we may write

$$q_i \equiv q_i(x_1, x_2, \ldots, x_{3N}, t) \equiv q_i(x_j, t) \tag{9}$$

where i and j take integer values from 1 to $3N - n$.

As an example of these concepts we can consider a single point mass particle constrained to move on the surface of a sphere of radius a. In this case, $N = 1$ and the three cartesian coordinates are related by the single constraint equation

$$x^2 + y^2 + z^2 - a^2 = 0 \tag{10}$$

which may be used to eliminate one of the 3 coordinates, leaving $3(1) - 1 = 2$ degrees of freedom. A little reflection on the situation leads us to conclude that the longitude and latitude angles of a spherical polar coordinate frame should serve satisfactorily as generalized coordinates. Thus we can write

$$q_1(x,y,z) = \theta = \tan^{-1}\frac{\sqrt{x^2 + y^2}}{z} \tag{11a}$$

$$q_2(x,y) = \phi = \tan^{-1} y/x \tag{11b}$$

which, for this simple case, can easily be "inverted" and solved for the cartesian coordinates [in fact θ and ϕ were actually obtained from x,y,z of (12)]:

$$\begin{aligned} x &= a \sin \theta \cos \phi \\ y &= a \sin \theta \sin \phi \\ z &= a \cos \theta \end{aligned} \tag{12}$$

In this rather trivial example, the generalized coordinates were taken to be angles; and frequently it will be convenient to choose distances and angles as the generalized coordinates. However, such esoteric entities as the Fourier coefficients of the equations of motion may serve as generalized coordinates.

We have noted that a system subject to holonomic constraints can be described in terms of its independent coordinates, with the equations of constraint (7) being used to eliminate the dependent coordinates. If there are f d.o.f. we can write (2) in the form

$$F_i = \frac{d}{dt}(m_i\dot{x}_i) \qquad i = 1, 2, ...,f \tag{13}$$

It proves efficacious to express the kinetic energy of the system, in terms of the cartesian coordinates, as

$$T = \sum_i \tfrac{1}{2} m_i \dot{x}_i^2 \tag{14}$$

from which we see that

$$\frac{\partial T}{\partial \dot{x}_i} = m_i\dot{x}_i \tag{15}$$

For a conservative system there exists, by definition, a potential energy function for the system which is a function only of the coordinates of the system,

$$V = V(x_i) \qquad i = 1, 2, ..., f \tag{16}$$

such that the force components are given by

$$F_i = -\frac{\partial V}{\partial x_i} \tag{17}$$

Now, with the aid of (15) and (17), we may write (13) in the form

$$\frac{d}{dt}\left(\frac{\partial T}{\partial \dot{x}_i}\right) = -\frac{\partial V}{\partial x_i} \tag{18}$$

We have now, by means of (18), expressed Newton's second law of motion in terms of two scalar energy functions. In cartesian coordinates the kinetic energy is only a function of the velocity components of the particles in the system and never a function of the cartesian coordinates. On the other hand, for most conservative forces, the potential energy function is only a function of the cartesian coordinates and (practically) never[1] contains velocity components. We assume that the equations describing the transformation to generalized coordinates, given by (9), can be inverted to yield the cartesian coordinates in terms of the generalized coordinates

$$x_i \equiv x_i(q_1, q_2, \ldots, q_f, t) \equiv x_i(q_j, t) \tag{19}$$

Because of the relation (19), the potential energy will be a function of the generalized coordinates, but not the generalized velocities. Consequently we can express

$$\frac{\partial V}{\partial x_i} = \sum_{j=1}^{f} \frac{\partial V}{\partial q_j}\frac{\partial q_j}{\partial x_i} \tag{20a}$$

When we use the chain rule to take derivatives, as in (20a), we *always* sum over the repeated indices [j in (20a)], and the dummy index j is always taken over the range from 1 to f. Consequently, in an effort to avoid writer's cramp (to say nothing of the savings in printer's ink) it has become customary to utilize the *Einstein summation convention* (originally introduced in the application to tensor calculus) in which the summation symbol is suppressed and the fact that a sum is to be taken is indicated by the repeated index. Accordingly we should express (20a) in the form

$$\frac{\partial V}{\partial x_i} = \frac{\partial V}{\partial q_j}\frac{\partial q_j}{\partial x_i} \tag{20b}$$

Note that the same index [i in (20a) or (20b)] is to be found on either side of the equation.

Having expressed the r.h.s. of (18) in terms of the generalized coordinates, we now investigate the l.h.s. of (18). We first note that the kinetic energy is a function of the cartesian velocities, which can be obtained from (19) as

$$\dot{x}_i = \frac{\partial x_i}{\partial q_j}\dot{q}_j + \frac{\partial x_i}{\partial t} = \dot{x}_i(q_k, \dot{q}_k, t) \tag{21}$$

---

[1] Electromagnetic forces of the type $q(\mathbf{v} \times \mathbf{B})$ constitute an important exception, however. See, for example, H. Goldstein, *Classical Mechanics* (Reading, Mass.: Addison-Wesley Publishing Co., Inc., 1950), Chap. 2.

where the first term on the r.h.s. represents a sum (since the indices are repeated), and the explicit dependence of $\dot{x}_i$ on the generalized coordinates [since, from (19), $\partial x_i/\partial q_j$ will depend on the q_k] is indicated. We can then write

$$\frac{\partial T}{\partial \dot{x}_i} = \frac{\partial T}{\partial q_j}\frac{\partial q_j}{\partial \dot{x}_i} + \frac{\partial T}{\partial \dot{q}_j}\frac{\partial \dot{q}_j}{\partial \dot{x}_i} \tag{22}$$

But from (9) we see that the generalized coordinates are not functions of the cartesian velocities, and so

$$\frac{\partial q_j}{\partial \dot{x}_i} \equiv 0 \quad \text{for all } i \text{ and } j \tag{23}$$

Furthermore, from (21), we notice that

$$\frac{\partial \dot{x}_i}{\partial \dot{q}_j} = \frac{\partial x_i}{\partial q_j} \tag{24}$$

so that (22) can be written as

$$\frac{\partial T}{\partial \dot{x}_i} = \frac{\partial T}{\partial \dot{q}_j}\frac{\partial q_j}{\partial x_i} \tag{25}$$

We now extract the total time rate of change of (25) which can be written as

$$\frac{d}{dt}\left(\frac{\partial T}{\partial \dot{x}_i}\right) = \frac{\partial q_j}{\partial x_i}\frac{d}{dt}\left(\frac{\partial T}{\partial \dot{q}_j}\right) + \frac{\partial T}{\partial \dot{q}_j}\frac{d}{dt}\left(\frac{\partial q_j}{\partial x_i}\right) \tag{26}$$

Now we note that

$$\frac{d}{dt}\left(\frac{\partial q_j}{\partial x_i}\right) = \frac{\partial}{\partial x_k}\left(\frac{\partial q_j}{\partial x_i}\right)\dot{x}_k + \frac{\partial}{\partial t}\left(\frac{\partial q_j}{\partial x_i}\right) = \frac{\partial}{\partial x_i}\left[\frac{\partial q_j}{\partial x_k}\dot{x}_k + \frac{\partial q_j}{\partial t}\right]$$

$$\frac{d}{dt}\left(\frac{\partial q_j}{\partial x_i}\right) = \frac{\partial \dot{q}_j}{\partial x_i} \tag{27}$$

and thus, with the aid of (20b), (26), and (27), we can write (18) in the form

$$\left[\frac{d}{dt}\left(\frac{\partial T}{\partial \dot{q}_j}\right) + \frac{\partial V}{\partial q_j}\right]\frac{\partial q_j}{\partial x_i} + \frac{\partial T}{\partial \dot{q}_j}\frac{\partial \dot{q}_j}{\partial x_i} = 0 \tag{28}$$

Inasmuch as the potential energy term does not (by hypothesis, for conservative systems) depend on the generalized velocities, we can rewrite (28) as

$$\left\{\frac{d}{dt}\frac{\partial}{\partial \dot{q}_j}(T - V) - \frac{\partial}{\partial q_j}(T - V)\right\}\frac{\partial q_j}{\partial x_i} + \left[\frac{\partial T}{\partial q_j}\frac{\partial q_j}{\partial x_i} + \frac{\partial T}{\partial \dot{q}_j}\frac{\partial \dot{q}_j}{\partial x_i}\right] = 0 \tag{29}$$

The student may recognize the double sum in the square brackets of (29) as being the derivative of the kinetic-energy function with respect to the cartesian coordinate x_i, and of course this term vanishes:

$$\frac{\partial T}{\partial x_i} \equiv 0 \tag{30}$$

It is customary[2] to call the difference between the kinetic energy and the potential energy functions, in the parentheses of (29), the *Lagrangian function*, or simply the *Lagrangian* of the system [although it is sometimes known as the *kinetic potential*] and to denote it by

$$L(q_j, \dot{q}_j, t) \equiv T - V \tag{31}$$

Note from (31) that the Lagrangian is to be expressed in terms of the generalized coordinates, q_j, the generalized velocities, $\dot{q}_j$, and perhaps the time. This is consistent with the differential operators which act on L within the braces of (29). Thus the procedure which is generally followed is to express the kinetic and potential energies in terms of the cartesian coordinates and velocities x_i and $\dot{x}_i$, then (19) and (21) are employed to transform to the generalized coordinates and velocities, in terms of which L is to be expressed. We then see that (29) may be written as

$$\left[\frac{d}{dt} \frac{\partial L}{\partial \dot{q}_j} - \frac{\partial L}{\partial q_j} \right] \frac{\partial q_j}{\partial x_i} = 0 \quad i, j = 1, 2, \dots, f \tag{32}$$

Now (32) represents a system of f equations (since i takes on all integer values between 1 and f), each of which contains a sum of f terms (since j also takes on all integer values from 1 to f, and the repetition of the subscript j indicates a sum over j is to be performed), and since the cartesian and generalized coordinates are each independent coordinates, the quantities $\partial q_j / \partial x_i$, for a fixed value of i, are likewise independent, and (32) reduces to a statement of linear independence, which can be satisfied *only* if the coefficients of $\partial q_j / \partial x_i$, for *all* j and i fixed, each separately vanish.[3] Thus the Lagrangian (energy) formulation of Newton's equations of motions can be expressed as

$$\left[\frac{d}{dt} \frac{\partial}{\partial \dot{q}_j} - \frac{\partial}{\partial q_j} \right] L(q_j, \dot{q}_j, t) = 0, \qquad j = 1, 2, \dots, f \tag{33}$$

for a conservative system.

From (15) and (31) we notice that, for conservative systems in which the

[2]J. L. Synge and B. A. Griffith, *Principles of Mechanics*, 3rd ed. (New York: McGraw-Hill Book Company, 1959), Chap. 15.

[3]E. A. Kraut, *Fundamentals of Mathematical Physics* (New York: McGraw-Hill Book Company, 1967), Secs. 1.4 and 5.5.

potential energy is velocity independent, we may express the ith component of the linear momentum of the system as

$$p_{x_i} = \frac{\partial L}{\partial \dot{x}_i} \qquad (34)$$

in cartesian coordinates (that is, when the generalized coordinates of the system are taken to be rectangular cartesian coordinates). This fact leads us to define the *generalized momentum* associated with the generalized coordinate q_j (sometimes called the *canonical momentum* or the momentum *conjugate* to the coordinate q_j) as

$$p_j\,(q_i,\,\dot{q}_i) = \frac{\partial L(q_i,\,\dot{q}_i)}{\partial \dot{q}_j} \qquad (35)$$

Although (35) is directly analogous to (34), there are significant differences: the generalized momentum is frequently a function of the generalized coordinates as well as the generalized velocities, and the generalized momentum will not necessarily have the dimensions of linear momentum. In a similar manner we may define the components of a *generalized force*, in analogy with (17), as

$$Q_j = -\frac{\partial V}{\partial q_j} \qquad (36)$$

which need not have the units usually associated with force (i.e., pounds, dynes, and newtons).

With the aid of (31), (35), and (36) we can express (33) in the form

$$Q_j + \frac{\partial T}{\partial q_j} = \dot{p}_j \qquad (37)$$

which differs in form from (2) by the presence of the term $\partial T/\partial q_j$. This term is often referred to as a fictitious force (examples of which are centrifugal and Coriolis forces) and its presence is due to the curvature of the generalized coordinate surfaces. Naturally, when the quantities in (37) are expressed in cartesian coordinates, (37) reduces identically to (2) when use is made of (30).

As indicated by (31), the Lagrangian may be an explicit function of time, which dependence may be introduced by means of the transformation equations from cartesian to generalized coordinates (9), even for an inherently conservative system. The total time rate of change of the Lagrangian may be written as

$$\frac{dL}{dt} = \frac{\partial L}{\partial q_i}\,\dot{q}_i + \frac{\partial L}{\partial \dot{q}_i}\frac{d\dot{q}_i}{dt} + \frac{\partial L}{\partial t} \qquad (38)$$

The first term on the r.h.s. of (38) can be replaced by means of (33) to yield

$$\frac{dL}{dt} = \frac{d}{dt}\left(\frac{\partial L}{\partial \dot{q}_i}\right)\dot{q}_i + \frac{\partial L}{\partial \dot{q}_i}\frac{d\dot{q}_i}{dt} + \frac{\partial L}{\partial t} = \frac{d}{dt}\left[\dot{q}_i\frac{\partial L}{\partial \dot{q}_i}\right] + \frac{\partial L}{\partial t} \tag{39}$$

We can now use (35) to rewrite (39) in the form

$$-\frac{\partial L}{dt} = \frac{d}{dt}[p_i\dot{q}_i - L] \tag{40}$$

from which we gather that if L does not depend explicitly on the time, the quantity in the square brackets is conserved. We also notice that (35) can be "inverted" or "solved" for all of the $\dot{q}_i$ in terms of the p_j and q_j and substituted back into the square brackets of (40) to yield a quantity which is (or can be) expressed as a function of only the p_j and q_j (and perhaps the time). This quantity is known as the *Hamiltonian function*, and is always expressed as a function of the generalized momenta and coordinates

$$H(p_j, q_j; t) = \sum_i p_i\dot{q}_i - L(q_j, \dot{q}_j; t) \tag{41}$$

This "change of variables" from the q_j and $\dot{q}_j$, appearing in the Lagrangian function, to the q_j and p_j appearing in the Hamiltonian function, has been effected by (41) with the use of (35), and arises not only in analytical mechanics but also in thermodynamics. For example, in Chap. 2 we saw that the Helmholtz energy, which is regarded as a function of volume and temperature, may be obtained from the Gibbs energy, which is expressed as a function of the temperature and pressure, according to [see Eqs. 2-18a and 2-16]

$$-A(V, T) = VP - G(T, P) \tag{2-18b}$$

The formal resemblance between (2-18b) and (41) can be seen more readily by considering a time independent Lagrangian for a system with one degree of freedom and writing (41) directly below (2-18b). The mathematical procedure employed to accomplish this change of variables and manifested by means of (2-18b) and (41), for example, is known as the *Legendre transformation*.[4] The Legendre transformation plays an important role in analytical mechanics, thermodynamics, and statistical physics, but we shall not pursue a determination of its properties any further here.

We now proceed to investigate the character of the Hamiltonian function and to determine its role in expressing the equations of motion for the system in analogy with (2) and (33). From the defining equation of the Hamiltonian, (41), we can write

$$dH = p_i d\dot{q}_i + \dot{q}_i dp_i - dL \tag{42}$$

[4]H. B. Callen, *Thermodynamics* (New York: John Wiley & Sons, Inc., 1960), Chaps. 5, 11.

[where we have reverted to the Einstein summation convention, having abandoned it in (41) to emphasize that the first term is to be summed over]. Since the Lagrangian depends functionally on the q_i, $\dot{q}_i$, and the time, we may write

$$dL = \frac{\partial L}{\partial q_i}dq_i + \frac{\partial L}{\partial \dot{q}_i}d\dot{q}_i + \frac{\partial L}{\partial t}dt \tag{43}$$

which becomes, with the aid of (33) and (35),

$$dL = \dot{p}_i dq_i + p_i d\dot{q}_i + \frac{\partial L}{\partial t}dt \tag{44}$$

Substitution of (44) into (42) leads to

$$dH = \dot{q}_i dp_i - \dot{p}_i dq_i - \frac{\partial L}{\partial t}dt \tag{45}$$

in terms of the independent coordinates p_i, q_i, and the time. But, since H is a function of the p_i, q_i, and time, we may quite generally express

$$dH = \frac{\partial H}{\partial p_i}dp_i + \frac{\partial H}{\partial q_i}dq_i + \frac{\partial H}{\partial t}dt \tag{46}$$

By equating (45) and (46) we see that the coefficients of the independent variable must satisfy

$$\dot{q}_i = \frac{\partial H}{\partial p_i} \tag{47a}$$

$$\dot{p}_i = -\frac{\partial H}{\partial q_i} \tag{47b}$$

$$\frac{\partial L}{\partial t} = -\frac{\partial H}{\partial t} \tag{47c}$$

The relations of (47a) and (47b) are known as *Hamilton's canonical form of the equations of motion* or simply as *Hamilton's canonical equations.* Notice that they constitute $2f$ first-order differential equations, whereas the Lagrange equations consist of f second-order differential equations. Thus both yield $2f$ integration constants which can be determined from a knowledge of the initial coordinates and velocities *or* momenta. Although Hamilton's canonical equations are first-order partial differential equations, they are generally coupled and consequently the computational labor involved in extracting a solution from them is practically the same as that involved in solving the Lagrange equations of motion. Note also that (47a) is an explicit description of $\dot{q}_i$, which we said earlier could be obtained from "inverting" (35); consequently (47a) gives us no new information that was not already made use of in obtaining H from (41). Of course if a particular generalized coordinate (momentum) does not appear explicitly in the Hamiltonian function, the corresponding canonical momentum (coordinate) is a constant of the motion. Coordinates which do not appear explicitly in the Hamiltonian function are called *cyclic* or *ignorable* coordinates[1] since the canonical momentum in the Hamiltonian is a constant and thus the effect is to reduce the number of d.o.f. in the Hamiltonian by 1 except that the constant momentum must be determined from initial conditions describing the system. Advantage is taken of any naturally occurring cyclic coordinates by means of the *Routhian* formulation of the equations of motion, which is discussed in many more advanced texts on analytical mechanics,[5] and which will not be pursued any further here. At this point the student may suggest that if the Hamiltonian is a constant of the motion and if it were possible to transform to a particular coordinate system such that *all* the generalized coordinates were cyclic, the solution of Hamilton's canonical equations would be trivial: the generalized momenta would all be constants and the generalized coordinates would all vary linearly with time. Such transformations do indeed exist; they are called *canonical transformations* or *contact transformations*, and are discussed under this title or under the heading of Hamilton-Jacobi theory in more advanced texts on classical mechanics. We shall not be vitally interested in contact transformations in applications to our work, but it is worthwhile for the student to be aware that such topics do exist.

We have seen from (40) and (41) that if the time does not appear explicitly in the Lagrangian function the Hamiltonian function will be a constant of the motion. This is both a necessary and sufficient condition for the constancy of H. Independent of whether or not H is a constant of the motion, we note that H, like L, has the dimensions of work or energy; and in many cases of interest H will be found to be equivalent to the total energy of the system. In particular, if the transformation equations (9) which define the generalized coordinates do not depend explicitly on the time, and if the potential energy is velocity-independent, it can be shown (and, in fact is shown in Ref. 1) that the Hamiltonian is the total system energy

$$H = T + V \tag{48}$$

a result which is valid even for relativistic mechanics (see Chap. 6 of Ref. 1). The requirements that the coordinate transformations be independent of time (i.e., that the coordinate axes be fixed in space relative to each other) and that the potential energy function be independent of velocities, are sufficient but not necessary conditions that the Hamiltonian function be equal

[5]See, for example, A. G. Webster, *The Dynamics of Particles and of Rigid, Elastic, and Fluid Bodies*, 2nd ed. (New York: Dover Publications, Inc., 1959), Chap. 5, and Refs. 1 and 2 *supra*.

to the system total energy. The usual example which is cited to demonstrate that the Hamiltonian may still be identified with the system energy when the potential energy is an explicit function of the particle velocity, is the situation in which a charged particle moves under the influence of an unchanging electromagnetic field. In the conservative tradition of textbook writers, we now pursue this illustration. The total force on a particle of mass m, charge q, and traveling with a velocity $\mathbf{v}$ in the presence of an electric field $\mathbf{E}$, and magnetic field $\mathbf{B}$, is given by the well-known Lorentz force[6]

$$\mathbf{F} = q[\mathbf{E} + \mathbf{v} \times \mathbf{B}] \tag{49}$$

where the electric and magnetic fields can be expressed in terms of the electrostatic potential ϕ, and the magnetic vector potential $\mathbf{A}$, as[6]

$$\mathbf{E} = -\nabla\phi - \frac{\partial \mathbf{A}}{\partial t} \tag{50a}$$

and

$$\mathbf{B} = \nabla \times \mathbf{A} \tag{50b}$$

Substitution of (50) into (49) leads to

$$\mathbf{F} = q\left[-\nabla\phi - \frac{\partial \mathbf{A}}{\partial t} + \mathbf{v} \times (\nabla\times\mathbf{A}) \right] \tag{51}$$

Making use of the vector identity[7]

$$\mathbf{a} \times (\nabla \times \mathbf{b}) = \nabla(\mathbf{a} \cdot \mathbf{b}) - (\mathbf{a} \cdot \nabla)\mathbf{b} - (\mathbf{b} \cdot \nabla)\mathbf{a} - \mathbf{b} \times (\nabla \times \mathbf{a}) \tag{52}$$

the last term on the r.h.s. of (51) can be written

$$\mathbf{v} \times (\nabla \times \mathbf{A}) = \nabla(\mathbf{v} \cdot \mathbf{A}) - (\mathbf{v} \cdot \nabla)\mathbf{A} - (\mathbf{A} \cdot \nabla)\mathbf{v} - \mathbf{A} \times (\nabla \times \mathbf{v}) \tag{53}$$

and since $\mathbf{v}$ is independent of the coordinates, whereas ∇ is the vector differential operator in terms of the coordinates, the last two terms on the r.h.s. of (53) vanish identically. We can now insert (53) into (51) and combine terms to obtain

$$\mathbf{F} = -\nabla[q(\phi - \mathbf{v} \cdot \mathbf{A})] - \left[\mathbf{v} \cdot \nabla\mathbf{A} + \frac{\partial \mathbf{A}}{\partial t} \right] \tag{54}$$

---

[6]E. R. Peck, *Electricity and Magnetism* (New York: McGraw-Hill Book Company, 1953), Chap. 7.

[7]See, for example, J. A. Stratton, *Electromagnetic Theory* (New York: McGraw-Hill Book Company, 1941), App. II.

wherein the last term can be seen to be the total time rate of change of the magnetic vector potential

$$\frac{d\mathbf{A}}{dt} = \frac{\partial \mathbf{A}}{\partial x_i} \frac{dx_i}{dt} + \frac{\partial \mathbf{A}}{\partial t}, \qquad i = 1, 2, 3$$

$$\frac{dA}{dt} = \nabla \mathbf{A} \cdot \mathbf{v} + \frac{\partial \mathbf{A}}{\partial t} \tag{55}$$

When the magnetic vector potential is constant in time the Lorentz force acting on the charged particle can be expressed as the gradient of a quantity which we can identify with the electromagnetic (velocity-dependent) potential energy

$$\mathbf{F} = -\nabla \psi \tag{56}$$

$$\psi = q(\phi - \mathbf{v} \cdot \mathbf{A}) \tag{57}$$

and thus the Lagrangian function becomes

$$L = T - \psi \tag{58a}$$

$$= \frac{mv^2}{2} - q(\phi - \mathbf{v} \cdot \mathbf{A}) \tag{58b}$$

The generalized momentum is then

$$\frac{\partial L}{\partial v} = \mathbf{p} = m\mathbf{v} + q\mathbf{A} \tag{59}$$

which can be inverted to yield the velocity

$$\mathbf{v} = \frac{\mathbf{p}}{m} - \frac{q}{m} \mathbf{A} \tag{60}$$

and the Lagrangian equation of motion becomes

$$\dot{\mathbf{p}} = m\mathbf{a} = -\nabla \psi \tag{61}$$

which is identical with Newton's second-law formulation (1), with the unbalanced force given by (56) and (57), when we remember that (by hypothesis)

$$\frac{d\mathbf{A}}{dt} = \frac{\partial \mathbf{A}}{\partial t} = 0 \tag{62}$$

The Hamiltonian function, given by (41), can be written as

$$H = \mathbf{p} \cdot \mathbf{v} - L = [mv^2 + q\mathbf{A} \cdot \mathbf{v}] - \left[\frac{mv^2}{2} - q(\phi - \mathbf{v} \cdot \mathbf{A}) \right]$$

$$H = \frac{mv^2}{2} + q\phi \tag{63}$$

We see that H in (63) is not expressed in its proper functional form (i.e., in terms of the generalized momentum), but in the form of (63) we can more readily identify the Hamiltonian with the total system energy. The first term in (63) is certainly the kinetic energy of the system, but the second term is patently not the velocity-dependent potential ψ. We can, however, see that the term $q\phi$ is the potential energy of the system by considering the work done by the electromagnetic field on the charged particle

$$W = \int \mathbf{F} \cdot d\mathbf{l} = \int q[\mathbf{E} + \mathbf{v} \times \mathbf{B}] \cdot d\mathbf{l}$$

$$= -\int \nabla(q\phi) \cdot d\mathbf{l} + \int q(\mathbf{v} \times \mathbf{B}) \cdot \frac{d\mathbf{l}}{dt} dt$$

$$= \int - d(q\phi) + q\int(\mathbf{v} \times \mathbf{B}) \cdot \mathbf{v} \, dt \tag{64}$$

The second integral vanishes identically because $\mathbf{v} \times \mathbf{B}$ is perpendicular to the velocity vector of the particle, and the potential energy of a conservative system is identified with the negative of the work done. Consequently we see that the Hamiltonian of this system, containing a velocity-dependent potential given by (57), is still the total energy of the system. The student should now be able to show that the functionally correct Hamiltonian for this system is

$$H = \frac{1}{2m}(\mathbf{p} - q\mathbf{A})^2 + q\phi \tag{65}$$

and Hamilton's canonical equations are

$$\dot{\mathbf{p}} = -\nabla H = -\nabla q \left[\phi - \frac{(\mathbf{p} - q\mathbf{A})}{m} \cdot \mathbf{A} \right] \tag{66}$$

$$= q[\mathbf{E} + \mathbf{v} \times \mathbf{B}] \tag{67}$$

and

$$\mathbf{v} = \frac{\partial H}{\partial \mathbf{p}} = \frac{\mathbf{p} - q\mathbf{A}}{m} \tag{68}$$

PROBLEMS

1. Satisfy yourself that (47) follows rigorously from (45) and (46).
2. Convince yourself of the veracity of equations (65) to (68). [*Hint*: to obtain (67) from (66) make use of (60), (62), (53), (55), and (50).]
3. An example of a system in which the total energy is constant is given by a frictionless "sleeping top," which is a top spinning about its vertical axis of symmetry. For such a system the potential energy is constant and may be called V_0. The

kinetic energy arises from rotation and may be written as $T = \frac{1}{2} I\dot{\theta}^2$, where θ is measured relative to a space-fixed set of axes. (a) Set up the Lagrangian for the system and obtain the Lagrange equations of motion. (b) Set up the Hamiltonian for the system and write Hamilton's canonical equations. (c) Show that the Hamiltonian is constant and equal to the total energy of the system.

4. The sleeping top of Prob. 3 is now viewed from a rotating reference frame ϕ, which is related to the space-fixed θ reference frame by means of

$$\phi = \theta - \omega_0 t$$

where the angular velocity ω_0 is constant. (a) Set up the Lagrangian and obtain the Lagrange equations of motion for the system in terms of ϕ and $\dot{\phi}$. (b) Set up the Hamiltonian for the system and write Hamilton's canonical equations in terms of $p_\phi = \partial L/\partial \dot{\phi}$. (c) Is H constant? Why? (d) Is H the total system energy? Why? [*Hint*: See for example J. W. Leech, *Classical Mechanics* (New York: Barnes & Noble Inc., 1965), Chap. 5.]

5. (a) Set up the problem of central force motion in a plane by writing the Lagrangian and solving the angular equation of motion in terms of the angular momentum of the system. (b) Show that Kepler's second law is obeyed for any central force motion, and reduce the radial equation of motion to a quadrature. (c) Obtain the Hamiltonian for the system and show that Hamilton's canonical equations are equivalent to the Lagrangian equations of motion. [*Hint*: write $T = M(\dot{r}^2 + r^2\dot{\theta}^2)\frac{1}{2}$ in plane polar coordinates and take $V = V(r)$. For further help consult Ref. 1.]

6. Consider a plane double pendulum consisting of a mass m_2 attached by means of a weightless rigid rod of length l_2 to a mass m_1 which is itself suspended from the origin of a fixed coordinate frame by a second massless rigid rod of length l_1. Since the system has two degrees of freedom, take the two generalized coordinates as the angles θ_1 and θ_2 which the two rods make with the vertical at any instant of time. (a) Express the displacements of the masses (x_1, y_1) and (x_2, y_2) in terms of the angles θ_1 and θ_2. Convert the expressions for the kinetic and potential energies in terms of the generalized coordinates and write the Lagrangian and the Hamiltonian functions. Is the system conservative? (b) Write the Lagrangian and Hamiltonian equations of motion and demonstrate their compatibility. (c) Let θ_1 and θ_2 be small angles and show that the equations of motion are coupled linear equations. [*Hint*: for a complete solution when the angles are small see, A. Sommerfeld, *Mechanics* (New York: Academic Press, Inc., 1964), Chap. 3.]

7. A simple pendulum bob of mass m is connected by a rigid massless rod of length l to the origin of a reference frame which executes simple harmonic motion in the x-direction according to the equation

$$x = A \sin \omega t$$

The pendulum is constrained to move in a vertical plane containing the x-axis. Take as the generalized coordinate the angle θ between the pendulum rod and the vertical. (a) Express the displacement (x,y) of m in terms of θ at any instant of time. Write the Lagrangian and Hamiltonian functions. (b) Is H constant? Why? (c) Is H the total energy of the system? Why? (d) Write Lagrange's and Hamilton's equations of motion and demonstrate their compatibility. (e) When θ is restricted to small values show that the equation of motion reduces to the equation describing a forced harmonic oscillator. Obtain a complete solution to this (simplified) equation.

Index